AF753407

FOCUS ON EYE RESEARCH

FOCUS ON EYE RESEARCH

O. R. IOSELIANI
EDITOR

Nova Science Publishers, Inc.
New York

For permission to use material from this book please contact us:
Telephone 631-231-7269; Fax 631-231-8175
Web Site: http://www.novapublishers.com

LIBRARY OF CONGRESS CATALOGING-IN-PUBLICATION DATA
Available upon request

ISBN 1-59454-434-4

Published by Nova Science Publishers, Inc. ✢ New York

CONTENTS

PREFACE

The consequences of aging populations combined with the strain to the human eye caused by computers and widespread poor nutritional practices has resulted in an upsurge of research dealing with vision.This new book presents leading-edge research in this field.

Age-related macular degeneration (AMD) constitutes the leading cause of legal blindness after 65 years of age in developed countries. Fuller knowledge of the etiology and pathogenesis of this disease is needed to advance its early diagnosis and its treatment. In Chapter 1, the authors discuss about the retinal aging and AMD form part of a continual deterioration in which the transition between aging and illness is signalled by a vision loss. Classically, the retinal pigmentary epithelium (RPE) was thought to be the main agent causing AMD, but researchers are currently finding that many other factors are involved, notably genetic, vascular (hypertension, arteriosclerosis) and environmental (exposure to UV light and oxidative damage). In aging and AMD, alterations occur in the choriocapillaris, RPE and the Bruch's membrane, which leads to a chronic inflammatory response. These damages result in deposits (drusen and basal laminar deposits), which hamper the normal diffusion of nutrients to the retina, injuring the outer retina. This situation can trigger retinal-choroidal atrophy or neovascularization. The inner retina also undergoes alterations, which, with the loss of vessels and the thickening of basal vascular membranes as well as of the inner limiting membrane (ILM), can bring about retinal ischemia. This can in turn induce the retinal macroglia (Müller cells and astrocytes) to reactivate and later die, and the disappearance of the macroglial cells could induced neuronal death in the inner retina. Retinal ischemia could provoke the migration of astrocytes and Müller cells towards the vitreous humour in search of a metabolic reserve, constituting epiretinal membranes. Despite the different hypotheses that seek to explain AMD, ischemia may be a major factor in the genesis of this pathology. The control of the risk factors and the habits that promote ischemia could help prevent the advance of this eye disease.

The goal of Chapter 2 will be to review recent scientific research developments in the pathogenesis of dry age-related macular degeneration (AMD), a major cause of blindness among the elderly. AMD is a late onset (after age 50), progressive degeneration of the retina associated with vision loss coupled with a spectrum of specific clinical, physiological and histopathological features. The early or dry stage of AMD is characterized by the accumulation of drusen, specific lipid rich deposits under the retina. The various paradigms for the pathogenesis of drusen are briefly reviewed, including genetic, lipofuscin/lysosomal failure, choroidal hypoperfusion, barrier, and retinal pigment epithelium (RPE) injury models.

Then, the scientific evidence to support a new interpretation of the RPE injury model is reviewed in depth, especially the proposed role of oxidant-mediated RPE cell membrane blebbing and dysregulated regulation of the RPE extracellular matrix. The clinical implications of this model are discussed.

To investigate the efficacy of a long-term treatment with Deflazacort (DFZ), a third generation synthetic glucocorticoid, in patients affected by retinitis pigmentosa (RP) complicated by cystoid macular edema (CME). A randomized group of 10 RP subjects were selected for this pilot study and treated with DFZ for one year according to a standard protocol. Far and near best corrected visual acuity (BCVA), fluorescein angiography (Heidelberg Retina Angiograph) and computerized perimetry (Humphrey Visual Field Analyzer) were statistically assessed. Near visual acuities, fluorescein angiographic findings and perimetric data improved significantly ($p<0.01$) while far BCVA varied only slightly ($p<0.05$). No ocular or systemic side effects were recorded. Further case-control studies, also involving a larger number of patients, are required to confirm these preliminary results. However, the present investigation from Chapter 3, seem to suggest that DFZ could be effective in reducing fluorescein angiographic findings and improving perimetric data and near visual acuities in RP patients, even though the pathogenesis of CME remains poorly understood.

The eye lens contains no vasculature and has no direct innervation. Its simple arrangement of long thin fibre-like cells, containing proteins and water, is organised to maintain transparency, which is retained for the greater part of life. This may be considered unusual in a structure believed to possess short-range order and one which contains a mixture of proteins with irregular shapes and varying physical and immunochemical properties. Any change in protein concentration that is sufficient to cause light to scatter rather than to refract, will cause opacification, the clinical manifestation of which is cataract. A uniform concentration of protein, however, is not the optimum design for a lens that needs to contribute a certain amount of refractive power to focus light onto the retina as well as to alter its shape to meet varying visual demands. Refraction occurs when light passes through a curved surface or across an interface between media of varying refractive index. In a lens with a uniform protein concentration and hence a constant refractive index, all refraction would take place at the lens surface. This would require a high protein concentration and/or a very curved lens in order to meet focussing requirements and would not allow for any change in lens shape. The distribution patterns of the various protein classes create a gradual change in refractive index across the lens, ensuring that functional demands are met without any detrimental effects to transparency of the tissue. Variations in the refractive index distribution exist in lenses from different species and some change in refractive index occurs with age. Chapter 4 discusses the contribution of the structural proteins to the functional requirements of the lens and presents comparative results of refractive index variations in human and animal lenses as well as showing how the refractive index may alter with age in the human lens.

In chapter 5, the authors present the results of using a mechanical stretching device to study the mechanism of accommodative lens shape changes at the level of the fibers.

The regulation of endothelial cell permeability is essential for maintenance of the delicate physiological environment of the retina. Retinal capillary barrier dysfunction is a hallmark of multiple ocular pathologies including diabetic retinopathy and macular edema leading to severe vision loss and blindness. In Chapter 6, the authors discuss several factors which alter the retinal microvascular barrier including exposure to angiogenic growth factors (VEGF), angiogenic inhibitors (endostatin, angiostatin), chemokines, reactive oxygen species, platelet phospholipids (sphingosine 1-phosphate), and the class of drugs known as the statins (simvastatin). VEGF, for example, increases barrier permeability in the retina via multiple signaling pathways which include a signal cascade culminating in activation of the cytoskeletal contractile apparatus. The balance between endothelial cell contractility and forces which promote intracellular adhesion both contribute to vascular barrier regulation via dynamics of the microfilament-based cytoskeleton and associated proteins. Alterations in cell-cell adhesion proteins are also associated with barrier permeability linked to retinopathies. The retinal endothelial cell cytoskeleton represents an important therapeutic target for the amelioration of retinal vascular pathology.

Identification, purification and characterization of a new protein from the serum of patients with Eales' disease is presented in Chapter 7. The protein was purified using preparative electrophoresis and HPLC. It resolved in α_2 globulin region. The purified protein had a retention time of 9.2 min in RP-HPLC. The molecular weight as determined by gel permeation chromatography was 88 kDa. Hence the protein is referred as 88 kDa protein. Periodic acid Schiff's staining revealed it as a glycoprotein. It was completely denatured above 70° C. Its isoelectric pH was 5. The protein was present in the vitreous and epiretinal membrane of Eales' patients and the blood of patients with systemic diseases like tuberculosis, leprosy and rheumatoid arthritis, but was absent in diabetic retinopathy and healed vasculitis of Eales' disease, as in the latter there is no inflammation. Hence 88 kDa protein is an acute phase protein produced in inflammatory conditions. The protein of different sources and diseases was immunologically the same.

The N terminal amino acid sequence by automated Edman's degradation chemistry is

Ala-Asp-Asp-Pro-Asn-Ser-Leu-Ser-Pro-Ser-Ala-Phe-Ala-Glu-Ala-Leu-Ala-Leu-Leu-Arg-Asp-Ser-
A D D P N S L S P S A F A E A L A L L R D S

X-Leu-Ala-Arg-Phe-Val
X L A R F V

Pigment epithelium-derived factor (PEDF), an extracellular serpin protein of 50-kDa, is a major antiangiogenic and neurotrophic factor in the eye. Because PEDF can prevent vessels from invading the cornea, vitreous and retina, and protect photoreceptors and cells from the inner neural retina from apoptotic cell death, its regulation plays an important role in ocular physiology and pathology. Interestingly, its levels are inversely associated with the progression of ocular diseases triggered by neovascularization and neuronal cell death. PEDF is present in high concentrations in the physiological interphotoreceptor matrix and vitreous where it associates with extracellular matrix components such as glycosaminoglycans/proteoglycans and collagens. The retinal pigment epithelium, the main source of PEDF for the eye expresses high levels of *PEDF* transcripts, from which the PEDF polypeptide chains are synthesized and, upon maturation, these are secreted into the interphotoreceptor matrix next to the neural retina. There is biochemical and immunological evidence for a neurotrophic PEDF receptor protein, and for interactions with signal transduction pathways for both neurotrophic and antiangiogenic activities. Regulation of the PEDF activities can be achieved by modulating the mechanisms for its production including transcriptional, and post-translational, secretion, degradation, or by interfering with its mechanisms of action, such as interaction with ECM components, receptors or signaling pathways. The authour's present in Chapter 8 some experimental evidence on PEDF regulation, and we discuss several possible mechanisms by which PEDF modulation could occur in the eye.

Mucin in the tear film forms the first line of ocular protection where it facilitates bacterial adhesion and removal from the eye, and forms the scaffold for tear defence proteins to be anchored in the tear film. *P. aeruginosa* is an opportunistic pathogen that has emerged as an important causative agent of bacterial keratitis. The interaction of mucin in tears and *P. aeruginosa* isolated from contact lens wear was undertaken in the present study to identify mucin species that bind to this bacterium and the nature of this interaction. Method: Open eye basal tears were collected from healthy volunteers, pooled, and tear constituents were thereafter separated by agarose gel electrophoresis. Separated tear proteins/glycoproteins were blotted to nitrocellulose for either characterisation by lectin staining or adhesion to biotin-labelled *P. aeruginosa* strains Paerl and 6294. Results: Tear mucin under reducing conditions, produced at least five mucin species greater than 200 kDa. Of these, Paerl and 6294 preferentially bound to the highest molecular weight mucin species near the origin of the gel, and shown by concurrent *S. nigra* lectin staining to contain sialic acid linked by an $\alpha(2\rightarrow6)$ linkage. The presence of $\alpha(2\rightarrow6)$ linked sialic acid was a unique feature of this mucin compared with the other species. The adhesion of *P. aeruginosa* to the distinct mucin species was not due to free biotin label, indicating its quite specific nature. Conclusion: A qualitative assay of biotin-labelled bacteria adhesion to mucins separated from tears by agarose electrophoresis was developed, where at least five high molecular weight glycoprotein species greater than 200 kDa were identified. The study from Chapter 9 observed the adhesion of ocular *P. aeruginosa* strains to a distinct tear glycoprotein species containing $\alpha(2\rightarrow6)$ linked sialic acid residues. Local variations in refractive index are the physical cause of light scattering in a material or tissue. The goal of Chapter 10 was to further add to the understanding of the process of light propagation in the crystalline lens by directly measuring local variations in refractive index by phase contrast microscopy. Refractive index was estimated by immersion refractometry. Cryo-sections of quick-frozen human donor lenses were embedded in a graded series of bovine serum albumin solutions, and in immersion oil, ranging in refractive index from 1.34 to 1.52. Fiber membranes in the lens cortex prove to have a refractive index considerably above that of fiber cytoplasm at the same location. Fiber membranes in the lens nucleus have a refractive index approximately the same as that of fiber cytoplasm at the same location. In the lens cortex, transparency is obtained by a high spatial order of the lens fiber lattice to compensate for the light scattering caused by differences in refractive index between fiber membranes and cytoplasm. In the lens nucleus, high spatial order is less important, because the minor differences in the refractive index between fiber membranes and fiber cytoplasm lead only to minimal scattering.

In: Focus on Eye Research
Editor: O.R. Ioseliani, pp. 1-37
ISBN: 1-59454-434-4

Chapter 1

Retinal Changes in Age-Related Macular Degeneration

A. Triviño*, A. I. Ramírez, J. J. Salazar, B. Rojas, R. De Hoz and J. M. Ramírez

Instituto de Investigaciones Oftalmológicas Ramón Castroviejo,
Facultad de Medicina, Madrid

Abstract

Age-related macular degeneration (AMD) constitutes the leading cause of legal blindness after 65 years of age in developed countries. Fuller knowledge of the etiology and pathogenesis of this disease is needed to advance its early diagnosis and its treatment. Retinal aging and AMD form part of a continual deterioration in which the transition between aging and illness is signalled by a vision loss. Classically, the retinal pigmentary epithelium (RPE) was thought to be the main agent causing AMD, but researchers are currently finding that many other factors are involved, notably genetic, vascular (hypertension, arteriosclerosis) and environmental (exposure to UV light and oxidative damage). In aging and AMD, alterations occur in the choriocapillaris, RPE and the Bruch's membrane, which leads to a chronic inflammatory response. These damages result in deposits (drusen and basal laminar deposits), which hamper the normal diffusion of nutrients to the retina, injuring the outer retina. This situation can trigger retinal-choroidal atrophy or neovascularization. The inner retina also undergoes alterations, which, with the loss of vessels and the thickening of basal vascular membranes as well as of the inner limiting membrane (ILM), can bring about retinal ischemia. This can in turn induce the retinal macroglia (Müller cells and astrocytes) to reactivate and later die, and the disappearance of the macroglial cells could induced neuronal death in the inner retina. Retinal ischemia could provoke the migration of astrocytes and Müller cells towards the vitreous humour in search of a metabolic reserve, constituting epiretinal membranes. Despite the different hypotheses that seek to explain AMD, ischemia may be a major factor in the genesis of this pathology. The control of the risk factors and the habits that promote ischemia could help prevent the advance of this eye disease.

*Correspondence concerning this article should be addressed to Dr. Triviño A. Instituto de Investigaciones Oftalmológicas Ramón Castroviejo. Facultad de Medicina, Pab VI, 4ª planta. Ciudad Universitaria s/n. UCM. 28040, Madrid. Tlf. 91 3947080; Fax. 91 394 1359; E-mail address: atrivino@med.ucm.es

1. Introduction

Among the most frequent causes of blindness in the aged population are retinal alterations. Macular problems of aging and particularly age-related macular degeneration (AMD) represent the main causes of legal blindness among subjects 65 years of age and older in developed countries. Despite technological advances, legal blindness caused by AMD has increased in relation to other diseases affecting vision [1,2,3]. Fuller knowledge of the etiopathogeny of AMD is indispensable for advancement both in early diagnosis as well as in treatment.

Retinal aging and AMD are part of a continual deterioration in which the transition between the aging and the illness are signalled by vision loss [4]. Classically, RPE has been cited as the prime cause of AMD, although currently it has been found that this pathology may involve many other factors, notably genetic and vascular ones, such as ischemia [5,6,7].

Also, the cell types involved in the development of this disease are been studied to determine exactly what occurs in AMD and thereby to avoid the maximum evolution of the disease, with the appearance of disciform lesions which increase the size of the blind area [6,8,9,10,11]. As AMD constitutes a pathology in the aging process leading to vision loss, we deem it helpful to determine how this pathology affects the population, how the components making up the retina undergo aging, and how this process affects the phenomenon of vision.

2. Epidemiology of AMD

Epidemiological data referring to the visual alterations of greatest frequency in the population show a clear growth of pathologies linked to aging, among other reasons for demographic changes. In the coming years world population is predicted to grow by two billion people, from 5.8 billion in 1996 to 7.9 in 2020, of which some 1.2 billion will be more than 60 years old, 75% of these living in developed countries by virtue of demographic shift [12].

As age is the prime marker of risk of visual deterioration and blindness, the figures for this problem are expected to increase as populations age, as expected for different age-related visual problems, especially those that are difficult to prevent or treat [13].

On a world scale, cataracts, trachoma and glaucoma constitute 70% of the preventable causes of visual deterioration and blindness, although in the developed world, diabetic retinopathy is the main cause. Similarly, if we take as a reference the total world population, then cataracts, glaucoma, diabetic retinopathy and AMD are the most frequent causes of blindness in the elderly. However, if we refer exclusively to the developed world, macular degeneration takes the forefront. Therefore, AMD is by far the primary cause of visual deterioration within the group of unpreventable diseases, being responsible for an estimated 8 million blind or severely incapacitated people [14]. Nevertheless, it should always be taken into account that the criteria used can change the figures for blindness, so that the WHO ranks AMD as the first cause of blindness, while the United States situates AMD in second place behind cataracts [15].

In terms of prevalence, there are roughly 7500 cases per million in developed countries, with a predominance of Caucasians, and more than 1000 if we consider the incidence of legal blindness from AMD, which accounts for some 200 cases per million [16]. Both incidence as well as prevalence depend on age. A recent publication in the Blue Mountains study reported an incidence that in 5 years reached some 15% among those over 80 years of age, and 7.4% from 60 to 70 years old [17].

3. Risk Factors in AMD

Several risk factors of AMD have been studied, many being subject to continual review. In terms of individuals, age is undoubtedly the risk marker of greatest magnitude, as evidenced by more than one study, although this fact certainly does not indicate that aging is the only cause of this disease.

The apparent predominance of the female gender has been questioned by many researchers and appears to be linked to the distribution of the populational pyramid and other methodologies [3].

The possible influence of race has also been masked by the differences in life expectancy of the different countries and the different habits or social and environmental factors. However, it has been observed that there is lower prevalence of this pathology in blacks, perhaps due to the protective effect of melanin in the pigmentary epithelium of the retina [2,3]

Family history appears to influence the development of the disease, implying a genetic component. In this field, a number of recent works have confirmed a genetic influence in drusen production [18,19,20]. The involvement of the gene ABCR [21,22], responsible for Stargardt disease, has been studied, as has the gene of the apolipoprotein E (Apo E). In the latter case, it has been suggested that the alleles of Apo E could alter lipid metabolism, affecting the lipid deposits of the Bruch's membrane, the formation of drusen, and the progress towards the exudative form of the disease [19]. The genetic implication of this pathology is reflected when the concordance of the AMD is analyzed in monozygotic and dizygotic twins. In some studies, the concordance in monozygotic twins was 100%, but 40% in dizygotic ones. However, the expressivity of AMD varies among monozygotic twins, supporting the possibility that this is a hereditary pathology influenced by environmental factors [23]. In addition, there are studies that indicate familiar susceptibility to this pathology ranging from 19 to 21%, although there is also marked variability in expressivity of AMD within a given family.

In terms of personal factors, all those related to vascular risk (arterial hypertension, type II diabetes, dislipemia, excess weight, smoking) usually increase the frequency of this disease with age. These, however, could give rise to spurious associations. For example, the association of hyperlipidemia with AMD could be related with arteriosclerosis of small vessels that feed the retina, in the same way as occurs in coronary vessels and in the heart [2,3].

A meta-analysis performed with the data from the Beaver Dam Eye Study, the Rotterdam Study, and the Blue Mountain Eye Study —that is, in American, European, and Australian communities— demonstrates that, apart from age, tobacco is the only risk factor consistently associated with any form of AMD, and thus can be considered as the prime factor of preventable risk [24]. Smoking causes injury by diminishing the concentration of antioxidants and altering the choroidal blood flow, as well as the metabolism of the RPE [2,3]. However, alcohol consumption does not appear to constitute a risk factor, as even the moderate consumption of red wine appears to exert a protective effect due to the quantity of antioxidants contained in this beverage [2,3].

Among ocular characteristics, attempts have been made to link AMD to hypermetropy and hypopigmentation of the iris. It has been postulated that blue eyes have a greater disposition to developing AMD, given that the melanin in the eye protects against free radicals on diminishing the light absorption of the photoreceptors [26].

Also, environmental factors have been studied, particularly in relation to environmental luminosity. Although studies are controversial, solar radiation has been deemed a moderate risk factor for AMD on the order of 1.4. Meanwhile, lens surgery also presents a risk factor, given that aphakic and pseudoaphakic patients have a higher rate of early signs of AMD. This could be because of a lack of protection of the lens, since this acts as an anti-UV filter [2].

It is very possible that the roles of antioxidants and of diet are becoming steadily more predominant, among other reasons for their relationship with the process of aging and vascular risk in general. A diet rich in antioxidants appears to provide protection against AMD, as these molecules can arrest the oxidative process, converting the free radicals into stable components before these can interact with the cell membranes to cause damage. The antioxidants that are beneficial against this pathology include: liposoluble vitamins E, C, A, carotenes (β-carotene), and xanthophils (lutein and zeaxanthine, which help filter the blue spectrum of sunlight, protecting the photoreceptors and the pigmentary epithelium from oxidative stress); oligoelements, which act as cofactors of antioxidant enzymes (zinc, copper, manganese, magnesium and selenium); as well as vitamin B6, folic acid, and the glutation, which also have been credited with being antioxidant agents [27,28].

The excessive consumption of fats, mainly linolenic acid, has been considered a possible risk factor for AMD. Nevertheless, the monounsaturated and polyunsaturated fatty acids found in fish could constitute a protective factor [29] .

It is assumed that all the risk factors mentioned above can contribute in different ways to the genesis of AMD.

4. Aging

4.1. Concept of Aging

Aging, universal in all living beings, can be defined as a process of the progressive loss of functions that culminates in death. Aging in humans is the consequence of the aging of their cells [30]. In recent years, a series of theories has been proposed to explain the mechanisms of cell aging. These theories can be divided into two large groups: those that consider aging to be a passive process, the result of the accumulation of alterations in nucleic acids, proteins and lipids; and those that consider aging to be an active, genetically programmed process [4,30,31,32,33,34].

Within the first group, we find the hypothesis of the exponential accumulation of errors in DNA, the hypothesis of free radicals, the hypothesis of inactivation of redundant copies of DNA, and the hypothesis of the shortening of telomeres [4,30,34,35,36]. Meanwhile, the theories of the second group are based fundamentally on the examples of programmed cell death (apoptosis) during embryonic development [34]. Therefore, in the theory of the cell clock, it is assumed that aging is the result of the activation of certain genes that bring about cell death. A variant on this theory would be one that explains aging as the result of an overexpression of genes that codify growth-inhibiting factors.

Currently, molecular mechanisms of aging are being proposed, combining some of the hypotheses from both groups. In this way, it is accepted that aging is to a certain extent genetically programmed, but it is believed that this program can be modified by activity [34] .

4.2. Anatomical-Physiological Changes Caused by Aging

During aging, a series of anatomical-physiological changes affects all organs, although more severely in some, such as the liver, spleen, kidneys, and nervous system [37]. In all organs, generalized cell loss occurs with aging, reaching great proportions in the case of the neurons (15%) [38]. In addition, the epithelia, gland tissues, and muscle tissue atrophy up to 50% [39]. Also, there is a decrease in intracellular water from 50% to 35%, and therefore the protoplasmically active mass of the noble parenchyma diminishes and the support tissues grow [4].

Aging prompts alterations also in the extracellular matrix (ECM), such as anomalies of ECM biosynthesis, postsynthetic modifications of ECM including degradation altered interaction among ECM components, and changes in cell-ECM adhesion [40,41]. Aged human fibroblasts appear to produce structurally and functionally abnormal fibronectine that exhibits reduced binding to native types I and II collagen [42,43].

Another characteristic of aging is a change in vascularization [37,44], with a reduced bood flow as a consequence of the sclerotic changes and other alterations in the vessels, with the appearance of amyloid deposits [34]. In the cells, deposits of lipofuscin (the aging pigment) appear, possibly in relation to the alterations of the mitochondria, a situation that may alter energy production [30]. Oxygen and glucose consumption also decline [37].

4.3. Changes Caused by Aging in the Organs Related to Vision

In the eye, a number of changes occur, involving the transparent media, the choroid and the retina. These changes trigger a number of sensorial defects such as reduced visual acuity, lower contrast sensitivity and altered chromatic vision [6,45,46,47]. Also, problems arise in relation to glare and adaptation to night vision [48]. In addition, the visual field shrinks and the blind spot expands [44].

Furthermore, there are electrophysical changes: the standard electroretinogram (ERG) registers a significant increase of implicit time and a decrease in the amplitude of a wave (response of photoreceptors) and b wave (response of bipolar and Müller cells) [49,50]. The multifocal electroretinogram shows that with aging the amplitude density is maximally reduced in the central 10° diameter of vision [51,52]. The changes in the ERG-waves could be due to a slowing of temporal adaptation [53]. The amplitude in the multifocal oscillatory potentials, which are thought to reflect the function of the inner retina and the rod-cone interactions, decreases lineally with age, while their latency increases with the age [54,55]. These sensory losses are the result of the changes that take place in the cellular and tissue context.

With aging, choroids progressively lose thickness from 200 μm at birth to 80 μm by 90 years of age. In this layer, there is a loss both of choriocapillaris density as well as the diameter of vascular lumen, while the width of the intercapillary pillars increases. Due to these histological changes, the subfoveal choroidal blood flow declines with age [56,57,58].

Meanwhile, in the retina, a series of histological alterations occurs. In the cells of the RPE, the nucleus becomes smaller and the cytoplasm accumulates lipofuscin as a result of cell metabolism [11,59,60,61,62,63,64]. Lipofuscin occupied 1% of the RPE cytoplasmic volume during the first decade of life and 19% of the cytoplasmic volumen by age 80 years. Reduction in functional cytoplasmic volume might impaired RPE function, for example phagocytosis which can lead to photoreceptor dead [65,66]. With light exposure, lipofuscin generates superoxide ions, singlet oxygen, hydrogen peroxide and lipid peroxides [67]. Lipofuscin fluorophore, A2E, mediates the blue-light-induced apoptosis of RPE cells by inhibiting the degrading capacity of lysosomes, disrupting membrane integrity due to its phototoxicity [68,69]. The metabolites of vitamin A (involved in phototransduction) could also be important in the development of photoreactivity of lipofuscin [70].

In the basal zone of RPE cells appear multiple autophagic vesicles, electrodense deposits, and remains of cell membrane that, for their situation between the plasma membrane and the basal layer of the RPE, constitute basal laminar deposits (BlamD). When located between the basal RPE and the inner collagen, these are called basal linear deposits (BlinD) [71].

In Bruch's membrane (the layer that separates the retina from the choriocapillaris) the changes translate as a diffuse thickening of this membrane This thickness seems to increase linearly with aging from approximately 2 μm at birth to approximately 4-6 μm in the tenth decade of life [56], and is caused by the infiltration of a PAS-positive material [59,60,72,73,74]. Electron microscopy has revealed that this material, is comprised of abnormal quantities of ECM material, including cell fragments, collagen aggregates and degenerated basal membranes [75,76,77,78] and lipids [79]. In addition, there is an increase in collagen fibers [80,81,82], and elastic fibres show greater density, even calcification [72]. Other ECM components such as the glucosaminoglucans and heparin sulphate, also grow in size with aging in this membrane. This may change the electronegative charge of the membrane and as a result alter its permeability [83].

An impaired ability to degrade the ECM might contribute to age-related Bruch's membrane thickening. Matrix metalloproteinases (MMPs) are zinc-dependent enzymes that catabolise ECM proteins, including collagen and elastin. Tissue inhibitors of metalloproteinases (TIMPs) regulate the activity of MMPs. RPE cells produce MMPs and TIMP-3. Inactive forms of MMP-2 and MMP-9 increase in the Bruch's membrane with aging, particularly in the submacular part. Abnormalities in metalloproteinase activity can result in changes in Bruch's membrane thickness [84,85,86] .

Lipids accumulating in a Bruch's membrane that is also structurally altered can interfere with the free metabolic exchange between the choriocapillaris and the RPE, and can contribute to the loss of retinal sensitivity. This situation of lipid accumulations can play a certain pathogenic role in the development of AMD [87,88].

The lipid accumulation in Bruch's membrane begins to increase substantially after 40 years of age. The quantity of lipids accumulated under the macula is greater than under the peripheral retinal, perhaps due to the great photoreceptor density in the macula or to the greater susceptibility to peroxidation of the lipids in the outer segments of the posterior pole.

In Bruch's membrane, the quantity of peroxidated lipids increases exponentially with age. These lipids are presumably derived from long-chain polyunsaturated fatty acids normally found in the outer segment of the photoreceptors, as for example docosahexanoic acid and linoleic acid. This fact supports the contention that at least some of the lipids that accumulate in the Bruch's membrane come from photoreceptors rather than from the blood [85,89,90]. Additionally, age-related declines in choriocapillaris density and lumen diameter might also decrease the clearance of debris from the Bruch's membrane, which would contribute to thickening with age [43].

Changes in the neurons of the retina have also been reported in the aging process, such as the appearance of lipofuscin granules in the cytoplasm, progressive loss of the dendritic tree, and the number of synapses, even causing neuronal death [6,34,91].

In the macular region, with aging, the nucleus of the outer nuclear layer moves towards the external plexiform layer [92], a situation which might be due to tractions triggered by the change in the shape of the cones in old age.

Also notable is the loss of photoreceptors [61,92,93,94]. With aging, there is a greater loss apparent among the rods than cones [61,95]. Rod density in the central retina diminishes by 30% between 34 and 94 years of age; however, the number of cones of the macular area remains stable. The survival of the cones depends on the presence of rods even though the latter are not functional, because the rods segregate survival factors for the cones [96,97,98,99]. A similar situation added to the alterations of the RPE could be related to pathological phenomena of aging, such as AMD, in which there is far more loss of rods than of cones [100].

Moreover, the external segments of the photoreceptors form bonds called circumvolutions (Fig.1). These structures are formed because the external segments continue growing beyond the limits existing in the young individual, with the growth range of these segments being greater than for phagocytosis [91,101].

In the rest of the retinal layers, the neurons show few changes with age. There is an accumulation of lipids in these nerve cells (Fig.2), especially in the ganglion cells, in which lipofuscin considerably increases. These cells can decrease by more than 25% in certain retinal zones [95]. Similar changes have also been observed in bipolar cells [9].

In the nerve fiber layer, a progressive loss in thickness was found, coinciding with the loss of ganglion cells with age [95]. Corpora amylacea were detected, appearing in electron microscopy micrographs as intracellular organelles (neurotubules, mitochondria, and dense bodies), which are located in the edematose axons [102] .

Retinal vessels also undergo changes in the aging process. Basal membranes of the capillaries show a swelling with lipofuscin infiltrates; in addition, endothelial cells and pericytes present a great quantity of lipofuscin that on occasion is expelled toward the vessel lumen [7] (Fig. 3). From 50 years on, endothelial cell loss of the peripheral retinal capillaries occurs, the vessels appearing completely acellular [103]. This extends to the central retina from 60 years on. Therefore, endothelial-cell loss and swelling of the basal membranes of the capillaries could impede or reduce the passage of oxygen and nutrients towards the retinal nerve tissue as well as the elimination of wastes, provoking chronic ischemia [104] .

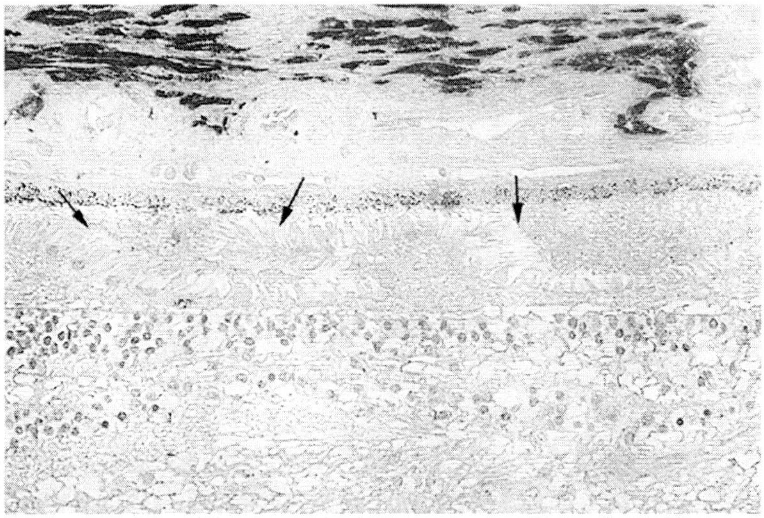

Fig. 1. Circunvolutions of photoreceptors. (arrows) H-E (x125) (From ref. 4).

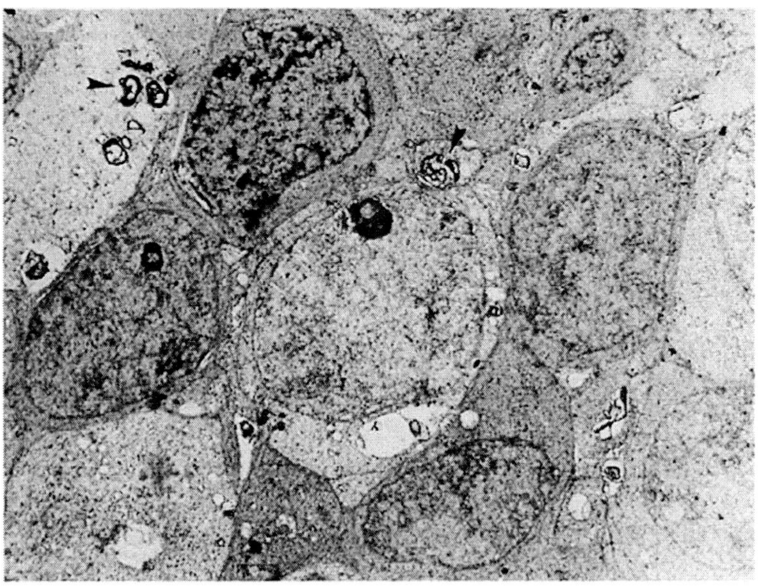

Fig. 2. Accumulation of lipofuscin (arrowhead) in the citoplasm of the cones and rods in the outer nuclear layer. (x3000) (From ref. 4).

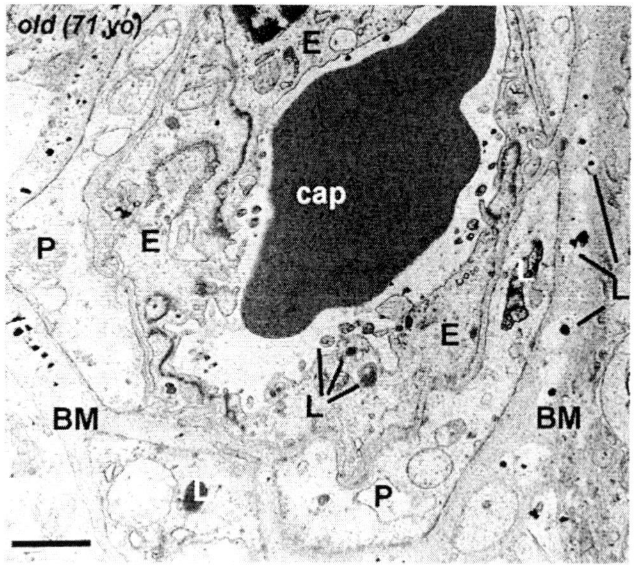

Fig. 3. NFL capillary of the old retina. The basal membrane is thicker than in young retina. The lipids and secundary lysosomes can be seen inside the basal membrane, endothelial cells and pericytes. (BM: basal membrane; cap: capillary; E: endothelial cell; L: secundary lysosomes; P: pericyte). (Bar = 1 μm) (From ref. 7).

4.4. Changes with Aging in the Retinal Glia

Currently, it is known that glial cells undergo changes with aging [4,105,106]. In the brain, a higher number of glial cells has been found, although it is not known whether this increase was a consequence of greater cell volume or a higher cell number [34,107]. It is still unknown whether this glial hyperactivity registered during aging is only a secondary response to neuronal atrophy and death, or whether the glia can be assigned an active role in the aging process of the nervous system [34].

Astrocytes and Müller glia are macroglial cells of the retina. These cells are intermediaries between the neurons and blood vessels, are arranged over the basal membrane of the capillaries, comunicating neurons and vessels. Müller glia extend radially across the entire retina. However, astrocytes are located primarily only in the ganglion cell layer (GCL) and in the nerve fibre layer (NFL). In the GCL, the astrocytes are stellate and form a honeycombed plexus. In the NFL, the astrocytes are elongated and arranged parallel to the axons of the ganglion cells and to the radial peripapillary capillaries [108] .

With aging the retinal astroglial cells diminish in such a way that the number of chambers of the honeycomb astroglial plexus in the GCL and the number of processes from astrocytes covering radial peripapillary capillaries in the NFL were significantly smaller in the group aged 60-89 than in the young group (Fig. 4). Moreover, this fall in the number of astrocytes continues to become more accentuated with age, as demonstrated by a comparison of persons aged 60-79 and persons aged over 80 [7]. In addition, the retinal astrocytes in persons over 60 years of age present a higher density of intermediate filaments, more abundant cytoplasmic organelles, and higher GFAP immunoreactivity than in young individuals, indicating greater cell activity [7] (Fig. 5). These astrocytes, which exhibit higher cell activity than in young people and higher density of intermediate filaments, are reactive astrocytes [109,110].

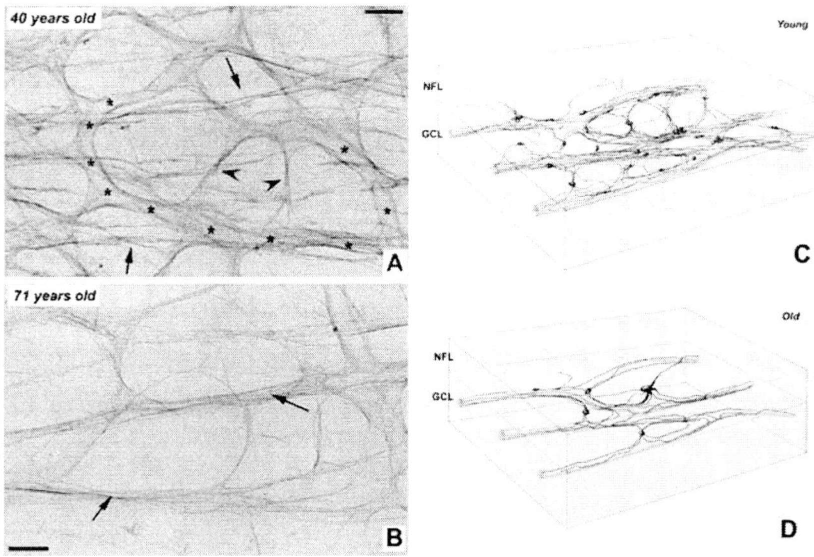

Fig. 4. (A,B) Shape and size of the chambers of the honeycomb plexus in the GCL. (*: blood vessels; retinal whole-mount, anti GFAP). (Bar = 25 μm). (C-D) Three-dimensional schemes of the astroglial honeycomb structure in the retinal ganglion cell layer (GCL). (NFL: nerve fiber layer). (From ref. 7). (A): Young individual: The capillaries are joined by numerous thick astroglial bundles (arrowheads). Arrows mark the astroglial bundles in the NFL. (B) Old individual: The honeycomb chambers have an irregular shape and are larger than in young individuals. Arrows mark the astroglial bundles of the NFL; these bundles show higher GFAP immunoreactivity than in young individuals. (C) Honeycomb structure of a young individual. There is a high density of astrocytes surrounding the capillaries of the GCL. (D) Honeycomb structure of an old individual. There is a reduction in the number of astrocytes in the GCL. The number of chambers in the GCL astroglial plexus is smaller than in the young individuals.

Reactive astrocytes are believed to protect the neurons against an ischemic process, eliminating excitotoxic neurotransmitters and ions, including glutamate, lactate, hydrogen, and potassium, which accumulate in the perineuronal space after ischemia. In the astrocytes, high levels of the enzyme glutamine synthase are found, and these, together with the specific transporters of glutamate, eliminate and detoxify extracellular glutamate and supply glutamine to the neurons [110,111]. In addition, the astrocytes store glucogen and have the potential for providing lactate. These cells also produce a great quantity of growth factors and cytokines, which may contribute both to neurotoxic as well as neuroprotective effects [112].

It has also been demonstrated that astrocytes are more resistant to oxidative damage than are neurons, which protects them against such damage. This potential is due to the fact that the astrocytes contain high concentrations of antioxidants such as reduced glutathion and vitamin C [113]. Consequently, a depression of these astroglial activities could induce neuronal dysfunction.

The reactive astrocytes appear to be in charge of keeping the neurons (in our case the ganglion cells) alive against ischemia, producing neurotrophic factors, increasing the expression of antioxidant enzymes (glutathion, vitamin C), and boosting glucose transport and production [113,114].

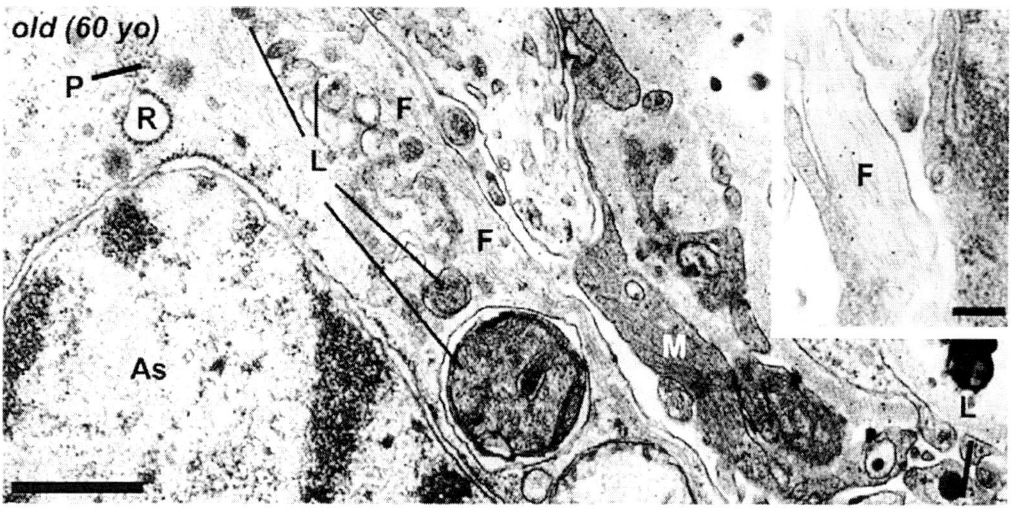

Fig. 5. Retina of an old individual. Astrocyte with large number of cytoplasmic organelles, glial filaments (F) and secundary lysosomes (L). The insert shows an astroglial process with only glial filaments inside. (As: astrocyte; M: Müller glia; P: polyribosomes; R: rough endoplasmic reticule). (Bar = 0.6 μm; Bar insert = 0.15 μm). (From ref. 7).

However, astrocytes have been found to be more vulnerable to oxidative damage in aged than in young individuals [115]. This is due to the fact that reactive astrocytes provoke changes in the geometry and volume of the extracellular space that can affect the diffusion of neuroactive substances. The extracellular space is not only the microenvironment of nerve cells but is also a major channel of communication between the neurons and astrocytes. The changes in the diffusion parameters during aging deteriorate the transmission of signals and can result in greater susceptibility of nerve tissue to ischemia due to stronger extracellular acidosis as well as the accumulation of potassium and toxic substances such as glutamate, which can damage neurons (Scheme 1).

In reactive astrocytes, the higher number of organelles and the vigorous cellular activity prompts a large quantity of lipofuscin to appear in the cells [27]. It has been noted that the astrocytes of subjects over 60 years of age have a great amount of lipofuscin in the cytoplasm [7] (Fig 5). The retinal astrocytes, and consequently lipofuscin are exposed to visible light (400-700 nm) and to high concentrations of oxygen (70 mmHg), which are ideal conditions for the formation of reactive oxygen that can damage cell protein and lipid membranes [27].

It has been postulated that human retinal astrocytes surrounding the capillaries are exposed to oxidative stress, being subject to high oxygen tensions. The reactive oxygen could damage the organelles and the plasma membrane of the astrocytes, raising the possibility of maintaining the cell mechanisms intact against ischemia. If, in addition, there is a greater concentration of toxic substances (e.g. glutamate) in the extracellular space (altered by the reactive astrocytes), then a massive inflow of glutamate, hydrogen, potassium, etc. becomes more likely due to the greater permeability of the cell membrane by the attack of the free radicals, provoking the cell to swell. Such cell edema could result in the splitting apart of intermediate filaments of the astrocytes and consequently the loss of immunoreactivity GFAP, followed by cell death [112] (Scheme 1). This could explain why the elderly have fewer astrocytes in the GCL, and it could also account for the disappearance of processes from the astrocytes in between the bundles of astroglial processes in the NFL [7] (Fig 4).

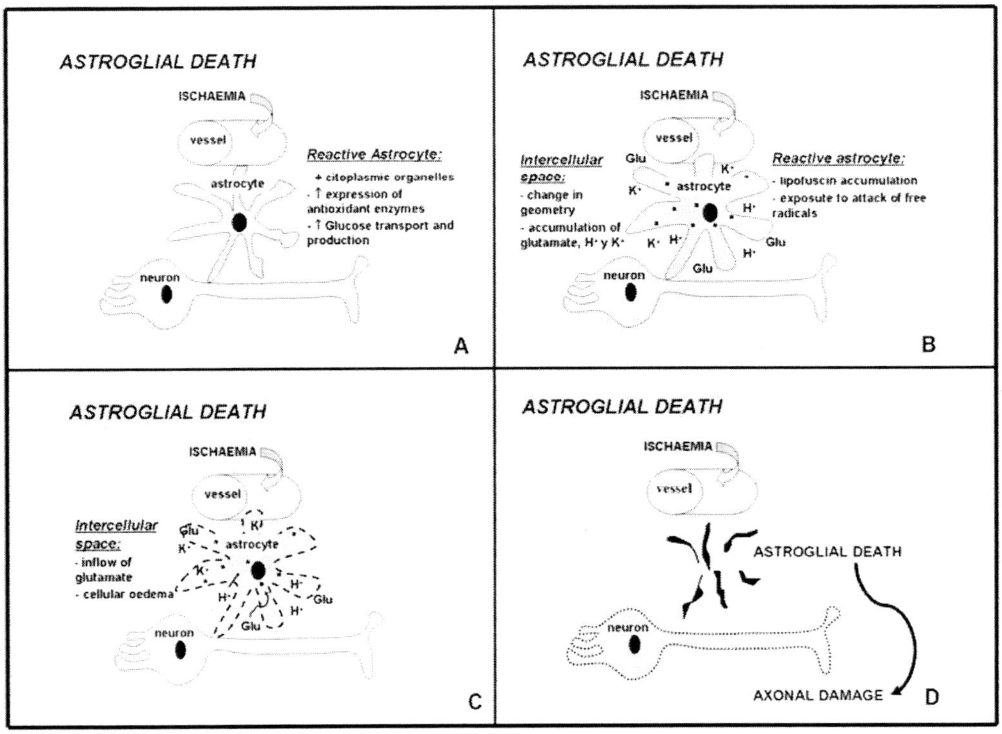

Scheme 1. Role of the astroglia in the ischaemia. (A) Reactive astrocytes. (B) Reactive astrocyte: changes in geometry and volume of the extra-cellular space. (C) Increases permeability of the cell membrane. (D) Breakdown of the astrocytes intermediate filaments, astroglial death and axonal damage.

In the aged, it has also been observed that the basal membrane of the ILM of the retina increases 12-fold with respect to young individuals [7] (Fig 6). This greater thickness could hinder the exchange of substances between the retina and the vitreous humour, as the latter is a metabolic reservoir of the retina (accumulating sugars, amino acids, potassium, glutation, etc.) and a deposit of waste materials [116]. Consequently, the situation of ischemia is aggravated in the inner retina by the difficulty of obtaining nutrients through this channel and of eliminating waste products that accumulate in the retina [7].

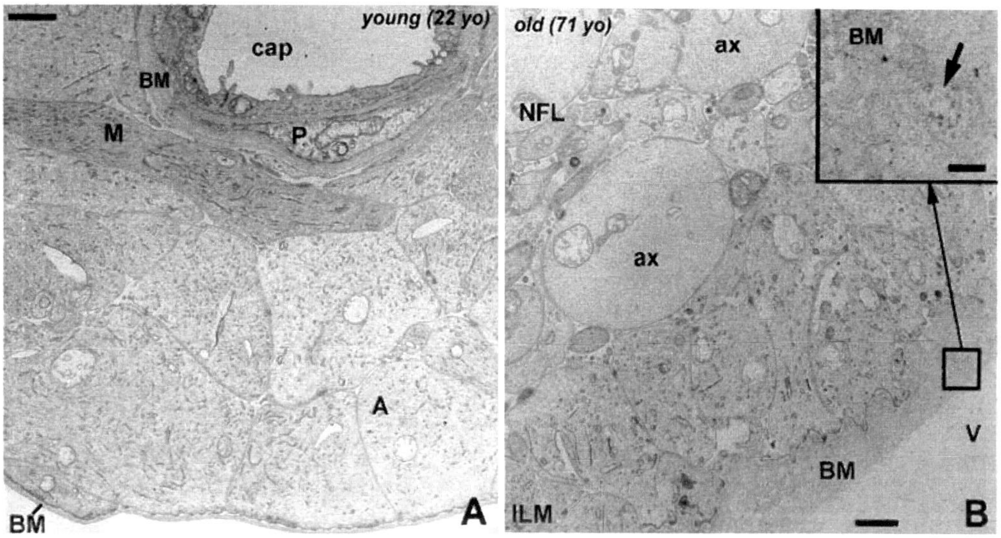

Fig. 6. (A) Retina of a young individual. The basal membrane of the ILM and the capillaries are very thin. (Bar = 1 μm). (B) The basal membrane of the ILM in old individuals is thicker than in young individuals, and inclusions can be seen in their interior (insert: arrow). (Bar = 1 μm; insert: bar = 200 μm). (A: astrocyte; ax: axon; BM: basal membrane; cap: capillary; ILM: inner limiting membrane; M: Müller cell; NFL: nerve fiber layer; P: pericyte; V: vitreous humor). (From ref. 7).

5. AMD

5.1. Etiopathogeny of AMD

The pathogenic sequence of AMD begins with the deterioration of the RPE due to metabolic disturbances in the pigmentary epithelium itself, the functions of which become altered as a consequence of the interaction of solar radiation or oxygen at the level of the outer segment discs of the photoreceptors [117]. As mentioned above, these have a high content in polyunsaturated acids, making them very susceptible to the attack of free radicals. Consequently, the photoreceptor discs that are phagocytosed by the RPE undergo incomplete digestion, with residual bodies appearing in the cytoplasm (lipofuscin granules) [64, 80].

The number of these granules increases with age, accumulating at first at the bottom and on the periphery of the cell, but in the fifth and sixth decade of life the granules are distributed throughout the cytoplasm, to the metabolic detriment of the normal cell [118]. The damage caused in the RPE provokes an inflammatory response in Bruch's membrane and in the choroid. RPE injury and inflammation foster the production of an abnormal ECM derived largely from the RPE and photoreceptor cells but also from cells in the choroid and from substances in the systemic circulation. This abnormal ECM may damage the retina, RPE, and choroid [43]. The waste materials produced by a biologically altered RPE are expelled from the cell, accumulating between the RPE and its basal membrane. This forms a linear deposit of an eosinophilous substance, amorphous or granular, which is known as the basal laminar deposit, constituting the first phase of AMD [9,72,77,119] (Fig.7). These deposits are formed primarily by granular and vesicular material, type-IV collagen, glucosaminoglucans, laminin, and fibronectin [120].

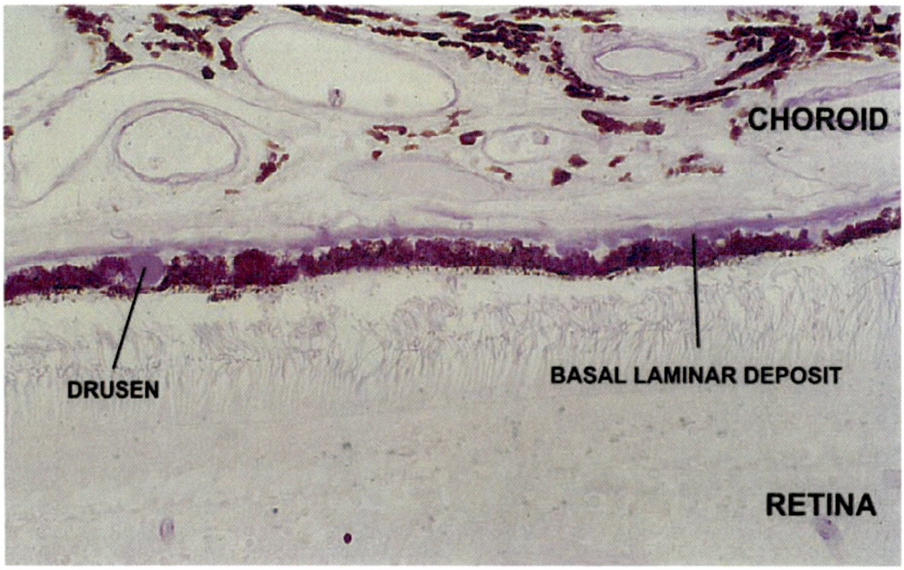

Fig. 7. Basal laminar deposit and drusen. (PAS; x175). (From ref. 6).

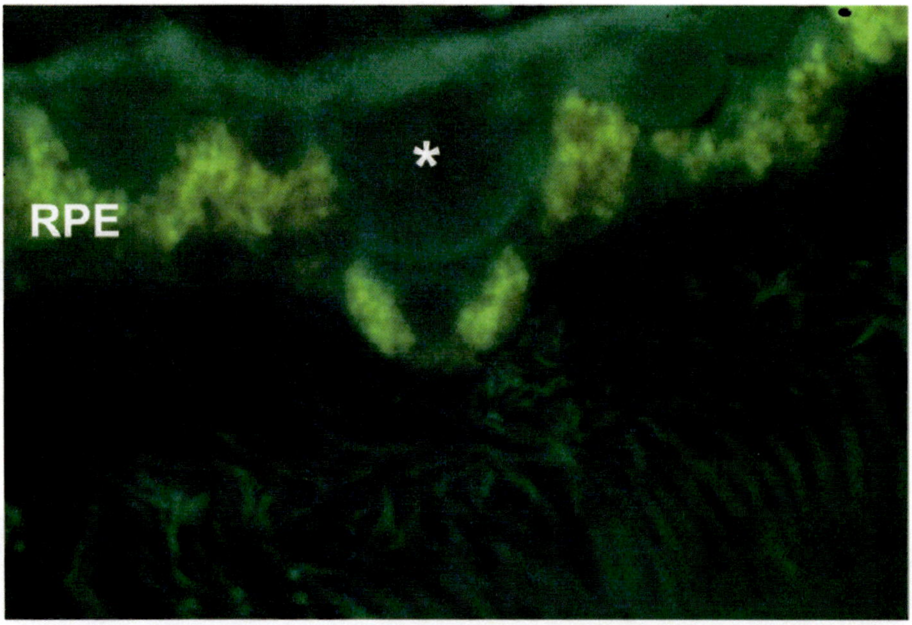

Fig. 8. Drusen with autofluorescent (*) (RPE: retinal pigmentary epithelium) (x500). (From ref. 6).

Other forms of deposit appear between the basal membrane of the RPE and the inner collagen of Bruch's membrane. These accumulations are comprised of extracellular masses of heterogeneous composition which are called drusen [9,59,121] (Fig.8,9). Many of the proteins present in the drusen are also components found in atherosclerosis, thermal elastosis, membranoproliferative glomerulonephitis type II, and Alzheimer' s disease [122]. Drusen contain serum amyloid-P component, apoliprotein E, vitronectin, immunoglobulin light chains, factor X, complement proteins, and Alzheimer's Ab-peptide [122,123]. A chronic local inflammatory component is initially associated with the formation of drusen, and it is hypothesised that the Ab-peptide activates the complement cascade involved in this formation. The debris from altered RPE cells may act as a chronic inflammatory stimulus for drusen formation [122,123].

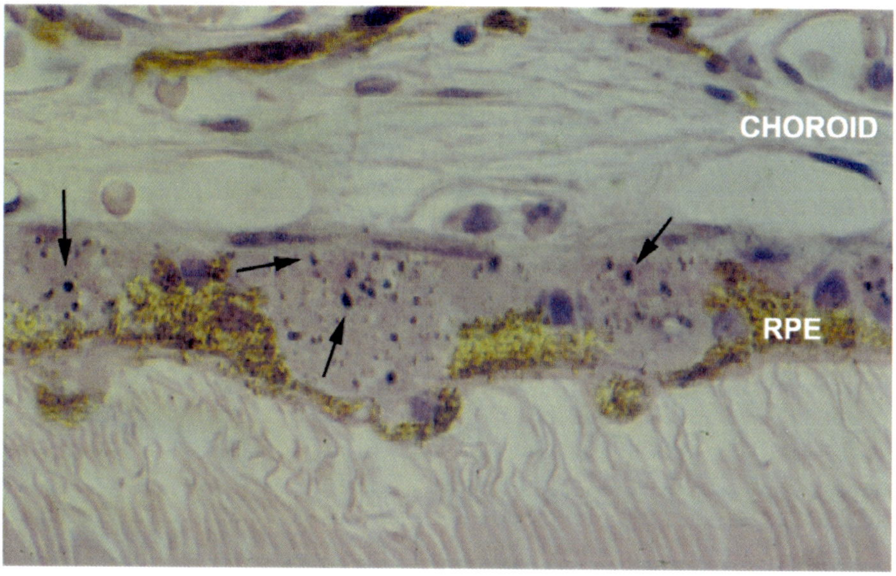

Fig. 9. Hard drusen with interior calcium deposits (arrows) (RPE: retinal pigmentary epithelium) (H-E) (x500). (From ref. 6).

Histologically, the drusen can be classified as soft or hard.

- *Soft drusen:* These constitute raised dome-shaped areas that can resemble serous detachment of the retinal pigmentary epithelium. These can coincide, reaching considerable size, and are generally related to the formation of neovessels [121,124]. This type of drusen is comprised of proteins and lipofuscin, presenting a granular aspect [80,125,126,127,128]. The size is related to the degeneration of extensive areas of RPE [64].
- *Hard drusen:* These, result from a disorder in some cells of the RPE [126], tend to present a globous form and contain dense vesicles, fibres, and granules or amorphous material of abnormal collagen and sometimes calcium [72,78,80] (Fig. 9). These drusen normally do not become complicated with choroidal neovascularizations, although if they become very numerous, this probability can increases [64,121].

In addition, at the same time as alterations appear in the RPE, changes occur in the Bruch's membrane. In AMD, swelling and disorganization of the collagen fibres are common [6,43]. The increase in the thickness of the Bruch's membrane is accompanied also by a progressive increase in lipid accumulations (Fig 10 A). These deposits of lipids or lipid-rich material could add resistance to the flow of solutes and water through the Bruch-RPE, as demonstrated by the studies that have measured the hydraulic conductivity of isolated Bruch's membranes [129,130,131]. This situation encourages the accumulation of advanced glycation end-products (AGEs) [132,133], contributing to the remodelling of the Bruch's membrane on diminishing its porosity. Also, the analysis of the lipid material shows the existence of a massive accumulation of esterified cholesterol in this membrane [88].

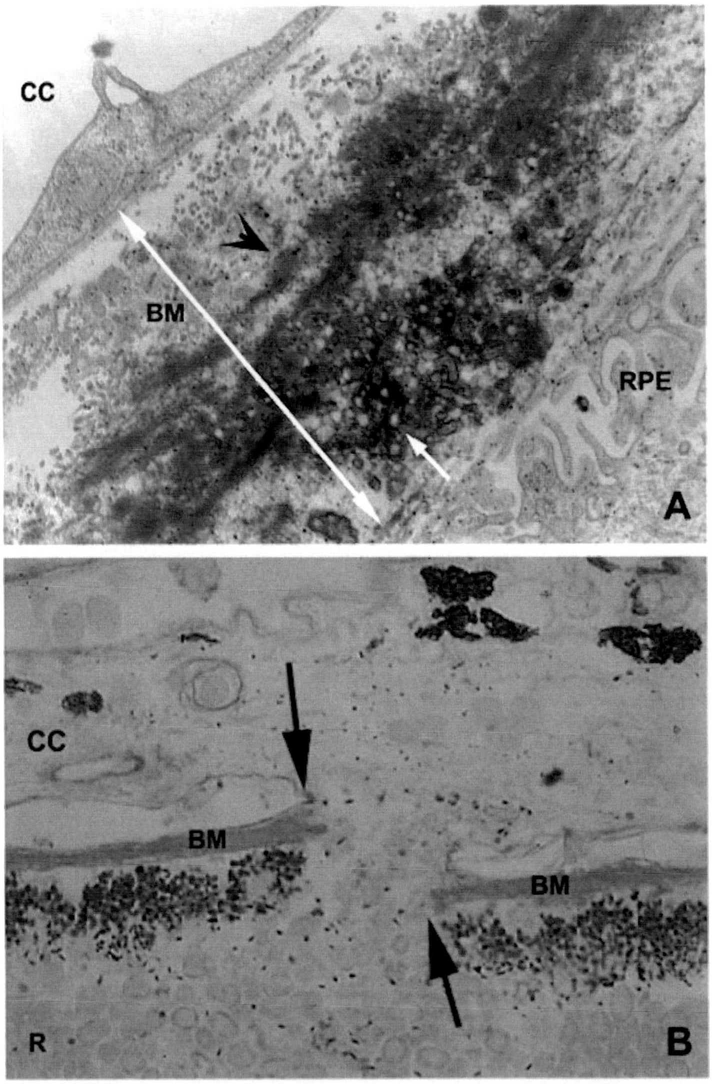

Fig. 10. Changes in the Bruch membrane. (BM: Bruch's membrane; cc: choriocapillaries). (A) Desorganization of the extracellular matrix (arrowhead: elastics fibres; arrows: granular material and vesicles; RPE: retinal pigment epithelium) (x 2000). (B) Tear in the membrane (arrows) (R: retina)(PAS; x300).

These lipid accumulations can act in two ways in the genesis of AMD:

- A hydrophobic barrier is created, interfering with the transport of nutrients and oxygen towards the retina, and retinal waste away from the retina [134].
- The deposits that accumulate under the RPE, which contain unsaturated fatty acids, are oxidized by light [135], thereby strengthening lipid peroxidation [136].

In addition, as a result of the greater lipid concentrations at the level of the drusen, there is an attraction of macrophages towards this membrane [121]. Also, the Bruch's membrane can present calcifications. In these zones, fractures can appear, through which neovessels can penetrate from the choriocapillaris to the retina [6,59,64,137] (Fig 10 B).

All these alterations induce atrophy of the RPE, which responds by releasing growth factors (e.g. VEGF) and forming choroidal neovessels responsible for the clinical manifestations of the disease [6,137]. The level of damage to the RPE, which gives rise to the basal laminar deposits and the drusen could progress in some eyes to a degenerative state with vision loss in two ways: the first involves a total degeneration of the RPE, triggering geographic atrophy; the second would be caused by the effects of the invasion of the choroidal neovessels which brings about a disciform lesion. The first clinically constitutes the dry form of the disease and the second the wet form.

Geographic atrophy (dry AMD)

At the onset of geographic atrophy, the RPE cells are found over drusen, and are often altered and dispigmented, with the adjacent photoreceptors being displaced, damaged, or even destroyed [80,138,139]. The basal laminar deposits reduce the bond between the RPE and the inner collagen of Bruch's membrane, predisposing the subject to serous detachment of the neuro-retina, with consequent injury to the photoreceptors [140,141,142] (Fig. 11).

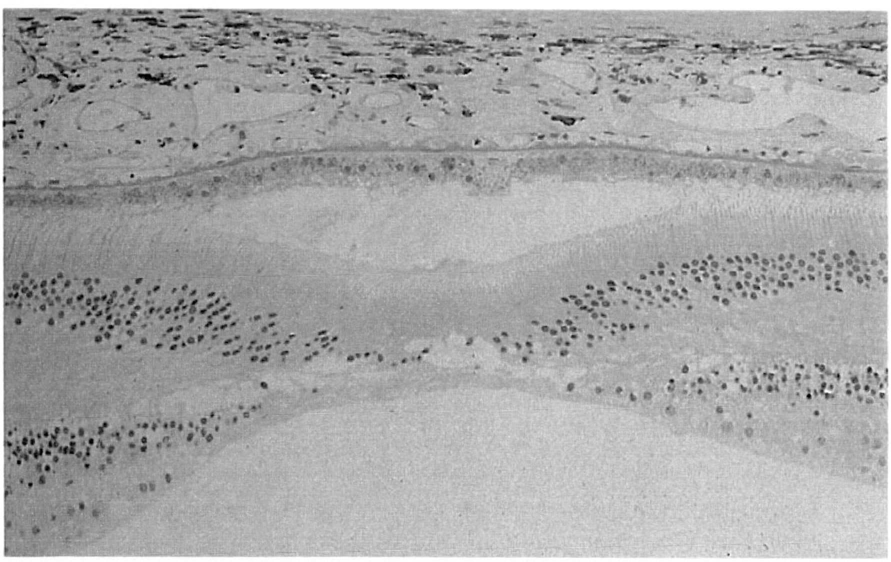

Fig. 11. Serous retinal detachment (H-E) (x125). (From ref. 6).

When both the RPE and the photoreceptors have degenerated, the basal laminar deposits can remain as drusen, or else they can calcify or disappear [9,77]. The macrophages as well as the pericytes of the choriocapillaris could contribute to the removal of this content, replacing it with fibrous tissue (Fig 12) [77,143].

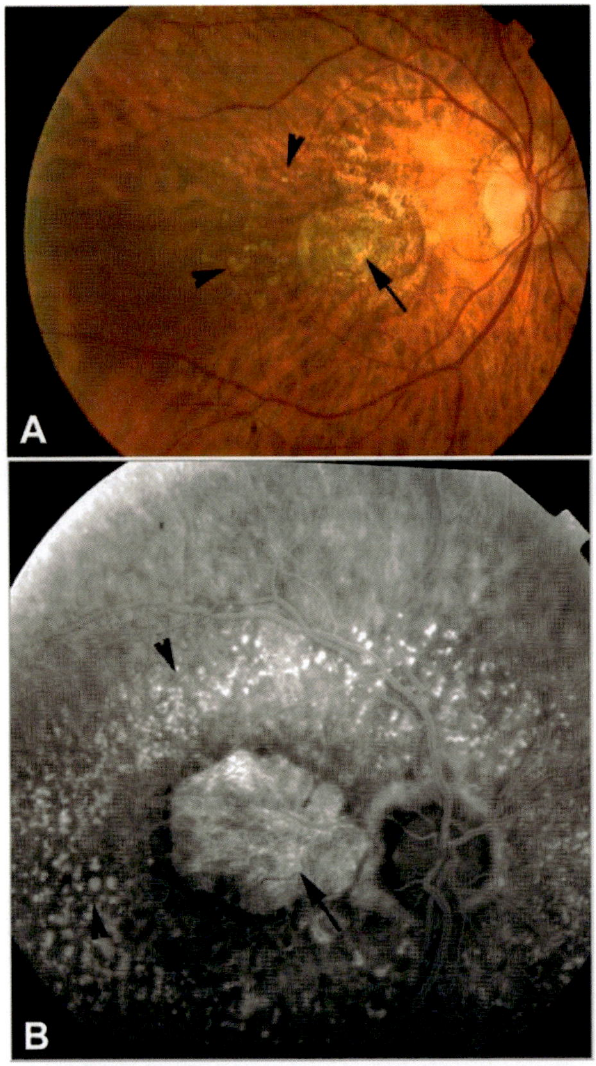

Fig. 12. Dry AMD. Hard drusen (arrowhead) and areas of atrophy (arrows) in EPR macular area. (A) Fundus picture. (B) Fundus fluorescein angiography.

Disciform degeneration (wet DMAE)

In response to aging, some eyes develop choroidal neovascularizations at the macular level. During the development of the neovascular processes, the blood vessels proliferate from the choriocapillaris to the Bruch's membrane. Afterwards, they penetrate the collagen tissue of this membrane and extend between the Bruch's membrane and the RPE. On occasions, they traverse the RPE, situating themselves under the sensorial retina (Fig.13). In both situations, the external hematoretinal barrier is broken. [80]. This process is more probable than it appears when it follows a strong deterioration of the RPE, with the presence of thick basal laminar deposits and confluent soft drusen [9,77].

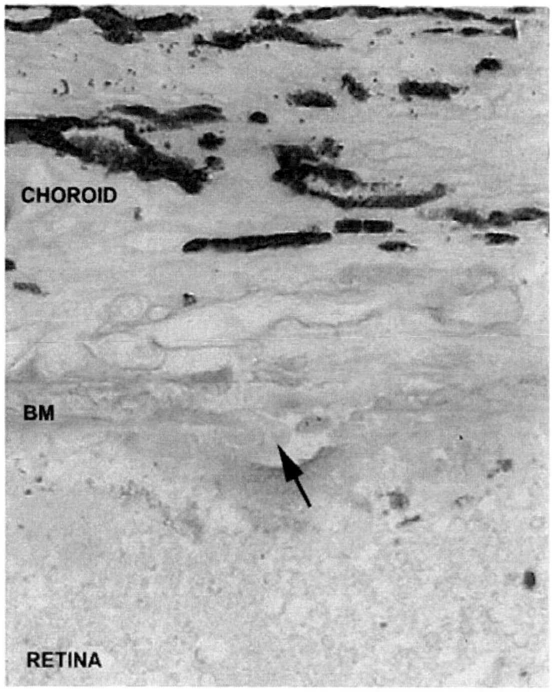

Fig. 13. Choroidal new-vessels (arrow) traversing the Bruch`s membrane (BM) and entering the subretinal space. (PAS) (x500). (From ref. 6).

The mechanism by which the choroidal vessels invade the Bruch's membrane is not precisely known. It is speculated that the vessels are attracted by factors such as the increase of the basal laminar deposit, the presence of macrophages in the Bruch's membrane, ischemia of the neurosensorial retina, the inability of the Bruch's membrane to diffuse metabolites, the alteration in the immunity to the retinal antigens S, and the accumulation of vasogenic substances in the Bruch's membrane [80].

Once the choroidal vessels have penetrated the Bruch membrane and have established themselves under the RPE, they tend to hemorrhage [72,144]. This blood spreads laterally, entering retinal zones weakened by the formation of basal laminar deposits and soft drusen. In this way, the RPE and its basal membrane are separated from the Bruch's membrane, forming a lump [64]. In addition, this fluid can accumulate between cells of the RPE and the neurosensorial retina, rapidly destroying the pigmentary epithelium and the photoreceptors in a broader area, with the subsequent vision loss [144,145].

This blood accumulation stimulates the proliferation of fibrous tissue, which produces a fibre-vascular plaque or scar tissue that constitutes a disciform scar. In some disciform lesions, the RPE, the photoreceptors, and the choriocapillaris can degenerate in the zones near the original disciform scar [144]. All this causes the surrounding zones that are geographically atrophied to increase the area of the blindness [64].

On clinical examination the eye of these patients present serous detachment of the macular retina, detachment of the RPE of the central retina, lipid exudates, and haemorrhages, all of these being signs of the existence of a choroidal neovascular membrane (CNVM) (Fig. 14). The CNVMs can be manifested ophthalmoscopically in two ways: the classical and occult way [146].

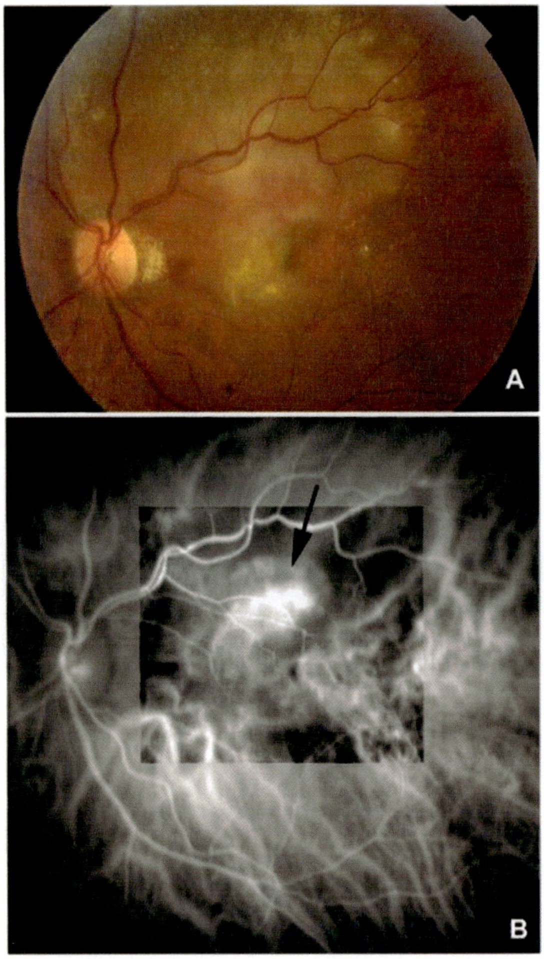

Fig. 14. Wet AMD. The presence of retinal serous detachment, haemorhages and exudates indicate the probable existence of a ocult choroidal neovascular membrane (arrow). (A) Fundus picture. (B) Fundus indocyanine green angiography.

The classical CNVM is a visible, well-defined membrane that is present in 15-20% of the exudative forms. The occult form, much more frequent than the classical CNVM, is found in 80% of all the exudative forms. The occult CNVM receives its name from its location under the RPE, which blocks its visibility. Suspicion of its presence is based on the appearance of different opthalmoscopic signs such as retinal serous detachment or the subtle exudates [146] (Fig 14).

5.2. How Might the Inner Retina be Involved in the Etiopathology of AMD?

The exact cause of AMD is not known, but, as discussed above, different factors have been postulated as risk factors, notably: genetic factors (mutation in the ABCR gene), cardiovascular diseases (hypertension, arteriosclerosis) and environmental factors (exposure to UV rays and to oxidative damage) [2,18]. The latter two factors could aggravate the situation of ischemia and oxidative damage that arises in normal retinal aging. Most studies on AMD focus only on the outer portion of the retina and the choriocapillaris, almost without considering the possible involvement of the inner retina in this pathology [7,147,148].

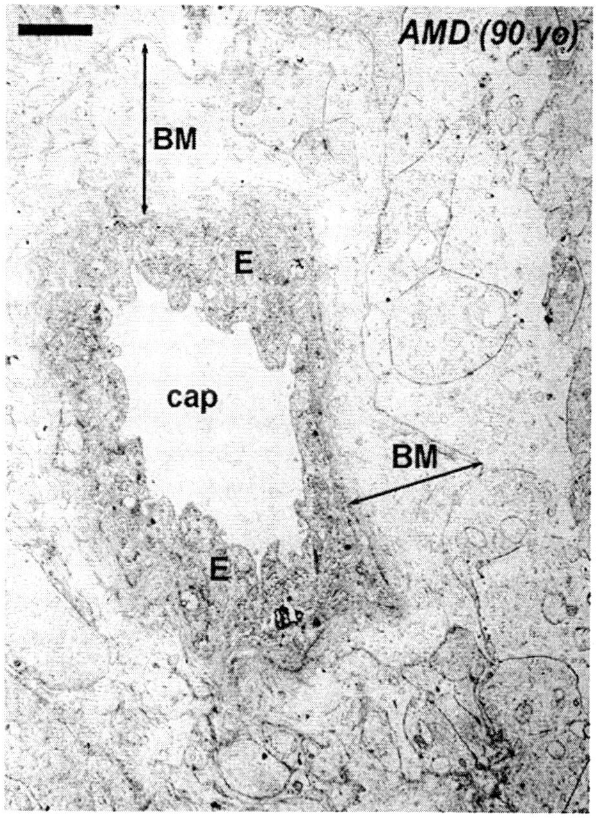

Fig. 15. AMD retina: Capillary (cap) of the NFL. The basal membrane (BM) is very thick and the endothelial cells (E) are severely damaged. (Bar = 2 μm). (From ref. 7).

The dysfunction of the RPE with the subsequent production of basal laminar deposits, drusen, and thickening of the Bruch's membrane, as well as choriocapillaris atrophy, diminishes the communication and diffusion of nutrients between the choroid and the photoreceptors, provoking the death of the latter [8,27,62]. However, if we compound this situation with a number of changes that bring about the death of the ganglion cells, we find that the situation becomes notably more serious.

The great convergence that the retina has in conducting visual signals should be taken into account: each eye has 125 million rods and cones but only 1 million ganglion cells [149]. Therefore, the disappearance of ganglion cells has a strong physiological impact. The changes observed in the inner retina among individuals with AMD [7] are equivalent to those found by other authors in the outer retina [1], and resemble an advanced process of retinal aging.

The basal membrane of the retinal capillaries considerably thickens in AMD with respect to normal aged individuals, exhibiting a thick outer layer of collagen appearing in contact with the Müller cells and astrocytes [7] (Fig. 15). There is a greater proportion of acellular capillaries that lose functionality, and therefore the situation of ischemia can be considerably exacerbated with respect to the aged individuals [7].

In retinas with AMD, a great quantity of hypertrophied and reactive astrocytes are found. Electron microscopy has revealed that these phagocyte the remains of ganglion cells that have died by necrosis or apoptosis (Fig. 16). Also, these cells contain a large amount of lipofuscin, as do the ganglion cells and their axons [7].

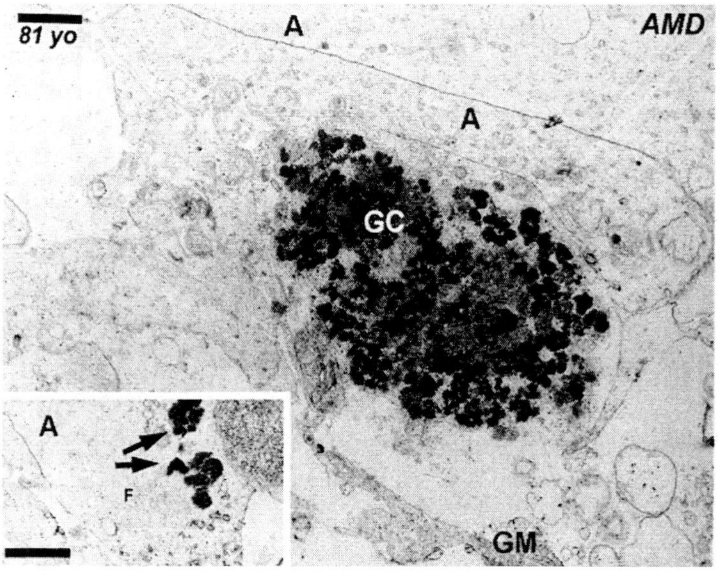

Fig. 16. AMD retina: Apoptotic ganglion cell. The insert shows an apoptotic nucleus phagocyted by an astrocyte (arrow). (A: astrocyte; F:glial filament GC: ganglion cell; GM Müller glia) (Bar = 1 μm). (From ref. 7).

The high degree of retinal ischemia that can occur in AMD, added to the decline in astroglial cells as a result of normal aging, could provoke the death of ganglion cells that cannot be defended against oxidative damage. In addition, the basal membrane of ILM of the retina doubles in thickness with respect to the normal aged individual, and can impede the exchange of substances between the retina and the vitreous humour (Fig. 17). Exacerbating this circumstance, the reactive astrocytes overcharged with lipofuscin can expel this into the ILM [7].

In individuals with AMD, astroglial protrusions have been found in the form of trunks, intensely GFAP(+), which cross through the ILM and lodge in the vitreous humour (Fig. 18 B,C). It has been confirmed that these protrusions are made up of astrocytes with very lengthy prolongations arrayed parallel to the ILM and forming a glial membrane. These prolongations communicate by numerous gap junctions. In addition, these astrocytes have microvilli in contact with the vitreous humour, where the basal membrane disappears, permitting direct contact between the vitreous humour and astrocytes [7] (Fig. 18 A).

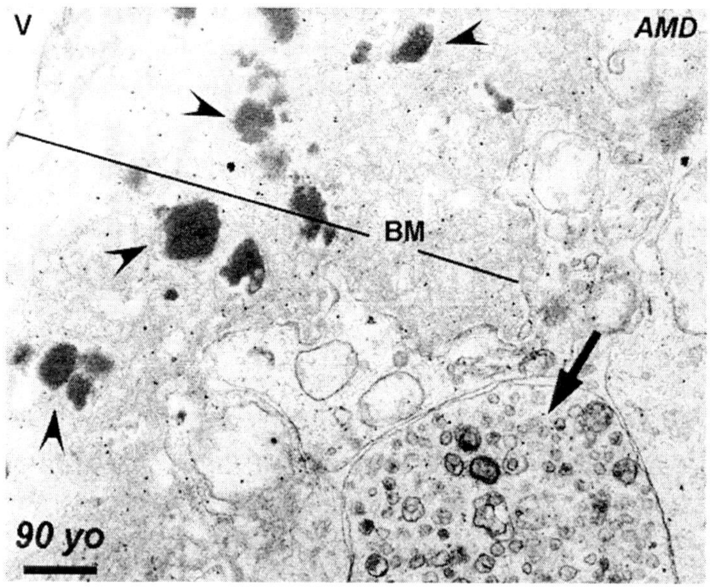

Fig. 17. AMD retina: Ganglion cell axon with membrane organelles undergoing degeneration in the cytoplasms (arrow). The basal membrane (BM) of the ILM is thicker than in the normal old retinas and has numerous lipids (arrowhead). (Bar = 500 μm). (V: vitreous humor). (From ref. 7).

In addition, in retinas with AMD, another, thicker, cell type intensely GFAP(+) has been found, columnar in shape and arranged parallel to the ILM, intermixed with the above-mentioned astrocytes (Fig 18 B, D) [7]. Electron microscopy has shown that these cells correspond to reactive Müller glia [7], which in pathological situations can express the protein GFA [150] (Fig 18 A).

Numerous studies have been made on subretinal neovascular membranes that appear in the AMD. These membranes are produced by the migration of choroidal endothelial cells across Bruch's membrane towards the subretinal space [151]. However, there are few studies available on these glial membranes in the inner retina in AMD [7,147].

On the other hand, many studies have demonstrated that epiretinal membranes, similar to those found in AMD, can appear by an inflammation, a retinal tear, or retinal occlusions [116]. Taking this last point into account, we note that the serious ischemia that can be triggered in the retina by AMD could cause the astrocytes to migrate towards the vitreous humour, where there is a metabolic reserve. These astrocytes, having microvilli, provide a broad surface of contact and therefore of exchange with the vitreous humour. Furthermore, these cells are linked by gap-junctions, and thus the astrocytes within the retina make contact with those in the vitreous humour. In this way, these cells could send nutrients from the vitreous humour towards the retina, and the waste products from the retina to the vitreous humour [7].

However, the factors that make the astrocytes and Müller glia migrate towards the vitreous humour in AMD are unknown; nor is it known whether these membranes could worsen the pathological situation of AMD by possible tractions of the retina and vitreous humour, provoking further retinal detachments.

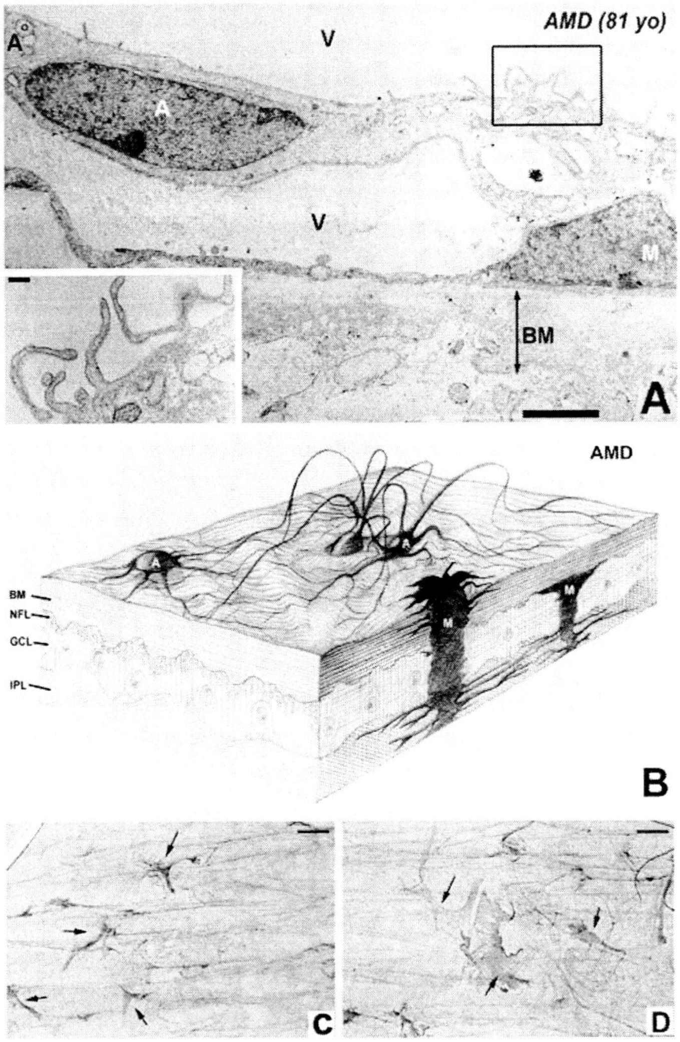

Fig. 18.- AMD retina: epiretinal astroglial membrane. (From ref. 7). (A) Astrocytes (A) and Müller cell (M) located in the vitreous humor (V). The Müller cell adheres to the vitreous face of the ILM. The insert shows the astrocyte microvilli without basal membrane in AMD retinas. (BM: basal membrane) (Bar = 2 μm; insert: bar = 0.4 μm). (B) Three-dimensional scheme of a glial membrane. The astrocytes (A) and the Müller cells (M) pass through the basal membrane (BM) of the inner limiting membrane (ILM) and form a glial membrane running parallel to the ILM in the vitreous humor. (IPL: inner plexiform layer; GCL: ganglion cell layer; NFL: nerve fiber layer). (C) The arrows show robust-bodied astrocytes with high GFAP immunoreactivity protuding from the retina to the vitreous humor. (D) Another type of glial cell can be seen in the astroglial membrane. These cells have a strongly GFAP(+) rectangular body and could be reactive Müller glia (arrow). (C.D: Retinal whole-mount, anti GFAP; Bar = 25 μm).

5.3. Pathogenic Theories on AMD

Various mechanisms have been implicated in the genesis of AMD [6], the most important being:

Vascular model or scleral rigidity [60]

This model holds that the same mechanisms that cause lipids to deposit on the systemic artery walls, in aging and in atherosclerosis, make AMD the result of the accumulation of lipids in the sclera and in the Bruch's membrane. These accumulations increase the rigidity of these tissues, in turn provoking greater choroidal vascular resistance. As a result, the choriocapillaris pressure augments and the choroidal blood flow diminishes.

The lipids deposited in the Bruch's membrane show the basal laminar deposits and drusen as well as the degeneration of the elastic tissue and the collagen, leading to calcification and fragmentation of the membrane. The combination of a high choriocapillaris pressure, the presence of the vascular endothelium growth factor (VEGF) and the rupture of the calcified Bruch's membrane cause choroidal neovascularization in the wet form of AMD. In addition, this model postulate that the drusen (which cause the atrophy of the RPE as part of the development of the dry form of AMD), together with the diminished choroidal flow, would also be added factors in the development of this situation.

Theory of solar radiation

In AMD a progressive deterioration, takes place in the outermost retinal tissues. Experimental studies have demonstrated that intense light damages the same region that is altered with AMD [152,153,154]. In the eyes of primates, the high-energy portion of the solar spectrum is the most dangerous to the retina. The visible high-energy photons and UV can cause molecular damage by a photochemical mechanism [118, 155]. This lesion increases with oxygen, spurring reactions of the free-radical chains (photodynamic effect) [156]. Melanin and lens opacity can protect the retina from AMD [118,157].

Accumulations of lipofuscin at the level of the RPE cause AMD with aging. Lipofuscin is composed of molecules so altered that they cannot be degraded by the native enzymes [64]. The damage caused in the molecular constituents of the retinal tissues at the macular level exceed the capacity of the retinal system for molecular reconstruction. Consequently, the retina progressively degenerates, causing a thickening of the RPE, with excretion of waste material towards the Bruch's membrane. In this membrane, the basal laminar deposits and the drusen later form, triggering geographic atrophy or disciform degeneration as the final phase of AMD [64,118].

Haematogenous photosensitization, [27,158]

AMD may be the result of photosensitization of the endothelium of the choriocapillaris, of the Bruch's membrane, and of the RPE by one superoxide anion and one oxygen anion generated by photoactive components of the blood. This photoactive compound could be protoporphyrin IX, precursor of the haemoglobin molecule located in the erythrocytes and plasma. This compound generates superoxide and oxygen anions in quantities that depend on the concentration of protoporphyrin IX and on the intensity and wavelength of the light emitted. In AMD the usual pattern of sinusoidal capillary lobules is replaced by a tubular capillary network, which has a lower surface: volume ratio [159]. This change might be due to primary damage to the choriocapillaris endothelium (e.g. oxidative damage mediated by protoporphyrins), might follow the loss of RPE cells (e.g. secondary to chronic oxidative damage) with attendant loss of VEGF and other trophic factors [160] or might arise from a combination of these processes. Photoreceptor death follows RPE cell loss [75,161]

Immune response in AMD

Recently, it has been found that many of the chronic degenerative diseases associated with age present an important inflammatory and immune component, and thus perhaps AMD also presents this same component.

Innate immunity involves activation by retinal or choroidal injury or infection. Antigen-specific immunity involves normal activation by foreign antigens and aberrant activation in AMD by molecular mimicry, antigen desequestration, neo-antigen formation, or antigen trapping. Innate immunity, antigen-specific immunity, and amplification cascades contribute to the pathogenesis of atherosclerosis, Alzheimer's disease and glomerular diseases. Innate immunity, antigen-specific immunity, and amplification cascades may contribute to AMD [162]

Oxidative damage in AMD

Oxidative aggression plays an important role in the etiopathogeny of AMD. Several epidemiological studies, such as the Eye Disease Case Control Study Group [163], the Baltimore Longitudinal Study on Aging [164] and the POLA Study [165], support this hypothesis. These are based on the analysis of blood markers of the antioxidative state under living conditions that can provoke oxidative aggression, such as light exposure and smoking. The results suggest that high concentrations of antioxidants (vitamins E and C, selenium and carotenoids) in the blood are associated with a lower risk of neovascular AMD. It also appears that a high plasma concentration of alpha-tocoferol is a protective factor against AMD, and that on the contrary a high plasma level of glutation peroxidase is associated with a higher prevalence of late forms of AMD.

Potential causes of oxidative aggression that merit emphasis are aging and ischemia. AMD has been related to progressive ischemia due to choriocapillaris sclerosis, though this may be secondary to the atrophy of the RPE. Ischemia would cause oxygenated free radicals and the expression of vascular endothelial growth factor (VEGF) involved in post-ischemic neovascularization processes. Aging, which has been associated with the theory of free radicals, is characterized at the cellular level by an increase in lipofuscin. This fluorescent pigment is composed of products of lipid oxidation bonded to wastes of protein origin. The accumulation of lipofuscin granules in the RPE is typical of aging and constitutes a sign of intense oxidative metabolism.

6. Conclusion

Retinal aging and AMD form part of a continual deterioration, in which the transition between aging and diseases is signalled by vision loss. On the basis of what has been discussed in this chapter, we offer a hypothetical sequence for the etiopathogeny of AMD.

Oxidative stress injures cells of the choriocapillaris and the retina. In the former, the lesions of the vascular endothelium provoke changes inside the vascular vessels, altering the blood flow and leading to ischemia. In the retina, this oxidative stress deteriorates the RPE, great quantities of lipofuscin accumulating in its interior, impeding the normal functioning of the cell. These injuries, at the level of the choriocapillaris-RPE zone, prompt a chronic inflammatory response, both in the Bruch membrane as well as in the choroid, giving rise to an abnormal ECM, which thickens the Bruch membrane. This thickening also involves lipid deposits which, expelled by the biologically altered RPE, constitute laminar deposits and drusen. Both accumulations, together with the thickening of the Bruch membrane, impede the normal diffusion of nutrients or waste products between the choroid and retina. This situation damages the outer retina, which could trigger retinal-choroidal atrophy or neovascularization (clinical manifestations of AMD).

In the inner retina, oxidative stress can also provoke neuronal and vascular alterations. The basal membranes of the capillaries thicken, lipofuscin accumulating both in these membranes and in the endothelium. This can hamper the exchange of normal nutrients and lead to ischemia. This situation in turn can prompt astrocytes to become reactive, in an attempt to regulate the antioxidant defences and protect the retinal neurons from free-radical attack. The reactive astrocytes are more susceptible to the attack of free radicals, resulting in the death of these cells. All these changes become more severe in AMD. The basal membranes both of the capillaries as well as of the ILM thicken considerably, accumulating lipids that hinder the diffusion of nutrients. There is a great loss of macroglial cells (Müller cells and astrocytes) and of neurons. Neuronal death can increase by the disappearance of the glia. However, some of the macroglial cells that remain can migrate towards the vitreous humour in search of nutrients. These cells form epiretinal membranes in an attempt to improve the situation of retinal ischemia. Nevertheless, it is not known whether these membranes could worsen the pathological situation of AMD.

Finally, it should be pointed out that in light of all the above, and despite the different hypotheses that seek to explain the disease, ischemia stands as an extremely important factor in the genesis of AMD. These facts should lead us to reflect, in the sense of trying to control risk factors and habits that favour ischemia, while its reversibility is still possible.

7. References

[1] Campochiaro, PA; Soloway, P; Ryan, SJ; Miller, JW. The pathogenesis of choroidal neovascularization in patients with age-related macular degeneration. *Molecular Vision*, 1999, 5, 34. <http.//www.molvis.org/molvis/ v5/p34>

[2] Hawkins, BS; Bird, A; Klein, R; West, SK. Epidemiology of age-related macular degeneration. *Molecular Vision*; 1999, 5, 26. <http.//www.molvis.org/ molvis/v5/p26>

[3] Serrano, P. Epidemiología de la degeneración macular asociada a la edad y ceguera en la vejez. In: Gómez-Ulla F, Marín F, Ramírez JM, Triviño A, editors. *La mácula senil.* Barcelona: EDIKA-MED; 1993, 55-71.

[4] Ramírez, JM; Triviño, A; Ramírez, AI; Salazar, JJ. La mácula senil. In: Gómez-Ulla F, Marín F, Ramírez JM, Triviño A, editors. *La mácula senil.* Barcelona: EDIKA-MED; 1993, 3-21.

[5] Harris, A; Chung, HS; Ciulla, TA; Kagemann, L. Progress in measurement of ocular blood flow and relevance to our understanding of glaucoma and age-related macular degeneration. *Progress in Retinal and Eye Research*; 1999, 18, 669-687.

[6] Triviño, A; Ramírez, JM; Salazar, JJ; Ramírez, AI. Fisiología de la degeneración macular asociada a la edad. In: Gómez-Ulla F, Marín F, Ramírez JM, Triviño A, editors. *La mácula senil.* Barcelona: EDIKA-MED; 1993, 23-33.

[7] Ramírez, JM; Ramírez, AI; Salazar, JJ; De Hoz, R; Triviño, A. Changes of astrocytes in retinal ageing and age-related macular degeneration. *Experimental Eye Research*, 2001, 73, 601-615.

[8] Adler, R; Curcio, C; Hicks, D; Price, D; Wong, F. Cell death in age-related macular degeneration. *Molecular Vision,* 1999, 5, 31. <http.//www.molvis.org/ molvis/v5/p31>

[9] Green, WR. Retina. In: Spencer WH, editors. *Ophthalmic pathology: an atlas and textbook.* Philadelphia: WB Saunders Company; 1985, 589-1291.

[10] Hjelmeland, LM; Cristofalo, VJ; Funk, W; Rakoczy, E; Katz, ML. Senescence of the retinal pigment epithelium. *Molecular Vision*; 1999. 5: 33. <http.//www. molvis.org/molvis/v5/p33>

[11] Lutty, G; Grunwald, J; Majji, AB; Uyama, M; Yoneya, S. Changes in choriocapillaris and retinal pigment epithelium (RPE) in age-related macular degeneration. *Molecular Vision*, 1999, 5, 35. <http.//www.molvis.org/molvis/ v5/p35>

[12] WHO: Blindness and visual disability. Part V of VII: Seeing ahead, projections into the next century. *Fact Sheet N 146.* February 1997.

[13] Serrano, P. Epidemiología de los problemas de visión en los ancianos. In: Ribera JM, editors. *Alteraciones de los órganos de los sentidos en el anciano.* Madrid: Editores Médicos SA, 1994, 31-44.

[14] WHO: Blindness and visual disability. Part III of VII: Other leading causes worldwide. *Fact Sheet N 144.* February 1997.

[15] Buch, H; Vinding, T; Nielsen, NV. Prevalence and causes of visual impairment according to World Health Organization and United States criteria in an aged, urban Scandinavians population: The Copenhagen City Eye Study. *Ophthalmology*, 2001, 108, 2347-2357.

[16] la Cour, M; Kiilgaard, JF; Nissen, MG. Age-related macular degeneration: epidemiology and optimal treatment. *Drugs Aging*, 2002, 19,101-133.

[17] Mitchell, P; Wang, JJ; Foran, S; Smith, W. Five-year incidence of age-related maculopathy lesions: The Blue Mountains Eye Study. *Ophthalmology*, 2002, 109, 1092-1097.

[18] Hammond, C; Webster, AR; Snieder, H; Bird, AC; Gilbert, CE; Spector, TD. Genetic influence on early age-realted maculopathy: a twin study. *Ophthalmology,* 2002, 109, 730-736.

[19] Simonelli, F; Margaglione, M; Testa, F; Capucci, G; Manitto, MP; Brancato, R; Rinaldi, E. Apolipoprotein E polymorphisms in age-realte macular degeneration in an Italian population. *Ophthalmic Research,* 2001, 33, 325-328.

[20] Gorin, MB; Breitner, JCS; De Jong, PTVM; Hageman, GS; Klaver, CCW; Kuehn, MH; Seddon, J M. The genetics of age-related macular degeneration. *Molecular Vision,* 1999, 5, 29 <http.//www.molvis.org/molvis/ v5/p29>

[21] Allikmets, R; Shroyer, NF; Singh, N; Seddon, JM; Lewis, RA; Bernstein, PS; Peiffer, A; Zabriskie, NA; Li, Y; Hutchinson, A; Dean, M; Lupski, JR; Leppert, M. Mutation of the Stargardt disease gene (ABCR) in age-related macular degeneration. *Science*, 1977; 277, 33, 1805-1807.

[22] Stone, EM; Webster, AR; Vandenburgh, K; Streb, LM; Hockey, RR; Lotery, AJ; Sheffield, VC. Allelic variation in ABCR associated with Stargardt disease but not age-related macular degeneration. *Nature Genetics*, 1998; 20, 328-329.

[23] Yates, JRW; Moore, AT. Genetic susceptibility to age-related macular degeneration. *Journal of Medical Genetics,* 2000, 37, 63-87.

[24] Smith, W; Assink, J; Klein, R; Mitchel, P; Klaver, CC; Klein, BE; Hofman, A; Jensen, S; Wang, JJ; de Jong, PT. Risk factors for age-realted macular degeneration: Pooled findings from three continents. *Ophthalmology*, 2001, 108, 697-704.

[25] Obisesan, TO; Kosoko, O; Hirsch, R; Carlson, L; Parrott, M; Obisesan, TO. Moderate wine consumption is associated with decreased odds of developing age-related macular degeneration in NHANES-1. *Journal of the American Geriatrics Society*, 1998, 46, 1-7.

[26] Mitchell, P; Smith, W; Wang, JJ. Iris color, skin sun sensitivity and age-related maculopathy. *Ophthalmology*, 1998, 105, 1359-1363.

[27] Winkler, BS; Boulton, ME; Gottsch, JD; Sternberg, P. Oxidative damage and age-related macular degeneration. *Molecular vision,* 1999, 5, 32 <http.//www. molvis.org/molvis/v5/p32>

[28] Mares-Perlman, JA; Fisher, AI; Klein, R; Palta, M; Block, G; Millen, AE; Wright, JD. Lutein and Zeaxanthin in the diet and serum and their relation to Age-Related Maculopathy in the Third National Health and Nutrition Examination Survey. *American Journal of Epidemiology,* 2001, 153, 424-432.

[29] Cho, E; Hung, S; Willett, WC; Spiegelman, D; Rimm, EB; Seddon, JM; Colditz, GA; Hankinson, SE. Prospective study of dietary fat and the risk of age-related macular degeneration. *American Journal of Clinical Nutrition*, 2001, 73, 209-218

[30] Zahn, RK. Edad y envejecimiento. In: Schmidt RF, Thews G, editors. *Fisiología humana*. Madrid: McGraw-Hill Interamericana; 1993; 866-871.

[31] Dice, JF. Cellular and molecular mechanisms of aging. *Physiological Reviews*, 1993, 73, 149-159.

[32] Miquel, J. Envejecimiento celular y molecular. Teorías del envejecimiento. In: Salgado A, Guillén F, editors. *Manual de Geriatría*. Barcelona: Ediciones Científicas y Técnicas; 1994; 1-20.

[33] Miquel, J; Fleming, JE. Testing ageing theories. In: Lints FA, Soliman MH. *Drosophila as a model organism for ageing studies*. Glasgow: Blackie; 1988; 17-29.

[34] Mora, F; Porras, A. Procesos involutivos del sistema nervioso. In: Delgado JM, Ferrús A, Mora F, Rubia FJ. *Manual de neurociencia.* Madrid: Editorial Síntesis SA; 1998; 915-928.

[35] Stadtman, ER. Protein oxidation and aging. *Science,* 1992, 257, 1220-1224.

[36] Toyokuni, S. Reactive oxygen species-induced molecular damage and its application in pathology. *Pathology International*, 1999, 49, 91-102.

[37] Miquel, J. Envejecimiento fisiológico, celular y subcelular. In: Leloir S, Ochoa S, Oro J, Scols A, editors. *Bioquímica y biología molecular*. Barcelona: Salvat Editores; 1986; 241-248.

[38] Miquel, J; Johnson, JE; Cervos-Navarro, J. Comparison of CNS aging in humans and experimental animals. Brain aging: neuropathology and neuropharmacology. In: Cervos-Navarro J, Sarkander HI, editors. *Aging*. New York: Raven Press; 1983; 231-258.

[39] McGill, JI; Liakos, GM; Goulding, N; Seal, DV. Normal tear protein profiles and age-related changes. *Journal of Gerontology,* 1984, 15, 149-154.

[40] Verzar, F. Aging of conective tissues. *Gerontologia*, 1957, 1, 363-378.

[41] Robert, L. Mechanisms of aging of the extracellular matrix: role of the elastin-laminin receptor. *Gerontology*, 1998, 44, 307-317.

[42] Chandrasekhar, S; Sorrentino, JA; Mills. AJ. Interaction of fibronectin with colagen: age-specific defect in the biological activity of human fibroblast fibronectin. *Proceedings of the National Academy of Sciences of the United States of America,* 1983, 80, 4747-4751.

[43] Zarbin, MA. Current Concepts in the pathogenesis of age-related macular degeneration. *Archives of Ophthalmology,* 2004, 122, 598-614

[44] Chevaleraud, JP. Oeil et sénescence. In: *Enciclopèdie Médico-Chirurgicale* (Paris); 1982, 21, 465 A10-12.

[45] Sekuler, R; Hutman, LP; Owsley, CJ. Human aging and spatial vision. *Science,* 1980, 209, 1255-1256.

[46] Spear, P. D. Neural bases of visual deficits during aging. *Vision Research*; 1993, 33: 2589-2609.

[47] Triviño, A; Serrano, P; Ramírez, JM; Vara, ML; García-Sánchez, J. Estudio de la edad sobre el test de sensibilidad al contraste en una población supuestamente normal. *Archivos de la Sociedad Española de Oftalmología,* 1988, 55, 259-264.

[48] Carter, JH. The effects of aging upon selected visual functions: color vision, glare sensitivity, field of vision, and accomadation. In: Alan R, editor. *Aging and human visual functions*. New York: Liss Inc; 1982, 121-130.

[49] Birch, DG; Anderson, JL. Standardized full-field electroretinography; Normal values and their variation with age. *Archives of Ophthalmology*, 1992, 110, 1571-1576.

[50] Weleber, RG. The effect of age on human cone and rod ganzfeld electroretinograms. *Investigative Ophthalmology and Visual Science,* 1981, 20, 392-399.

[51] Fortune, B; Jonhson, CA. Decline of photopic multifocal electroretinogram responses with age is due primarily to preretinal optical factors. *Journal of the Optical Society of America A: Optics and Image Science, and Vision,* 2002, 19, 173-184.

[52] Gerth, C; Garcia, SM; Ma, L; Keltner, JL; Werner, JS. Multifocal electroretinogram: age-related changes for different luminance levels. *Graefe's Archive for Clinical and Experimental Ophthalmology*, 2002, 240, 202-208.

[53] Jackson, GR; Ortega, J; Girkin, C; Rosenstiel, CE; Owsley, C. Aging-related changes in the multifocal electroretinogram. *Journal of the Optical Society of America A: Optics and Image Science, and Vision,* 2002, 19, 185-189.

[54] Kurtenbach, A; Weiss, M. Effect of aging on multifocal oscillatory potencials. *Journal of the Optical Society of America A: Optics and Image Science, and Vision,* 2002, 19, 190-196.

[55] Bonnel, S; Mohand-Said, S; Sahel, JA. The aging of the retina. *Experimental Gerontology,* 2003, 38, 825-83.

[56] Ramrattan, RS; Van der Schaft, TL; Mooy, CM; de Bruijn, WC; Mulder, PGH; de Jong, PTVM. Morphometric analysis of Bruch'S membrane,the choriocapillaris and the choroid in ageing. *Investigative Ophthalmology and Visual Science,*1994, 35, 2857-2864.

[57] Pauleikhoff, D; Harper, C; Marshall, J; Bird, AC. Aging changes in Bruch's membrane:a histochemical and morphologic study. *Ophthalmology*, 1990 , 97, 171-178.
[58] Grunwald, J; Harisprasad, S; Dupont, J. Effect on aging on foveolar choroidal circulation. *Archives of Ophthalmology,* 1998, 116, 150-154.
[59] Eagle, RC. Mechanisms of maculopathy. *Ophthalmology*, 1984, 91, 613-625.
[60] Friedman, E; Tso, MOM. The retinal pigment epithelium.II. Histology changes associated with age. *Archives of Ophthalmology,* 1968, 79, 315-320.
[61] Gao, H; Hollyfield, JG. Aging of the human retina. Differential loss of neurons and retinal pigment epithelial cells. *Investigative Ophthalmology and Visual Science,* 1992, 33, 1-17.
[62] Green, WR. Histopathology of age-related macular degeneration. *Molecular Vision,* 1999, 5, 27. <http.//www.molvis.org/molvis/ v5/p27>
[63] Hogan, MJ. Role of the retinal pigment epithelium in macular disease. *Transactions American Academy of Ophthalmology and Otolaryngology*, 1972, 76, 64-80.
[64] Young, RW. Pathophysiology of age-related macular degeneration. *Survey of Ophthalmology,* 1987, 31, 291-306.
[65] Feeney-Burns, L; Hilderbrand, ES; Eldridge, S. Aging human RPE: morphometric analysis of macular, equatorial, and peripheral cells. *Investigative Ophthalmology and Visual Science,* 1984, 25, 195-200.
[66] Sundelin, SP; Wihlmark, U; Nilsson, SEG; Brunk, UT. Lipofuscin accumulation in cultured retinal pigment epithelial cells reduces their phagocytic capacity. *Current Eye Research*, 1998, 17,851-857.
[67] Wassell, J; Davies, S; Bardsley, W; Boulton, M. The photoreactivity of the retinal age pigment lipofuscin. *Journal of Biological Chemistry*, 1999, 274, 23828-23832.
[68] Schutt, F; Davies, S; Kopitz, J; Holz, FG; Boulton, ME. Photodamage to human RPE cells by A2-E, a retinoid component of lipofuscin. *Investigative Ophthalmology and Visual Science,* 2000, 41, 2303-2308.
[69] Sparrow, JR; Nakanishi, K; Parish, CA. The lipofuscin fluorophore A2E mediates blue light-induced damage to retinal pigmented epithelial cells. *Investigative Ophthalmology and Visual Science,* 2000, 41, 1981-1989.
[70] Eldred, GE; Lasky, MR. Retinal age pigments generated by self assembling lysosomotropic detergents. *Nature*, 1993, 361, 724-726.
[71] Curcio, CA; Millican, CL. Basal linear deposit and large drusen are specific for early age-related maculopathy. *Archives of Ophthalmology,* 1999, 117, 329-339.
[72] Sarks, SH. Ageing and degeneration in the macular region: A clinico-pathological study. *British Journal of Ophthalmology,* 1976, 60, 324-341.
[73] Spencer, WH. Symposium: Macular Diseases. Pathogenesis: Light microscopy. *Transactions American Academy of Ophthalmology and Otolaryngology,* 1965, 69, 662-667.
[74] Spencer, WH. Histopathologic observations of aging changes and disease processes in the subretinal tissues of the macular region. *Excerpta Medica,* 1971, Tomo I, 479-484.
[75] Green, WR; Key III, SN. Senile macular degeneration: A histopathologic study. *Transactions of the American Ophthalmological Society,* 1977, 75, 180-254.
[76] Green WR. Clinicopathologic studies of senile macular degeneration. In: Nicholson, editor. *Ocular Pathology Update.* New York: Masson; 1980; 115-144.

[77] Sarks SH. Drusen and their relationship to senile macular degeneration. *Australian Journal of Ophthalmology,* 1980, 8, 117-130

[78] Burns, RP; Feeney-Burns, L. Clinicomorphologic correlations of drusen and Bruch's membrane. *Transactions of the American Ophthalmological Society*, 1980, 78, 206-223.

[79] Holz, FG; Sheraidad, G; Pauleikhoff, D; Bird, AC. Análisis of lipid deposits extracted from human macular and peripheral Bruch's membrane. *Archives of Ophthalmology*, 1994, 5, 196-200.

[80] Grey, RHB. The ageing macula and disciform degeneration. In: *Vascular disorders of the ocular fundus. A colour manual of diagnosis*, London: Butter- Worths; 1991, 55-80.

[81] Hogan, MJ; Alvarado, J. Studies on the human macula. IV. Aging changes in Bruch's membrane. *Archives of Ophthalmology*, 1967, 77, 410-420.

[82] Hogan, MJ, Alvarado, JA; Weddell, JE. *Histology of the human eye. Chapter Eight: Choroid.* Philadelphia: WB Saunders Company; 1971; 320-392.

[83] Hewitt, AT; Nakazawa, K; Newsome, DA. Analysis of newly synthesized Bruch's membrane proteoglycans. *Investigative Ophthalmology and Visual Science*, 1989, 30, 478-486.

[84] Alexander, JP; Bradley, JMB; Gabourel, JC; Acott, TS. Expression of matrix metalloproteinases and inhibitors by human retinal pigment epithelium. *Investigative Ophthalmology and Visual Science*, 1990, 31, 2520-2528.

[85] Leu, ST; Batni, S; Radeke, MJ; Johnson, LV; Anderson, DH; Clegg, DO. Drusen are cold spots for proteolysis: expression of matrix metalloproteinases and their tissue inhibitor proteins in age-related macular degeneration. *Experimental Eye Research*, 2002, 74,141-154.

[86] Guo, L; Hussain, AA; Limb, GA; Marshall, J. Age-dependent variation in metalloproteinase activity of isolated human Bruch's membrane and choroid. *Investigative Ophthalmology and Visual Science*, 1999, 40, 2676-2682.

[87] Mullins, RF; Russell, SR; Anderson, DH; Hageman, S. Drusen associated with aging and age-related macular degeneration contain proteins common to extracellular deposits associated with atherosclerosis, elastosis, amiloidosis, and dense deposit disease. *FASEB Journal,* 2000, 14, 835-846.

[88] Curcio, CA; Millican, CL; Bailey, T; Kruth, HS. Accumulation of colesterol with age in human Bruch's membrane. *Investigative Ophthalmology and Visual Science,* 2001, 42, 265-274.

[89] Kamei, M; Hollyfield, JG. TIMP-3 in Bruch's membrane:changes during aging and in age-related macular degeneration. *Investigative Opthalmology and Visual Scieence,*1999, 40, 2367-2375.

[90] Bailey, TA; Alexander, RA; Dubovy, SR; Luthert, PJ; Chong, NHV. Measurement of TIMP-3 expression and Bruch's membrane thickness in human macula. *Experimental Eye Research,* 2001, 73, 851-858.

[91] Weale, RA. Retinal senescence. *Progress in Retinal and Eye Research,* 1986, 5, 53-73.

[92] Gartner, S; Henkind, P. Aging and degeneration of the human macula. I. Outer nuclear layer and photoreceptors. *British Journal of Ophthalmology,* 1981, 65, 23-28.

[93] Feeney-Burns, L; Burns, RP; Chun-Lan, G. Age-related macular changes in humans over 90 years old. *American Journal of Ophthalmology,* 1990, 109, 265-278.

[94] Liem, ATA; Keunen, JEE; Van Norren, D; Van de Kraats, J. Rod densitometry in the aging human eye. *Investigative Ophthalmology and Visual Science,* 1991, 32, 2676-2682.

[95] Curcio, CA; Drucker, DN. Retinal ganglion cells in Alzheimer's disease and aging. *Annals of Neurology,* 1993, 33, 248-257.

[96] Mohand-Said, S; Deudon-Combe, A; Hicks, D; Simonutti, M; Forster, V; Fintz, AC; Leveillard, T; Dreyfus, H; Sahel, JA. Normal retina releases a diffusible factor stimulating cone survival in the retinal degeneration mouse. *Proceedings of the National Academy of Sciences of the United States of America,* 1998, 95 , 8357-8362.

[97] Mohand-Said, S; Hicks, D; Dreyfus, H; Sahel,JA. Selective transplantation of rods delays cone loss in a retinitis pigmentosa model. *Archives of Ophthalmology*, 2000, 118, 807-811.

[98] Mohand-Said, S; Hicks, D; Leveillard, T; Picaud, S; Porto, F; Sahel, JA. Rod-cone interactions: developmental and clinical significance. *Progress in Retinal and Eye Research,* 2001, 20, 451-467.

[99] Fintz, AC; Audo, I; Hicks, D; Mohand-Said, S; Leveillard, T; Sahel, J. Partial characterization of retina-derived cone neuroprotecion in two culture models of photoreceptor degeneration. *Investigative Ophthalmology and Visual Science*, 2003, 44, 818-825.

[100] Medeiros, NE; Curcio, CA. Preservation of ganglion cell layer neurons in age-related macular degeneration. *Investigative Ophthalmology and Visual Science,* 2001, 42, 795-803.

[101] Marshall, J; Grindle, J; Ansell, PL; Borwein, B. (1979): Convolution in human rods: an ageing process. *British Journal of Ophthalmology,* 1979; 63, 181-187.

[102] Avendano, J; Rodrigues, MM; Hackett, JJ; Gaskins R. Corpora amylacea of the optic nerve and retina: A form of neuronal degeneration. *Investigative Ophthalmology and Visual Science*, 1980, 19, 550-555.

[103] Cogan, DG. Doyne Memorial Lecture: Development and senescence of the human retinal vasculature. *Transactions of the Ophthalmological Societies of the United Kingdom,* 1963, 83, 465-489.

[104] Rivard, A; Fabre, J-E; Silver, M; Chen, D; Murohara, T; Kearney, M; Magner, M; Asahara, T; Isner, JM. Age-dependent impairment of angiogenesis. *Circulation*, 1999, 99, 111-120.

[105] Morán, M; Gómez-Ramos, P. Glial changes in aging and Alzheimer's disease. In Castellano B; González B; Nieto-Sampedro M; editors. *Understanding glial cells.* Boston: Kluwer Academic Publishers; 1998, 385-401.

[106] Vernadakis, A. Changes in astrocytes with aging. In: Federoff S; Vernadakys A; editors. *Astrocytes. Biochemistry, physiology, and pharmacology of astrocytes.* Orlando: Academic Press, INC; 1986, 377-407.

[107] Soffié, M; Hahn, K; Terao, E; Eclancher, F. Behavioural and glial changes in old rats following environmental enrichment. *Behavioural Brain Research,* 1999, 101, 37-49.

[108] Ramírez, JM; Triviño, A; Ramírez, AI; Salazar, JJ; García-Sánchez, J. Immunohistochemical study of human retinal astroglia. *Vision Research*, 1994, 34, 1935-1946.

[109] Ridet, JL; Malhotra, SK; Privat, A; Gage, FH. Reactive astrocytes: cellular and molecular cues to biological function. *Trends in Neuroscience,* 1997, 20, 570-577.

[110] Nieto-Sampedro, M; Verdú, E. Lesiones del sistema nervioso: respuesta neuronal y reparación. In: Delgado J M; Ferrús A; Mora F; Rubia, FJ; editors. *Manual de neurociencia.* Madrid: Editorial Síntesis SA; 1998, 929-969.

[111] Kettenmann, H; Faissner, A; Trotter, J. Neuron-glia interactions in homeostasis and degeneration. In: Greger R; Windhorst U; editors. *Comprehensive human physiology. From cellular mechanisms to integration.* Berlin: Springer-Verlag; 1996, 533-543.

[112] Liu, D; Smith, CL; Barone, FC; Ellison, JA; Lysko, PG; Li, K; Simpson, IA. Astrocytic demise precedes delayed neuronal death in focal ischemic rat brain. *Molecular Brain Research*, 1999, 68, 29-41.

[113] Wilson, JX. Antioxidant defense of the brain: a role for astrocytes. *Canadian Journal of Physiology and Pharmacology,* 1997, 75, 1149-1163.

[114] Sabbatini, M; Barili, P; Bronzetti, E; Zaccheo, D; Amenta, F. Age-related changes of glial fibrillary acidic protein immunoreactive astrocytes in the rat cerebellar cortex. *Mechanisms of Ageing and Development*, 1999, 108, 165-172.

[115] Syková, E; Mazel, T; Simonová, Z. Diffusion constraints and neuron-glia interaction during aging. *Experimental Gerontology,* 1998, 33, 837-851.

[116] Williams, GA; Blumenkranz, MS. Vitreous humor. In: Tasman and Jaeger, editors. *Duane's Ophthalmology on CD-ROM.* Lippincott-Raven; 1998.

[117] Lindquist, TD; Grutzmacher, RD; Gofman, JD. Light-induced maculopathy. *Archives of Ophthalmology,* 1986, 104: 1644-1647.

[118] Young, RW. Solar radiation and age-related macular degeneration. *Survey of Ophthalmology*, 1988, 32, 252-269.

[119] Loeffler; KU; Lee, WR, Van der Schaft, TL; De Bruijn, WC; Mooy, CM; Ketelaars, DAM; De Jong, PTVM. Is basal laminar deposit unique for age-related macular degeneration? *Archives of Ophthalmology*, 1992, 110, 15-16.

[120] Kindcaid, MC. Pathology of AMD. In: Hampton GR; Nelsen PT, editors. *Age–Related Macular Degeneration: Principles and Practice.* New York: Raven Press, Ltd; 1992, 37-61.

[121] Killingsworth, MC; Sarks, JP; Sarks, SH. Macrophages related to Bruch's membrane in age related macular degeneration. *Eye*, 1990, 4, 613-621.

[122] Mullins, RF; Russell, SR; Anderson, DH; Hageman,GS. Drusen associated with aging and age-related macular degeneration contain proteins common to extracellular deposits associated with atherosclerosis, elastosis, amyloidosis, and dense deposits disease. *FASEB Journal*, 2000, 14, 835-846.

[123] Johnson, LV; Leitner, WP; Rivest, AJ; Staples, MK; Radeke, MJ, Anderson, DH. The Alzheimer's Ab-peptide is deposited at sites of complement activation in pathologic deposits associated with aging and age-related macular degeneration. *Proceedings of the National Academy of Sciences of the United States of America,* 2002, 99, 11830-11835.

[124] Bressler, NM; Bressler, SB; Seddon, JM; Gragoudas, ES; Jacobson, LP. Drusen characteristics in patients with exudative versus non-exudative age-related macular degeneration. *Retina,* 1988, 8, 109-114.

[125] Farkas, TG. Drusen of the retinal pigment epithelium. *Survey of Ophthalmology*, 1971, 16, 75-87.

[126] Farkas, TG; Krill, AE; Sylvester, VM; Archer, D. Familial and secondary drusen: histologyc and functional correlations. *Transactions American Academy of Ophthalmology and Otolaryngology,* 1971, 75, 333-343.

[127] Farkas T.G., Sylvester V., Archer D. (1971): The ultrastructure of drusen. *American Journal of Ophthalmology*, 1971, 71: 1196-1205.

[128] Farkas T.G., Sylvester V., Archer D., Altona M. The histochemistry of drusen. *American Journal of Ophthalmology*, 1971, 71, 1206-1215.

[129] Bird, AC; Marshall, J. Retinal pigment epithelial detachment in the elderly. *Transactions of the Ophthalmological Societies of the United Kingdom,* 1986, 105, 674-682.

[130] Moore, DJ; Hussain, AA; Marshall J. Age-related variation in the hydraulic conductivity of Bruch's membrane. *Investigative Ophthalmology and Visual Science*, 1995, 36,1290-1297.

[131] Starita, C; Hussain, AA; Pagliarini, S; Marshall, J. Hydrodynamics of ageing Bruch's membrane: implication for macular disease. *Experimental Eye Research,* 1996, 26, 565-572.

[132] Handa; JT; Matsunaga, H; Aotaki-Keen, A; Hjelmeland, LM; Hjelmeland, LM; Verzij, N; Te Koppele, JM; Lutty, GA; Handa, JT; Miyata, T. Increase in the advanced glycation end product pentosidine in Bruch's membrane with age, *Investigative Ophthalmology and Visual Science*, 1999, 40, 775-779.

[133] Hillemkamp, J; Hussain, AA; Jackson, TL; Cunningham, JR; Marshall, J. The influence of path length and matriz components on ageing characteristics of transport between the choroid and the outer retina. *Investigative Ophthalmology and Visual Science*, 2004, 45,1493-1498.

[134] Marshall, J; Hussain, AA; Starita, C; Moore, DJ, Patmore, AL. Aging and Bruch's membrane. In: Marmor MF; Wolfensberger TJ; editors. *The Retinal Pigment Epithelium.* New York: Oxford University; 1998, 669-692

[135] Cousins, SW; Espinosa-Heidmann, DG; Alexandridou, A; Sall, J; Dubovy, S; Csaky K. The role of aging, high fat diet and blue light exposure in an experimental mouse. Model for Basal Laminar Deposit Formation. *Experimental Eye Research*, 2002, 75, 543-553.

[136] Connor, WE; Neuringer, M; Reisbick, S. Essential fatty acids : the importance of n-3 fatty acids in the retina and brain. *Nutrition Reviews,* 1992, 50, 21-29 Nutr Rev 1992; 50: 21-29.

[137] Zarbin, MA. Age related macular degeneration: review of patogenesis. *European Journal of Ophthalmology,* 1998, 8, 199-206.

[138] Mishima, H; Hasebe, H; Kondo, K. Age changes in the fine structure of the human retinal pigment epithelium. *Japanese Journal of Ophthalmology,* 1978, 22, 476-485.

[139] Sarks, SH. Drusen patterns predisposing to geographic atrophy of the retinal pigment epithelium. *Australian Journal of Ophthalmology,* 1982, 10 (2) , 91-97.

[140] Braunstein, RA; Gass, JDM. Serous detachments of the retinal pigment epithelium in patients with senile macular disease. *American Journal of Ophthalmology,* 1979, 88: 652-660.

[141] Gass, JD. Drusen and disciform macular detachment and degeneration. *Transactions of the American Ophthalmological Society,* 1972, 70 , 409-436.

[142] Gass, JD. Drusen and disciform macular detachment and degeneration. *Archives of Ophthalmology*, 1973, 90, 206-217.

[143] Duvall, J; Tso, MOM. Cellular mechanisms of resolution of drusen after laser coagulation. *Archives of Ophthalmology*, 1985, 103, 694-703.

[144] Gass, JD. Pathogenesis of disciform detachment of the neuroepithelium. I. General concepts and clasification. *American Journal of Ophthalmology*, 1967, 63, 573-585.

[145] Small, ML; Green, WR; Alpar, JJ. Senile macular degeneration. *Archives of Ophthalmology,* 1976, 94, 601-607.

[146] Marin, F; Gomez-Ulla, F. Degeneración macular exudativa asociada a la edad. In: Gómez-Ulla F; Marín F; Ramírez JM; Triviño A; editors. *La mácula senil.* Barcelona: EDIKA-MED, 1993, 129-153.

[147] Madigan, MC; Penfold, PL; Provis, JM; Balind, TK; Billson, FA. Intermediate filament expression in human retinal macroglia. Histopathologic changes associated with age-related macular degeneration. *Retina*; 1994. 14: 65-74.

[148] Penfold, PL; Madigan, MC; Provis, JM; Billson, FA. Changes of the retinal pigment epithelium and glia in aged human retinae. *Excerpta Medica*, 1991, 620-626.

[149] Hubel, DH. *Eye, brain and vision.* New Cork: WH Freeman and Company; 1998, 233.

[150] Tyler, NK; Burns, MS. Alterations in glial cell morphology and glial fibrillary acidic protein expression in urethane-induced retinopathy. *Investigative Ophthalmology and Visual Science*, 1991, 32, 246-256.

[151] Hinton, DR; He, S; Lopez, PF. Apoptosis in surgically excised choroidal neovascular membranes in age-related macular degeneration. *Archives of Ophthalmology*, 1998, 116, 203-209.

[152] Radnot, M; Jobbagyi, P ; Heszberger, I. Les données a l'ultrastructure de la rétine humaine sous l'éffect de la lumiere. *Ophthalmologica,* 1969, 159, 460-471.

[153] Sykes, SM; Robison, WGJr; Waxler, M; Kuwabara, T. Damage to the monkey retina by broad-spectrum fluorescent light. *Investigative Ophthalmology and Visual Science,* 1981, 20, 425-434.

[154] Tso, MOM; Fine, BS; Zimmerman, LE. Photic maculopathy produced by the indirect ophthalmoscope. I. Clinical and histopathologic study. *American Journal of Ophthalmology,* 1972, 73: 686-699.

[155] Oraedu, ACI; Voaden, MJ; Marshall, J. Photochemical damage in the albino rat retina: morphological changes and endogenous amino acids. *Journal of Neurochemistry,* 1980, 35, 1361-1369.

[156] Zrenner, E. Light-induced damage to the eye. *Fortschritte der Ophthalmologie*, 1990, 87 (SUPPL.), S41-S51.

[157] Mainster, MA. Light and macular degeneration: A biophysical and clinical perspective. *Eye,* 1987, 1, 304-310.

[158] Gottsch, JD; Pou, S; Byone, LA; Rosen, GM. Hematogenous photosensitization. A mechanism for the development of age-related macular degeneration. *Investigative Ophthalmology and Visual Science*, 1990, 31, 1674-1682.

[159] Torczynski, E; Tso, MOM. The architecture of the choriocapillaris at the posterior pole. *American Journal of Ophthalmology*, 1976, 81, 428-440.

[160] Korte, GE; Burns, MS; Bellhorn, RW. Epithelium-capillary interactions in the eye: the retinal pigment epithelium and the choriocapillaris. *International Review of Cytology,* 1989, 114 , 221-248.

[161] Sarks, JP; Sarks, SH; Killingsworth, MC. Evolution of geographic atrophy of the retinal pigment epithelium. *Eye,* 1988, 2, 552-577.

[162] Cousins, SW; Csaky, KG. Immunology of the age-related macular degeneration. In: Jennifer IL; editors. *Age related macular degeneration.* New York: Marcel Dekker; 2002, 27-65.

[163] Anand, R; Bressler, SB; Davis, MD; Ferris III, FL; Klein, R; Lindblad, AS; Milton, RC; Sperduto, RD. Risk factors associated with age-related macular degeneration: A case-control study in the Age-Related Eye Disease Study: Age-Related Eye Disease Study report number 3. *Ophthalmology,* 2000, 107, 2224-2232.

[164] West, S; Vitale, S; Hallfrisch, J; Munoz, B; Muller, D; Bressler, S; Bressler NM. Are antioxidants or supplements protective for age-related macular degeneration? *Archives of Ophthalmology,* 1994, 112, 222-227

[165] Delcourt, C; Papoz, L; Cristol, J-P; Leger, CL; Descomps, B; Tessier F; Delcourt, C. Age-related macular degeneration and antioxidant status in the POLA study. *Archives of Ophthalmology*, 1999; 117, 1384-1390.

In: Focus on Eye Research
Editor: O.R. Ioseliani, pp. 39-80
ISBN: 1-59454-434-4

Chapter 2

PATHOGENESIS OF EARLY AGE-RELATED MACULAR DEGENERATION (AMD): A NEW HYPOTHESIS

Scott W. Cousins*,[1] Maria E. Marin-Castano,[1] Karl G. Csaky[2] and Diego G. Espinosa-Heidmann[1]
[1]Department of Ophthalmology, Bascom Palmer Eye Institute, Miami, FL;
[2]National Eye Institute, National Institute of Health, Bethesda, MD.

ABSTRACT

The goal of this chapter will be to review recent scientific research developments in the pathogenesis of dry age-related macular degeneration (AMD), a major cause of blindness among the elderly. AMD is a late onset (after age 50), progressive degeneration of the retina associated with vision loss coupled with a spectrum of specific clinical, physiological and histopathological features. The early or dry stage of AMD is characterized by the accumulation of drusen, specific lipid rich deposits under the retina. The various paradigms for the pathogenesis of drusen are briefly reviewed, including genetic, lipofuscin/lysosomal failure, choroidal hypoperfusion, barrier, and retinal pigment epithelium (RPE) injury models. Then, the scientific evidence to support a new interpretation of the RPE injury model is reviewed in depth, especially the proposed role of oxidant-mediated RPE cell membrane blebbing and dysregulated regulation of the RPE extracellular matrix. The clinical implications of this model are discussed.

Key words: Dry Age-related Macular Degeneration, response to injury, reactive oxygen intermediates, blebbing, extracellular matrix turnover, actin cytoskeleton, Hsp25/27, matrix metalloproteinases, subRPE deposits, blue light, hydroquinone, laser, animal model, aging, gender, cigarette smoke, and fat diet.

---

* Reprint requests: Scott W. Cousins, M.D.; Diego G. Espinosa-Heidmann, M.D. William L. McKnight Vision Research Center, 1638 N.W. 10th Avenue (D-880), Miami, FL 33136. Tel.: (305) 326-6329; (305) 326-6329; Fax: (305) 326-6536; E-mails: scousins@med.miami.edu; despinosa@med.miami.edu

DEFINITION OF DRY (EARLY) AMD

Age-related macular degeneration (AMD) is a late onset (after age 50), progressive degeneration of the retina associated with vision loss coupled with a spectrum of specific clinical, physiological and histopathological features (Figure 1).(1;2) AMD affects 30% of people older than age 70, and is the leading cause of blindness in the elderly.(3;4) Fourteen million people may be affected in the United States, and over 60 million worldwide. Since the population older than 60 years is the fastest growing segment in western society, the burden of AMD will become a huge global public health problem.(3;4)

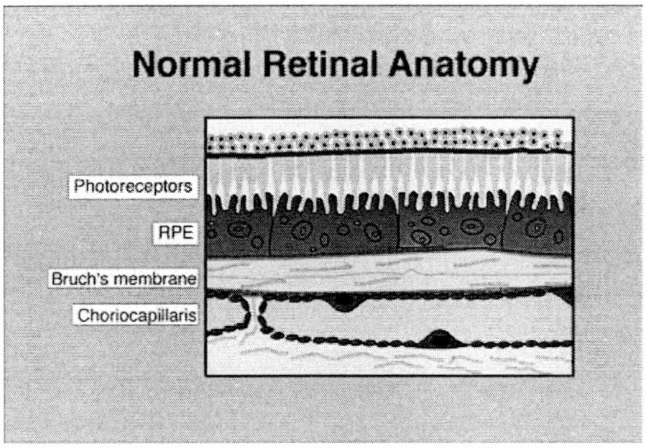

Figure 1: Schematic cross-section of the outer retina anatomy where Age-related Macular Degeneration (AMD) takes place. It shows the normal relation between photoreceptors, retinal pigment epithelial (RPE) cells, Bruch's membrane (BM), and choriocapillaris. The basement membranes of the RPE cells (red line) and endothelial cells (green line) constitute the innermost and outermost layers of BM respectively, demarcating the site where the early phases of the disease occur.

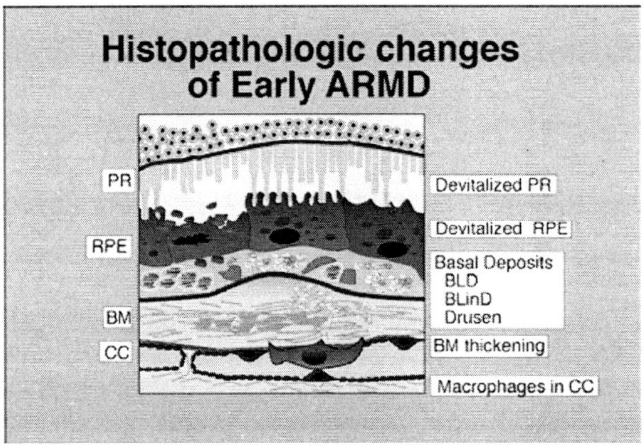

Figure 2: Histopathologic changes of early Age-related Macular Degeneration (AMD). The schematic drawing shows the typical sub-Retinal Pigment Epithelium (RPE) deposits located in Bruch's Membrane (BM). Basal laminar deposits (BLD) are normally located between the RPE cell membrane and the RPE basement membrane (above red line) while basal linear deposits (BLinD) and drusen are located in the inner collagenous layer (below red line) of BM. Other histologic findings of this early stage of the disease are also shown such as devitalized photoreceptors (PR) and RPE cells, BM thickening, and invasion of macrophages. CC= Choriocapillaris.

The clinical presentation of AMD progresses through two stages: early and late.(5) Early AMD ("atrophic" or "dry" degeneration) is characterized by accumulation of various lipid rich extracellular deposits under the RPE (Figure 2).(5-7) Ultimately, early AMD can progress into late or severe atrophic AMD characterized by death of RPE and photoreceptors (called geographic atrophy) (Figure 3).(5;7) Another form of late AMD ("exudative" "neovascular" or "wet" degeneration) is characterized by endothelial invasion and pathological neovascularization under the retina (Figure 4).(5;7) Wet AMD is always preceded by early disease (Figure 5).(7)

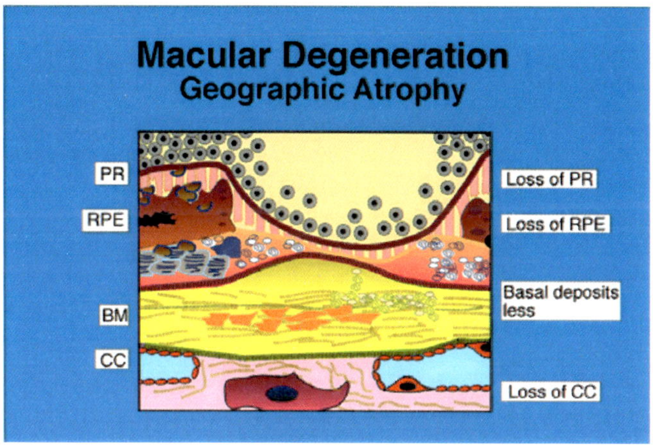

Figure 3: Histopathologic changes of the late phases of dry Age-related Macular Degeneration known as Geographic Atrophy. The schematic drawing shows loss of photoreceptor (PR), Retinal Pigment Epithelial (RPE) cells, and choriocapillaris (CC) vessels characteristic of this stage. There is also a marked decrease in the amount of subRPE deposits in Bruch's membrane (BM). Macrophages can be found at the edges of areas of geographic atrophy.

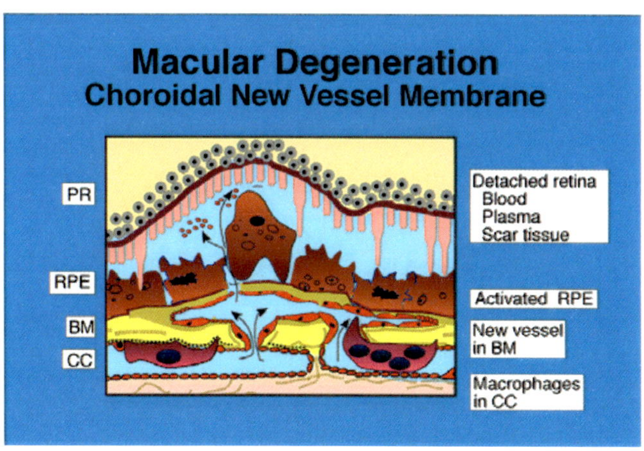

Figure 4: Histopathologic changes of the late phases of wet Age-related Macular Degeneration (AMD) known as Choroidal Neovascularization (CNV). The schematic drawing shows a breach in the continuity of Bruch's membrane (BM) with invasion of neovessels from the choriocapillaris (CC). As a consequence of this alteration there is escape of blood and plasma, which detaches the retina and eventually leads to the formation of scar tissue. There is also activated Retinal Pigment Epithelial (RPE) cells proliferating over the lesion and the presence of macrophages.

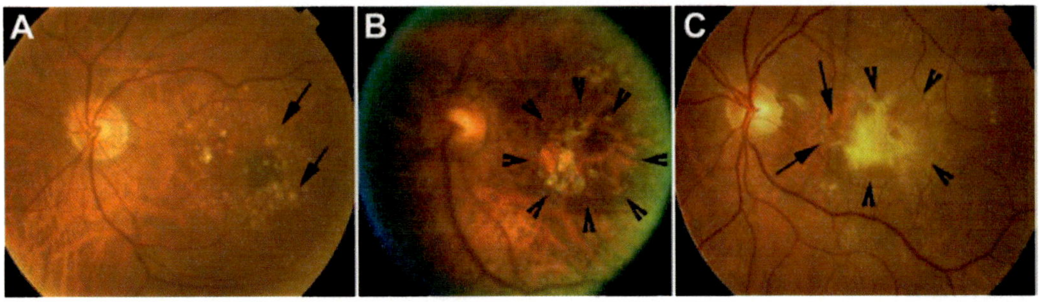

Figure 5: Color fundus photographs of patients with different stages of Age-related Macular Degeneration. A. Drusen (black arrows) are generally the earliest sign of AMD consisting in multiple, discrete, round, slightly elevated, variable-sized, sub-RPE deposits in the macula and elsewhere in the fundus of both eyes. Generally they are described clinically as hard or soft drusen depending in their size and how well defined their boundaries are. B. Geographic atrophy characterizes the dry form of AMD. The photograph shows a window defect (black arrowheads) in which there is a diminished number of photoreceptors, RPE cells, and atrophy of the choriocapillaris. C. Choroidal neovascular (CNV) membrane characterizes the wet form of AMD. The photograph shows a typical subfoveal CNV lesion characterized by a disciform scar (black arrowheads) and subretinal hemorrhage (black arrows).

Death or dysfunction of retinal photoreceptors is the ultimate cause of vision loss.(8) However, the initial pathogenic target of AMD is the retinal pigment epithelium, its extracellular matrix (called Bruch's membrane), and the subjacent vascular bed (called the choriocapillaris), the blood supply for the outer retina.(3)

Bruch's membrane (BrM) is traditionally considered to be a five-layered stratified extracellular matrix.(3;9;10) In addition to acting as a structural support element, BrM also provides a semipermeable filtration barrier through which major metabolic exchange takes place between the RPE and the choriocapillaris. In the center is the elastic fiber layer sandwiched between the inner and outer collagenous layers. Finally, two basal lamina define the innermost and outermost layers. The innermost layer is the basal lamina of the RPE and the basement membrane of the endothelial cells that form the choriocapillaris, is the external layer.(3;9;10) The collagen layers contain striated collagen fibers mainly type I, III, and V.(3;10) Type I confers tensile strength to the tissue, type III is normally present in tissues with elastic properties, and type V acts to anchor basement membranes to stromal matrixes.(10;11) The inter-fiber matrix of BrM is comprised largely of glycosaminoglycans such as heparan sulfate (25%) and chondroitin/dermatan sulfate (75%), which provides an electrolytic barrier to diffusion as well as important regulatory roles by binding extracellular proteins and growth factors in processes such as cell adhesion, cell migration and differentiation.(11-13)

The basement membrane of both the choriocapillaris and RPE are comprised of mostly type IV collagen.(10;11) Type VI collagen is also present and is associated with the choriocapillaris.(10;11) It has been suggested that this collagen is the product of pericytes and may act to anchor fenestrated capillaries to the underlying choroid. The basement membranes also contain laminin, heparan sulfate proteoglycans, and fibronectin.

Subretinal Deposits and AMD

Numerous biochemical and anatomical changes occur in BrM as part of the aging retina in the absence of apparent retinal dysfunction, including collagenous thickening, calcification and lipid infiltration.(10;11) The accumulation of specific deposits under the RPE is the prominent histopathological feature of eyes with early AMD, when visual function is still not irreversibly impaired.(7;14) They were initially described by Donders in 1854.(4) These deposits are generically termed "drusen" when observed by ophthalmologists upon clinical examination of the retina,(15) but histopathological examination allows three main types of sub-RPE deposits to be distinguished by location, thickness and content: basal laminar deposits (BLD), basal linear deposits (BLinD) and nodular drusen.(7;16)

BLD and BLinD are both diffuse deposits that accumulate on opposite sides of the basal lamina of the RPE; thus the RPE basement membrane is the crucial dividing line to distinguish the location of BLD from BLinD (Figure 2).(7) BLD is the accumulation of amorphous material of intermediate electron density between the plasma membrane and the basement membrane of the RPE, often containing banded structures (wide-spaced collagen), patches of electron dense fibrillar or granular material, and occasionally, membranous debris.(7;17) They are distributed throughout the retina, including the periphery as well as the macula. Therefore BLD underlie rods as well as cones. BLinD are diffuse, amorphous accumulations within the inner collagenous zone of BrM, external to RPE basement membrane, with similar content variations.(7) BLinD are characterized by coated and non-coated vesicles as well as some membranous and empty profiles.(7) Biochemically, deposits contain phospholipids, triglycerides, cholesterol, cholesterol esters, unsaturated fatty acids, peroxidized lipids, and apolipoproteins.(18-21)

In contrast to BLD or BLinD, nodular drusen are discrete, dome shaped deposits within the inner collagenous zone of BrM (i.e., external to the RPE basal lamina). Thus, nodular drusen are often contiguous with BLinD, and can be difficult to distinguish from BLinD without electron microscopy.(4) In addition to the biochemical content of diffuse deposits, nodular drusen may also specifically contain vitronectin, immunoglobulins, amyloid, complement and many other poorly characterized components.(18-21) Further, low-grade monocyte infiltration within the choriocapillaris is often present underlying areas of deposits.(19;21)

Clinically deposits of AMD are classified based on fundoscopic features of morphology and size.(18) Although multiple classifications exists, most clinicians now use size to classify drusen: small or "hard" (<63 μm) and intermediate, large, or "soft" (>63 μm) (Figure 5A).(18) When hard or soft drusen coalesce to the point of losing their boundaries they are then classified as "diffuse". Although the clinical detection of drusen is usually necessary to diagnose AMD, occasionally the diagnosis can be made in the absence of drusen based on the presence of pigmentary changes indicative of RPE degeneration.(22;23) The specific contribution of drusen to AMD complications and progression is not clear, but the presence of macular drusen is considered a strong risk factor for the development of the late forms of the disease, geographic atrophy and CNV (Figure 5B & 5C).(22;24;25)

The histological correlates of clinically observed drusen are controversial. Most experts agree that small hard drusen observed clinically consist mostly of nodular drusen histologically. However, no consensus exists among experts for the specific composition of clinically evident large soft drusen, and definitive information is lacking that clarifies the specific contributions of each of the three ultrastructural deposit types. Some postulate that BLinD are specific for AMD, whereas others believe only large nodular drusen define AMD.(26;27) Some investigators postulate that BLD are an aging change without disease significance, whereas others believe that they are an early manifestation of AMD and that they can evolve into linear deposits.(28;29) Nevertheless, many eyes with clinical AMD express all three deposit subtypes, and conversely, examples have been published in which conditions with clinical drusen-like deposits reveal histology dominated by thick variants of any one of the three subtypes.(19;30) Furthermore, histological, immunohistochemical, and ultrastructural studies of surgical-excised choroidal neovascular membranes (CNV) have shown that the cellular and extracellular constituents of CNV are the same regardless of the underlying disease, with the exception of the amount of BLD and the presence of BLinD, which is virtually exclusively found in CNV specimens from patients with AMD.(31)

Pathogenic Mechanisms for Subretinal Deposit Formation

Lack of scientific consensus exists regarding the origin of drusen, but at least five different paradigms are currently proposed to explain deposit formation in AMD.

Genetic Hypothesis

Twin and sibling studies clearly indicate that AMD has a genetic component, and two genetic models have been proposed.(32-34) One model proposes that genetic mutations of protein(s) specific to retinal or RPE function cause the disease, similar to the pathogenesis of retinitis pigmentosa. This hypothesis has been supported by the identification of several specific mutations for various hereditary maculopathies, especially Stargardt's disease, Best's disease, Familial drusen and Sorsby's Fundus dystrophy.(35-39) To date, none of these genes seem to be associated with AMD, although a recent report suggests that defects in the fibulin-5 gene (a member of the gene family associated with Familial Drusen) may be correlated with some cases of AMD.(40-42) Also mutations in genes associated with retinitis pigmentosa or pattern dystrophies of the macula have not been found to play a role in AMD.(43)

Alternatively, mutations or polymorphisms in general metabolic pathways that interact with outer retinal function may serve as susceptibility cofactors in AMD.(42;44;45) The association of AMD with polymorphisms of apolipoprotein E supports this model.(46) Second, complement has been observed within drusen and in the choriocapillaris in eyes with AMD. Recently, four different research groups independently identified the same polymorphism in complement factor H in association with AMD, explaining up to 40% of the genetic risk. Complement H is a regulatory protein that promotes clearance of complement deposited through the alternative pathway. This observation raises the hypothesis that dysregulation of the complement system may contribute to AMD pathogenesis.

Lysosomal Failure/Lipofuscin Hypothesis

The role of RPE in phagocytosis of photoreceptor outer segment shedding (i.e., the regular cyclical release of outer segment cell membrane debris) was first recognized with the advent of the electron microscope in the 1930's, and became fully characterized with the development of modern cell biology in the 1960's-70's. The RPE must phagocytose and catabolize huge amounts of photoreceptor outer segments during a lifetime.(47) Failure of this process results in retinal damage, first demonstrated in a spontaneous rat model of dysfunctional phagocytosis.(48) Also, histological observation of RPE accumulation of aging pigments (so called lipofuscin) suggested that faulty lysosomal degradation of outer segments might contribute to AMD.(47;49;50)

The modern version of this model proposes that an age-related failure in RPE lysosomal enzymatic degradation of phagocytosed photoreceptor membranes and RPE-derived proteins causes dry AMD.(49;51;52) Initially, incomplete degradation of phagocytosed phospholipids and other materials leads to the accumulation of a potentially cytotoxic byproduct, lipofuscin, within the RPE cytoplasm.(14) Lipofuscin, which includes numerous distinct biochemical components, can be directly cytotoxic by disrupting lysosomal and cell membranes.(14) It is also a powerful chromophore for visible light, resulting in the production of oxidants like singlet oxygen upon blue light exposure.(49;50) According to this model, however, lysosomal failure ultimately causes failure to digest phagocytosed outer segments or cellular proteins, which then leads to transcellular transport of undigested material, which is deposited under the RPE as drusen.(14) Extensive basic science research has investigated the biochemical properties of lipofuscin and its components.(53;54) However, very little data support a specific role of lysosomal failure as a mechanism for its accumulation, or for the secretion of subRPE deposits.(55;56) Two potential mechanisms that have been postulated include oxidant-mediated biochemical modifications of cell proteins leading to loss of catabolic sites for enzymatic digestion(57-59) and genetic mutations in RPE proteins which lead to misfolding thereby altering access to degradation pathways.(41)

Choroidal Hypoperfusion Hypothesis

Primary decrease of choroidal blood flow has been proposed to cause deposits in AMD, presumably by slowing removal of RPE-derived waste materials from BrM and diminution of nutrients or oxygen delivered to the outer retina.(60;61) Decreased choroidal blood flow has been observed in AMD eyes, especially after fluorescein angiography or computer-assisted image analysis of video ICG angiography.(62;63) Two structural changes might contribute to hypoperfusion. Decreased density or diameter of choriocapillaris lumens can result in decreased blood flow through the choriocapillaris and reduction of diffusion-mediated removal of waste material derived from the RPE. Secondly, increased scleral rigidity with age can cause increased resistance to blood flow with decreased choroidal perfusion and impaired RPE transport.(61;64) Some have proposed that the submacular choroid is a vascular watershed area, suggesting a possible role for relative ischemia as a component in the pathogenesis of wet AMD.(61;65) However no data is available to determine whether choroidal blood flow abnormalities are primary or reflect a change secondary to another pathogenic component of AMD.

Barrier Hypothesis

This model postulates that an acquired defect in BrM permeability impedes the flow of nutrients and oxygen from the choroid into the RPE, and waste products from RPE into the choroid. Nutrient depletion would cause RPE degeneration. RPE-derived waste products would subsequently accumulate as drusen. However, no mechanism has been proposed to explain how the initial barrier evolves into specific deposits subtypes like severe BLD, BLinD and drusen.

Marshall and colleagues suggested that deposition of plasma derived lipids (cholesterol, cholesterol esters, triglycerides, and fatty acids among others) and proteins (apolipoproteins) may create the barrier.(66-68) By using laser ablation of the different layers of BrM, they showed that hydraulic resistance to water flow lies in the inner collagenous layer, where deposits are normally located.(67) This barrier then produces a decline in the hydraulic conductivity of the Bruch's membrane-choroid complex with aging, decreasing then the exchange of fluids and nutrients between the choroidal and retinal pigment epithelium compartments.

Alternatively, Curcio and colleagues have proposed that lipids (and proteins) abnormally produced and secreted by the RPE cells may cause the barrier. This hypothesis was supported by studies that indicated that esterified cholesterol (EC) and fatty acids found in AMD deposits required biochemical processes found in RPE (specifically the presence of acyl co-A cholesterol acyl transferase-1 and –2 activity) and not resembling the biochemical composition of lipids derived from low-density lipoproteins in plasma. (Curcio C, et al. IOVS 2002; 43: ARVO E-Abstract 862). Furthermore, the RPE is known to synthesize a wide range of proteins found in drusen, including vitronectin, collagen, apolipoproteins and even complement.(20;69;70)

RPE Injury Hypothesis

The theory that drusen were derived from damaged RPE was originally postulated by Donders, who proposed that drusen were derived from RPE nuclei (Donders, 1854). Others suggested aberrant secretion of basement membrane components (Muller, 1856) or a combination of both processes (Coats, 1905).(4) In its modern version, the RPE injury hypothesis proposes that deposit formation is secondary to chronic, repetitive but nonlethal RPE injury.(71;72) Two separate phenomena must be distinguished: the injury stimulus and the cellular response. The most widely implicated injury stimuli are various oxidants, especially those induced by RPE exposure to visible light or those derived from endogenous metabolism.(49;50) Environmental oxidants derived from cigarette smoke, pollution or industrial byproducts have also been proposed to contribute to AMD (Cousins SW, et al IOVS 2003; ARVO E-Abstract 1619). More recently, inflammatory-derived injury stimuli have also become implicated, including oxidants, complement, immune complexes and factors produced by macrophages or monocytes.(72;73) Inflammatory cells might be responsible for drusen progression into choroidal neovascularization by secretion of growth factors and cytokines that will damage the choriocapillaris and stimulate the invasion of neovessels into the subretinal space.(31;74;75)

Irrespective of the injury, this model proposes that all stimuli result in a final common pathway of cellular responses that cause the actual deposits. Cellular responses that can lead to deposit formation include RPE cell membrane blebbing and dysregulation of extracellular matrix production and breakdown. Accumulation of subRPE blebbed material in the setting of imbalanced breakdown and resynthesis of basement membrane and BrM extracellular matrix is proposed to produce the various deposits of AMD. Repetitive injury ultimately can kill RPE, leading to late dry AMD.(3)

Hypothetical Model for Dry AMD

Our research is based on the RPE injury hypothesis. We postulate that the pathogenesis and progression of dry macular degeneration is characterized by three distinct stages (Figure 6): (1.) Initial RPE oxidant injury causes extrusion of cell membrane "blebs", together with decreased activity of matrix metalloproteinases (MMPs), promoting bleb accumulation under the RPE as BLD.

Numerous endogenous or exogenous oxidants can induce blebbing; (2.) RPE cells are subsequently stimulated to increase synthesis of MMPs and other molecules responsible for extracellular matrix turnover (i.e. producing decrease collagen), affecting both RPE basement membrane and BrM. This process leads to progression of BLD into BLinD and drusen by admixture of blebs into BrM, followed by the formation of new basement membrane under the RPE to trap these deposits within BrM. (Strunnikova NV, et al. IOVS 2003; ARVO E-Abstract 3145). We postulate that various hormones and other plasma-derived molecules related to systemic health cofactors are implicated in this stage; (3.) Macrophages are recruited to sites of RPE injury and deposit formation. Macrophage recruitment may be beneficial or harmful depending upon their activation status at the time of recruitment.(74;76) Nonactivated or scavenging macrophages may remove deposits without further injury. Activated or reparative macrophages, through the release of inflammatory mediators, growth factors or other substances, may promote complications and progression.(31;74;75)

Stage I: RPE Oxidant Injury and Nonlethal Blebbing

Oxidants and the RPE

A massive literature is available for the biochemistry of oxidants and effects of anti-oxidant defense systems in protection from injury in nonocular systems, and significant research addresses protective actions of anti-oxidant in the retina and RPE. Several recent reviews provide more details for the interested reader.(50;77;78) Nevertheless, a brief review is relevant to the understanding of our hypothesis.

Reactive oxygen intermediate (ROI) is an umbrella term used to describe a variety of related oxidants, including free radicals, hydrogen peroxide, and singlet oxygen.(49) Free radicals are molecules that contain one or more unpaired electrons in their outer orbits, such as superoxide anion, the hydroxyl free radicals, and the lipid peroxyl radicals. Singlet oxygen and hydrogen peroxide contain their full complement of electrons but in an unstable or reactive phase. In the cell, ROI are constantly being produced by enzymes involved in oxidative processes. Stimuli known to increase the production of ROI include irradiation, aging, inflammation, elevated partial pressure of oxygen, air pollutants, cigarette smoke, and reperfusion injury among others.(79-81) If produced in excess or if they leak from isolated intracellular compartments, these ROI extract electrons from other molecules.

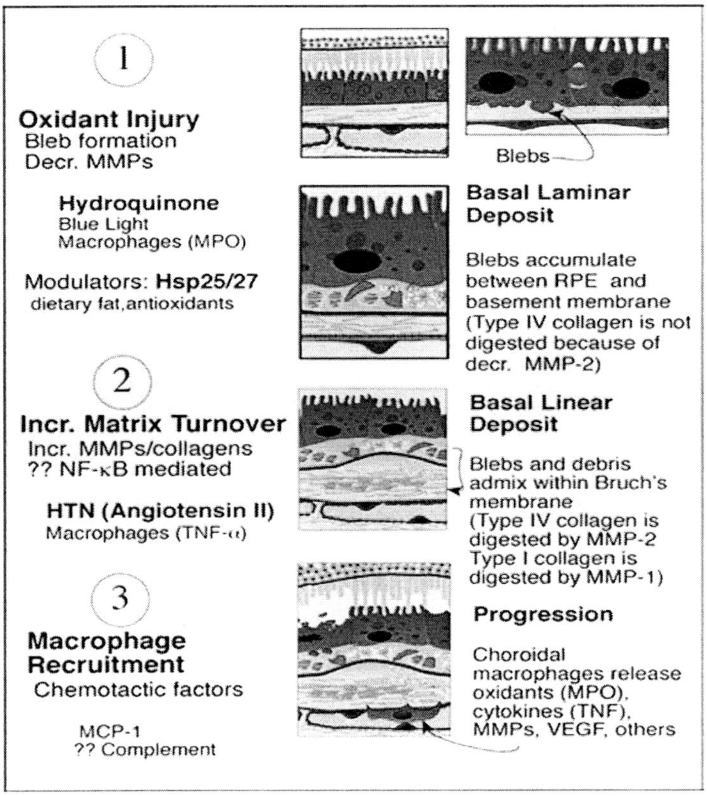

Figure 6: Schematic drawing of the early stages of dry Age-related Macular Degeneration in which three distinct phenomena contained in our hypothetical "response to injury" paradigm are summarized. ***First stage:*** Oxidant injury to the RPE causes bleb formation and decreased MMPs. Different sources of oxidants might trigger this response such as blue light, hydroquinone, and macrophages. Modulators involved are Hsp25/27, dietary fat, and antioxidants. Blebs accumulate between RPE and basement membrane. ***Second stage:*** Increased matrix turnover characterized by increased MMPs and decreased collagens. Modulators involve systemic processes such as hypertension (HTN) and macrophages (via TNF-α through NF-kB activation). BLDs progress into basal linear deposits and drusen and are located within Bruch's membrane inner collagenous layer external to the RPE basement membrane. ***Third stage:*** Macrophages are recruited by chemotactic factors to the site of injury and are responsible for the release of cytokines, angiogenic factors, oxidants and others that may perpetuate the RPE injury maintaining the vicious cycle, and promoting progression to the late stages of the disease (i.e. CNV).

Lipofuscin may be one major source of endogenous RPE-derived ROI. Lipofuscin is a family of highly fluorescent lipid aggregates that accumulate in lysosomes and cytoplasm of many cells with age, but especially within RPE.(54;82) Since lipofuscin is a mixture of molecules, its origin is probably multifactorial. One major component of RPE lipofuscin is derived from incompletely digested photoreceptor membranes, resulting in a molecule called A2E (N-retinylidene-N-retinylethanolamine).(49;54;83) A2E is a major photosensitizing chromophore for visible blue light, resulting in the generation of singlet oxygen, superoxide anion, hydrogen peroxide, and lipid hydroperoxides all of which may act as an injury stimulus to RPE cells.(49;50) However, the RPE contain several other potential chromophores in addition to lipofuscin, including melanin and other molecules.(84-86)

Another potential oxidative injury stimulus in AMD may occur during inflammation. Histopathology of AMD demonstrates that all stages of the disease, including drusen, geographic atrophy and choroidal neovascularization (CNV), are associated with inflammatory cells, especially macrophages.(18;19;31;87;88) One well-characterized inflammatory oxidant is myeloperoxidase (MPO), a heme protein secreted by neutrophils and macrophages that converts its substrate, hydrogen peroxide into an active oxidant.(72) RPE metabolism results in high quantities of hydrogen peroxide synthesis, which by itself is a weak oxidant and is neutralized by catalase and other anti-oxidant enzyme systems.(89-91) However, in the setting of MPO release, RPE-derived hydrogen peroxide can become a powerful oxidant. Macrophage-derived MPO will remain extracellular, but may initiate or potentiate the RPE injury response by catalyzing hydrogen peroxide into the formation of powerful oxidants such as hydroxyl radicals, hydroperoxides, hypochlorous acid and tyrosyl radicals.(73;92) Among their actions, MPO-derived oxidants induce injury to the cell membrane and modify cell surface proteins and receptors.(73;92-94)

Although oxidants derived from blue-light exposure, inflammation or endogenous metabolism are more frequently implicated in RPE injury, we also postulate that environmental oxidants may also contribute to deposit formation. Cigarette smoking is the strongest environmental risk factor for all forms of AMD.(95) The epidemiologic data indicate that cigarette smoking influences the development and severity of AMD, either by the direct actions of oxidants or toxins in cigarette smoke, or indirectly, by the smoking effects on other AMD risk factors like cardiovascular disease.(95) Cigarette smoke-related toxins in tar contain high concentrations of potent oxidants such as the quinones and nitric oxide.(96-99) Quinones are a general term for a ubiquitous class of compounds, which are derivatives of (poly) aromatic phenols.(100) Quinones are common in natural products (especially in plants like tobacco), endogenous biochemicals or metabolites of phenolic compounds.(101-103) Although cigarette smoke contains a complex mixture of quinones, hydroquinone (HQ) is the most abundant.(97;104) All quinones can become oxidants by a similar mechanism.(105-107) Hydroquinone competes with the normal substrate of mitochondrial oxidases associated with electron transport, and undergoes redox cycling with its corresponding semiquinone radical. As a result, HQ metabolism in the mitochondria generates superoxide anion, which in turn, damages mitochondrial membranes and leaks into the cytoplasm. In the cytoplasm, superoxide can be converted into hydroxyl anion and hydroxyl radicals to participate in protein oxidation or lipid peroxidation as explained above. We have shown that HQ can induce blebbing in RPE and subretinal deposits in mice (Suner I.J., et al. IOVS 2004; ARVO E-Abstract 1810).

Molecular Targets of RPE Oxidant Reactions

Several molecular targets are susceptible to damage from oxidation reactions, including DNA, carbohydrates, cellular proteins and cell membranes. Oxidative modifications in key cellular molecules can often produce a cytotoxic chain reaction that contributes to the pathogenesis of many diseases (i.e. atherosclerosis, diabetes, retinopathy of prematurity, cancer, and AMD).(79-81) For example, oxidation-induced breaks in DNA are a major mechanism for cell death due to ionizing radiation.(108) However, we believe that oxidative damage to cell membranes and cellular proteins is more important in AMD.

RPE cell membranes are highly susceptible to lipid peroxidation. As for all cells, RPE cell membranes are comprised of a phospholipid bilayer, and each phospholipid molecule consists in a pair of fatty acids and a polar head group attached to a glycerol backbone.(109) Phospholipids in RPE and photoreceptor membranes are especially rich in polyunsaturated fatty acid (PUFAs), particularly docosahexanoic acid (DHA).(49) The susceptibility of PUFAs to oxidation correlates directly with the number of double bonds (i.e. DHA contains 6 double bonds), which renders the RPE cell membrane especially susceptible to lipid peroxidation and blebbing.(49;110) Importantly, DHA and its precursor, the essential fatty acid linoleic acid, are derived entirely from dietary intake, so that RPE membrane PUFA concentration is strongly influenced by diet.(111)

Cellular proteins are also important targets of oxidant-induced modification. Typical chemical modifications include breakdown of disulfide bonds, tyrosylation, acetlylation and many other biochemical changes that can alter function of the molecule.(112) Accordingly, several well-described pathways exist (i.e., ubiquitin) to remove these damaged biomolecules.(113) Although any cellular protein is potentially susceptible, the actin cytoskeleton is especially vulnerable to oxidant-induced damage, as described below.

Nonlethal Blebbing

Nonlethal cell membrane blebbing is the process by which a cell can pinch off part of its plasma membrane and cytosol in an attempt to discard damaged cellular organelles, molecules and lipid membranes (Hageman GS, Mullin RF, Clark WG, et al. IOVS[ARVO Abstract]1995;36:S432).(114-117) Nonlethal blebbing has been demonstrated to especially affect epithelial cells in liver, kidney, and eye.(72;114;118) Since blebs are short lived (half life of hours), they are difficult to demonstrate histologically.

Nonlethal blebbing is related to, but different from, apoptosis and physiological membrane outpouching.(119-121) Apoptosis is diffuse membrane blebbing secondary to cell death, nuclear fragmentation and metabolic dysfunction, leading to widespread failure to maintain the actin cytoskeleton.(122;123) Physiologic membrane outpouching (i.e., lamellapodia, exocytosis, endocytosis, microspikes and other surface changes) is induced by receptor mediated, focal changes in the cytoskeleton.(124-127) Nonlethal blebbing (without nuclear fragmentation) is an injury-induced cell response characterized by the formation of "focal adhesions" (membrane plaques of Hsp25/27, actin and other proteins), aggregates of cytoplasmic actin filaments and stress fibers, followed by blebbing.(72;114;128) Several injury stimuli induce blebbing in nonocular cells, especially drugs, oxidants, physical membrane damage and certain cytokines.(119;129-134)

Blebbing was first introduced as a possible pathogenic mechanism in drusen formation by Feeney-Burns, who observed bleb-like structures in human drusen.(135) Subsequently Ryan's laboratory demonstrated RPE budding in monkeys with drusen, and in different rabbit models of RPE injury.(136-138) These observations demonstrated the occurrence of RPE blebbing in vivo. Our lab hypothesizes that nonlethal cell membrane blebbing is the primary cause for the accumulation of subRPE deposits (BLD) that become BLinD and drusen.

We have used a genetically modified human RPE cell line containing green fluorescent protein anchored to the inner leaflet of the plasma membrane to demonstrate nonlethal blebbing in response to various types of injury (Figure 7).(72;139-143) Blebbing can be induced by oxidant injury with blue light, MPO or hydroquinone (Monroy D., et al., IOVS, 2001, 42(4), ARVO Abstract, 4060; Suner I.J., et al. IOVS 2004; ARVO E-Abstract 1810).(3;72) Cytoplasmic actin aggregates are observed after nonlethal blebbing, but not with lethal oxidant injury (Figure 8). Interesting, blebbing is not induced by treatment with cytokines like tumor necrosis factor, which can induce lethal blebbing and apoptosis in other cell types. Also, lipid peroxidation is suggested in MPO-induced blebbing since the susceptibility to blebbing can be increased by loading the RPE with PUFA (linoleic acid) 24 hours prior to oxidant exposure. Further, this lipid-enhanced blebbing can be prevented by pre-treatment of RPE with alpha-tocopherol (vitamin E), a lipid soluble antioxidant known to inhibit cell membrane lipid peroxidation (Sall J.M. et al. IOVS 1999, 40(4), ARVO Abstract, 4857).(144)

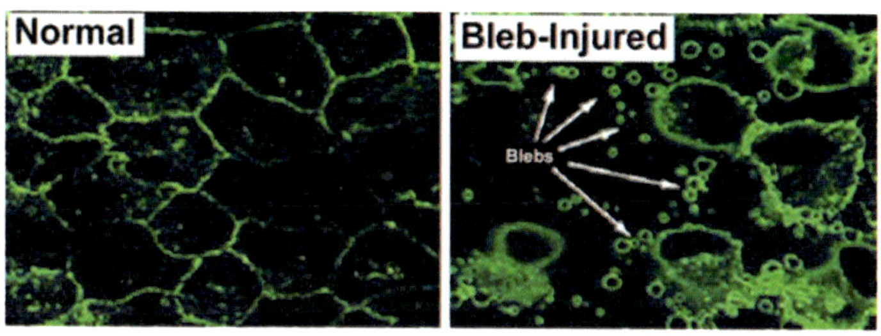

Figure 7: Fluorescent GFP-RPE derived blebs before and after exposure to oxidant-mediated injury. The figure to the left shows a spontaneously transformed human adult RPE cell line (ARPE 19, a standard line for RPE cell biology) that has been genetically modified by retroviral transduction with a construct containing green fluorescent protein-fernesylated r Ras [GFP-RPE] which anchors the fluorescent marker to the inner leaflet of the plasma membrane. The figure to the right shows the same culture of RPE cells after exposure with 100 μM of hydroquinone. The white arrows point the blebs indicating oxidant-mediated injury.

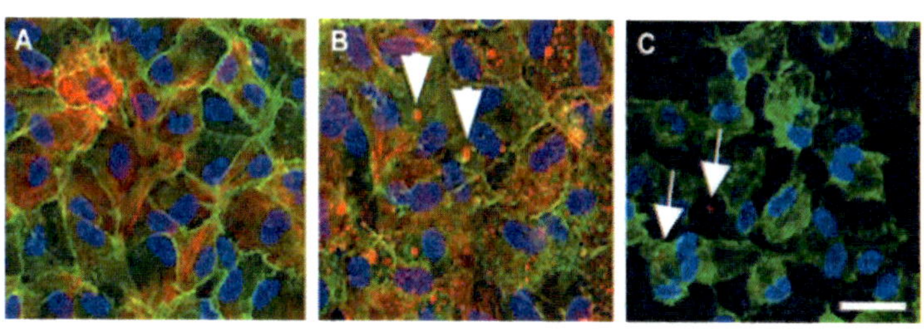

Figure 8: Morphologic changes of RPE F-actin fibrils after phalloidin staining. A. Confocal image of ARPE-GFP-c' Ras control cells with normal cytoskeletal architecture. Green label = inner leaflet of the plasma membrane; Red label = F-actin fibrils; Blue (DAPI) label = Nuclei. B. Morphologic changes after nonlethal oxidative injury (100 μM of hydroquinone). F-actin fibrils were partially rearranged into aggregate structures (white arrowheads). C. After a lethal injury (300 μM of hydroquinone), ARPE-GFP-c' Ras cells show completely disassembled F-actin fibrils (white arrows) and loss of cytoplasmic actin aggregates. Scale bar 50 μM.

Regulation of Actin Cytoskeleton Turnover and its Relationship with Blebbing

All forms of blebbing, including non-lethal blebbing, are closely interrelated with the actin cytoskeleton.(129;145-152) The actin cytoskeleton consists of the cortical cytoskeleton (the scaffold that supports the plasma membrane) and the microfilaments (the cytoplasmic network of actin filaments responsible for intracellular transport and compartmentalization).(153) The cytoskeleton is a dynamic structure undergoing continuous turnover by disassembly and reassembly of G-actin monomers, which are added to the active edge of a growing filament. Cytoskeletal turnover is mediated by a large system of interacting proteins generically referred to as the actin polymerizing protein system (APP). The identity of these proteins is a rapidly growing field, and includes kinases, phosphatases, cleavage proteins and elongating proteins. Their individual specific function and regulatory interactions remain essentially unknown. However, in general, the APP functions as a coordinated system such that individual molecular regulators of cytoskeleton dynamics exert their actions on the entire APP in coordinated fashion.(129;145-152)

The molecules that regulate the APP system have only recently become elucidated, and very little information is available to relate these molecules to disease pathogenesis. Interestingly, oxidant injury is an effective activator of increased cytoskeleton turnover, presumably secondary to direct oxidative changes of disulfide bonds within actin filaments.(129;154-157) The best characterized inhibitor/ stabilizer of cytoskeleton turnover is heat shock protein 25/27 (Hsp25/27). This molecule belongs to the family of small heat shock proteins (which includes α-β crystallins) and serves a dual role as cytoskeleton stabilizer and chaperone protein.(156-161) Furthermore, studies on overexpression of this protein indicate that it can protect against cell death induced by hyperthermia, anticancerous drugs, and inflammatory cytokines.(162-165)

Our data indicate that RPE, ganglion cells and photoreceptor outer segments express high levels of Hsp25/27.(72;166) Oxidant injury can induce a rapid upregulation of Hsp25/27 protein through the activation of presynthesized heat shock factors (hsf-1,-2,-3) which upon oxidation form trimers that become very potent transcription factors (Figure 9).(156-161) Upon phosphorylation, Hsp25/27 acts as an F-actin cap-binding protein, binding to the active edge of a growing microfilament, causing a transient delay in actin cytoskeleton reassembly and repair (Figure 9).(129;145-152;154-161;167;168) Transient delay in reassembly allows the unsupported plasma membrane to be forced outward by the hydrostatic forces of the cytoplasm, and a vesicle or bleb forms if cortical cytoskeleton and microfilaments do not completely reform within the outpouched membrane (Figure 9). Phosphorylation of Hsp25/27 is mediated through the MAP kinase cascade, but is directly phosphorylated by MAPKAP 2 kinase (MK2), which in turn is phosphorylated by p38 kinase (or p38).(129;169) Thus, drug inhibition of p38 will block MK 2 and Hsp25/27 phosphorylation, a potential therapeutic target for drusen inhibition.

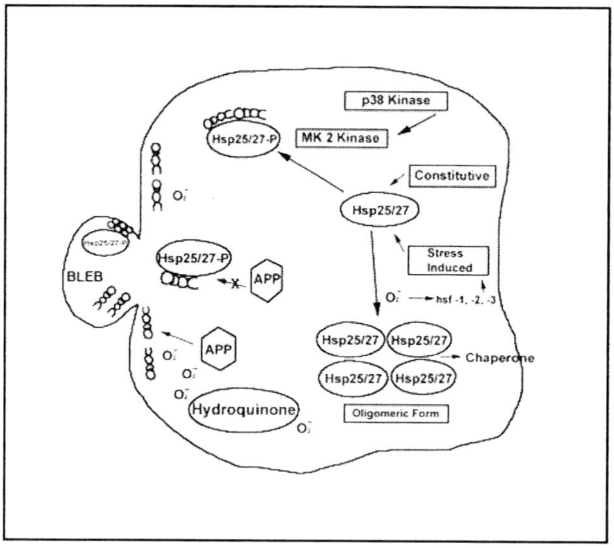

Figure 9: Regulation of the actin cytoskeleton turnover and its relationship to blebbing. The schematic drawing shows the phosphorylation of Hsp25/27 through the MK-2 kinase pathway and the capping of actin filaments which prevents the reassembly of the growing actin microfilaments that make the cytoskeleton in the cytoplasm by interfering with the function of the actin polymerizing proteins (APP) system and to disassembled aggregates in damaged cell membrane (i.e., dense plaques) after oxidant injury. Oxidant injury also causes Hsp25/27 to polymerize into large oligomers after which it becomes a potent chaperone molecule capable of binding to other proteins to protect them from injury stimuli, by promoting protein folding, and scavenging cytoplasmic oxidants. Also, oxidant injury can induce a rapid upregulation of Hsp25/27 protein through the activation of presynthesized heat shock factors (hsf-1,-2,-3) which upon oxidation form trimers that become very potent transcription factors.

STAGE II: DYSREGULATED EXTRACELLULAR MATRIX TURNOVER

The normal anatomy and physiology of extracellular matrix (ECM) in most tissues requires continuous turnover of collagen and other matrix components by a tightly regulated balance in production of matrix molecules, matrix metalloproteinases (MMPs) and tissue inhibitors of metalloproteinases (TIMPs).(170) Relatively small dysregulation in the ratio of these factors can produce profound changes in the ECM, including thickening and deposit formation.(171;172) Accordingly, dysregulated turnover of ECM is a major mechanism of disease pathogenesis in many tissue sites, including renal disease, atherosclerosis, lung disease and others.(170-177) The capacity of oxidant injury to regulate production of ECM, especially to modulate the expression and activity of MMP-2 has been documented in different cell types.(178-182) Unfortunately, minimal information is available concerning normal turnover in healthy BrM or dysregulated turnover in AMD eyes.

Ample evidence supports the idea that MMPs and their tissue inhibitors (TIMPs) play an important role in AMD. The RPE is capable of producing many matrix components found in Bruch's membrane.(183-186) RPE expresses high levels of pro-matrix MMP-2 and active MMP-2, which is the major RPE enzyme synthesized for the degradation of matrix type IV and I collagens, and laminin. Oxidative injury to the RPE may not only produce blebbing but also dysregulated ECM turnover.(3;4;49;71;72;114;144;187)

Our results have shown that blebs form and accumulate in the absence of activated MMP-2, which otherwise induce breakdown of type IV collagen present in the basement membrane of the RPE.(187) Sustained oxidant injury in a time-dependent manner is capable of downregulating MMP-2 activity in an in-vitro system of RPE cells, correlating with an increase in bleb levels as well as the latent MMP-2 protein (Monroy D., et al., IOVS, 2001, 42(4), ARVO Abstract, 4060). Also, type IV collagen accumulation, the main component of the RPE basement membrane, correlated with the absence of MMP-2 activity. Accordingly, we have shown in vivo (see below) that reducing MMP-2 activity leads to an increase in deposit formation by RPE cells. This allows the blebs to become trapped between the RPE cell membrane and the basement membrane to form BLD.

One source of ECM dysregulation is the activational state of estrogen receptors. Estrogens receptors regulate the expression of genes relevant in the turnover of ECM such as MMP-2.(188-192) Estrogen deficiency may predispose to a dysregulated synthesis and degradation of ECM, leading to the accumulation of collagens and other proteins between the RPE and its basement membrane.(193-195) Our lab has confirmed the presence and functionality of estrogen receptors α and β in human RPE.(183) The regulation of these receptors by estrogen is done in a dose-dependent fashion and probably in part mediated through NF-κB. This data taken together with animal studies in mice (see below) suggest that estrogen regulation of ECM synthesis and turnover may, in part, explain gender differences in the deposit severity of AMD patients.

For the BLD deposits to progress into linear deposits a second hit is needed. ECM upregulation with MMP-2 activation is necessary for collagen and BLD deposit degradation. This will ultimately displace subRPE deposits into the inner layer of BrM where BLinD and drusen are histologically found. Preliminary work in our lab has shown that the three components of the renin/angiotensin/converting enzyme system are present in the RPE suggesting that local activation of circulating angiotensin I into the bioactive peptide, angiotensin II, probably occurs in the RPE (Marin-Castano ME, et al., IOVS, 2003; 44: ARVO E-Abstract, 2282/B121; Marin-Castano ME, et al., IOVS, 2004; 45: ARVO E-Abstract, 1811/B622). Angiotensin II is an octapeptide hormonal growth factor derived from angiotensin I by the action of angiotensin converting enzyme (ACE).(196-201) Angiotensin I is derived from angiotensinogen, a liver-derived pro-peptide that is cleaved by renin into angiotensin I. Angiotensin II acts by two specific cell surface receptors AT1 and AT2.(196;197;200;202) Both are typical seven transmembrane G-coupled receptors, but AT1 and AT2 seem to antagonize each other. AT1 generally activates kinases, phospholipase C, adenylate cyclase and NADPH.(203-208) AT2 activates MAPK phosphatases and guanylate cyclase.(209;210)

More recently our lab has shown the expression of angiotensin II receptors in human and murine RPE cells (Marin-Castano ME, et al., IOVS, 2004; 45: ARVO E-Abstract, 1811/B622). Through interactions with its two receptors, angiotensin II can regulate the synthesis of molecules important in the maintenance of the extracellular matrix, especially MMP-2 and -9, therefore, time course analysis have been performed demonstrating that angiotensin II upregulates MMP-2 activity as well as MMP-9 activity in the RPE in a concentration dependent fashion (Marin-Castano ME, et al., IOVS, 2004; 45: ARVO E-Abstract, 1811/B622). Additionally inhibition assays have been able to show that Candersartan (AT1 receptor antagonist) and PD123319 (AT2 receptor antagonist) attenuate the angiotensin II associated MMP activity which support the hypothesis that angiotensin II might regulate extracellular matrix molecules expression in systemic diseases such as hypertension (HTN).

Some evidence has supported the notion that systemic vascular disease, especially HTN is an important risk factor for AMD.(22;211) In several cross sectional and case control studies, systemic HTN was associated with increased prevalence and progression of AMD.(212-214) The potential high importance of HTN and drusen formation was recently demonstrated in a primate model of AMD were Jonas et al. observed a dramatic increase in the severity and incidence of drusen.(215) Although no specific mechanism were determined, we believed that using angiotensin II as a surrogate for HTN might be the second hit for the progression of BLD into drusen and severe basal linear deposits. Furthermore, based on receptor functions in other cells, we hypothesize that angiotensin II might induce significant upregulation of matrix turnover through ATI/AT2 receptors, and might also affect Hsp25/27 and blebbing, thus contributing to BLD progression into BLinD and drusen.

STAGE III: INFLAMMATION, MACROPHAGES AND DRY AMD

In the past three years, the concept that inflammatory mechanisms play an important role in the pathogenesis of both dry and wet AMD has emerged as a major paradigm shift. Several laboratories have identified complement and immune complexes in drusen, but their pathogenic role has not been defined. This information has been recently reviewed.(18;21)

Other investigators (especially Hinton, Mullins, Penfold and Grossniklaus) have observed that choroidal monocytes/ macrophages are present in human specimens of both early and late AMD.(18;19;21;31;88;216) Macrophages have been detected along the choriocapillaris-side of Bruch's membrane underlying areas of thick drusen or other deposits.(87;217-220) Processes from choroidal monocytes have been noted to insert into Bruch's membrane deposits, presumably for the purpose of scavenging debris.(87) The contribution (beneficial or harmful) of these cells in drusen pathogenesis or progression is uncertain.

Monocytes and macrophages belong to the family of circulating bone marrow derived mononuclear leukocytes. The monocyte (the circulating cell) and the macrophage (the tissue-infiltrating or cell culture equivalent) are important effectors in tissue repair, cell injury, inflammation and innate immunity.(76) Monocytes can be recruited into many normal tissues by specific chemotactic factors, where they become macrophages. At the risk of oversimplification, blood-derived macrophages can be subdivided into one of three functional phenotypes: scavengers of cell debris and antigen presenting cells to T lymphocytes ("scavenging" macrophages); inflammatory effector cells ("inflammatory" macrophages); and modifiers of other processes in cell biology, especially wound repair, angiogenesis and matrix turnover ("reparative" macrophages).(76)

Our laboratory has postulated that macrophages might contribute to progression of drusen and induction of CNV.(74;75) They may also regulate the size and severity of CNV and contribute to retinal damage leading to vision loss, but this issue will not be addressed here.(75) We propose that different subsets of individuals may exist in terms of cytokine and growth factor production by circulating macrophage, reflecting generalized differences in the activation state of circulating monocytes: a "low-active" scavenging macrophages versus a "partially activated" reparative subset.(74) Low active macrophages will scavenge RPE debris without damage, perhaps serving a protective function. However, partially active macrophages may inappropriately promote complications, especially CNV formation.(76)

Based upon the assumption that choroidal macrophages are derived from circulating blood monocytes,(221) we determined if monocyte populations from individual AMD patients exhibited heterogeneity in terms of cytokine production in culture or in mRNA expression of freshly isolated cells, and if high levels served as a biomarker of risk for progression into neovascular AMD.(74) We focused on TNF-α expression, a potent cytotoxic and proangiogenic cytokine for wet AMD.

Human monocytes were obtained from control and AMD subjects. TNF-α is expressed by freshly isolated monocytes and produced by macrophages in culture after stimulation with RPE derived blebs and cytokines. Typically macrophages in culture, after stimulation produced a 2-3 fold increase in TNF-α. However, extremely high variability in baseline TNF-α expression from isolated macrophages was observed among different subjects, spanning 200-300 fold range.(74) This finding suggested that the subset of patients with high TNF-α reflected the presence of partially activated monocytes in the blood. When subdivided, the wet AMD group revealed higher median values than dry. Thus, our data indicate that AMD patients with blood monocytes expressing high TNF-α levels demonstrate almost 5-fold increased odds ratio for the presence of neovascular AMD.(74)

These results are consistent with the hypothesis that the pre-existing macrophage activation state, defined as level of cytokine or mediator expression of the circulating monocyte, might determine the negative or positive consequence of macrophage recruitment as a disease modifier. Macrophages with low expression might remove deposits safely whereas macrophages with high expression might produce mediators that contribute to disease progression.

Animal Model for Sub-RPE Deposits

Animal models are extremely useful in preclinical testing of theories of disease pathogenesis and therapeutic interventions. However, until recently, no animal models for dry AMD were available. The available literature has reported several models for dry AMD that we have summarized below including our own preferred model.

Animal Models for Dry AMD

Protoporphyric Mouse Model

By feeding albino mice (Balb CJ) with griseofulvin, Gottsch et al. were able to induce liver dysfunction, which causes elevations of protoporphyrin IX concentrations in blood and induces reactive oxygen species by photosensitizing this compound after exposing the animals to blue light.(222) The concept behind the model was that initial deposits may be produced by the choriocapillaris endothelium and may contribute to an overall thickening of the choriocapillaris basement membrane. The typical BLDs occurred later, as a result of altered choriocapillaris permeability or RPE photosensitization. This model was the first one to stress the importance of reactive oxygen species in the development of subRPE deposits and that the latter were the result of a light mediated phenomenon.(222)

Genetically Manipulated Mouse Models of Hyperlipidemia with APO E Abnormalities

These animal models have been useful to elucidate the complicated nature of lipids in the pathogenesis of AMD with contradictory results regarding deposit formation. Dithmar et al. showed that the APO E null mice did not develop BLDs or RPE degeneration, but electron-lucent particles were present in BrM indicating a mild form of basal linear deposits-like debris that correlated with older age.(223) Kliffen et al. on the other hand, showed that typical BLDs developed in mice expressing the mutant APO E3 after consuming a high fat diet, without light exposure.(224) In summary, APO E3 is important in hepatic processing of VLDL remnants, and its absence results in increased VLDL in the blood, which may ultimately contribute to modify the composition of lipids in RPE cells.(225;226) Additionally, APO E isoforms may also contribute to transport and solubilization of extracellular lipids in tissues and its importance in AMD might be related to a role in BrM lipid transport and deposit accumulation.(225-227)

Mutated Cathepsin D Transgenic Mouse Model

Rakoczy et al. developed a mouse line (mcd/mcd) which expresses an inactive form of cathepsin D that impairs the process of phagocytosing photoreceptor outer segments in RPE cells.(228) This animal reproduces features associated with the early stages of AMD including BLD and BLinD with RPE cell proliferation and atrophy, photoreceptor degeneration, and accumulation of photoreceptor breakdown products in the RPE cells. The hypothesis states that any change, genetic or environmental, that might lead to an accelerated photoreceptor outer segment breakdown product accumulation in the RPE layer will compromise RPE cell function, initiating changes similar to those observed in AMD.(228)

Macrophage depletion model

Macrophage chemotactic protein-1 (MCP-1 or CCL-2) is an important macrophage chemoattractant. Mice genetically deficient in MCP-1 demonstrate diminished recruitment of blood-derived macrophages into various tissues. Furthermore, genetically deficient mice lacking the CCR2 receptor for MCP-1 develop less severe CNV, consistent with the important role of macrophages in regulating severity of CNV. Recently, Ambati et al. have published data to indicate that MCP-1 deficient mice develop spontaneous histopathologic changes identical to human AMD, including drusen and CNV.(229) If true, this model will be useful in studies of AMD pathogenesis. However, validation of the model has been problematic. Furthermore, MCP-1 null mice are susceptible to chronic infections, and the possible role of inapparent systemic infection as a confounding variable in this model has been raised.

Retinal Iron Overload and Degeneration in a Transgenic Mouse Model for Retinal Degeneration

Using a transgenic animal model for retinal degeneration based in disruption of two important iron regulating proteins, ceruloplasmin and hephaestin, Hahn et al. provided evidence showing that iron overload in the retina might be relevant for the pathogenesis of retinal degeneration, including AMD.(230) These results were based on previous studies in postmortem AMD-affected maculas showing the presence of excessive iron in the RPE and BrM of human subjects. The rationale is based upon the concept that increased concentrations of iron, which can generate highly reactive hydroxyl radicals via the Fenton reaction and induce oxidative stress in the macula, may lead to AMD.(231)

C57BL/6 Mouse Model for Dry AMD

The utility of animal models to evaluate mechanism of deposit pathogenesis is illustrated by recent data from our laboratory and others to evaluate mechanisms for age, gender, environmental toxins, and to test current hypothesis (Cousins SW, et al. IOVS 2003; 44: ARVO E-Abstract 1619/B515; Suner IJ, et al., IOVS 2004; 45: ARVO E-Abstract 1810/B621).(71;144;187;232)

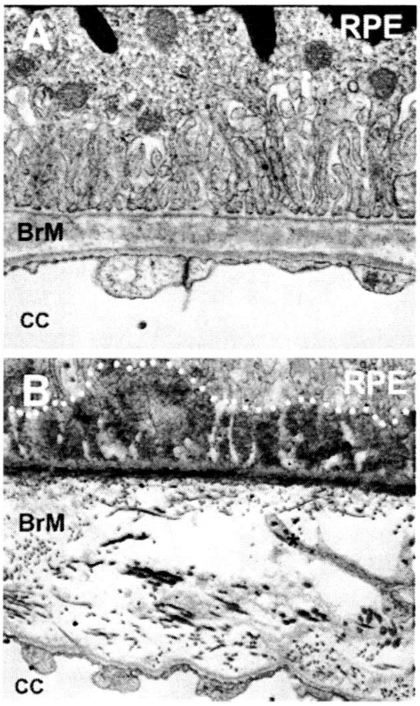

Figure 10: Transmission electron microscopy of the outer retina and choroid from mice from different age groups fed on high fat diets for 4.5 months and exposed to blue light. A. Young mice usually revealed normal anatomy. B. Old mice revealed moderately severe subRPE deposits (under white, dashed line) consisting of BLD containing banded structures and marked collagenous thickening of BrM. Invasion by a cellular process (black asterisk) apparently emanating from the choriocapillaris is evident. RPE= Retinal pigment epithelium, BrM= Bruch's membrane, CC= Choriocapillaris. (Magnification: x25,000)

We were able to modify the composition of fats in the lipid bilayer of RPE cell membranes and study the role of aging as a susceptibility factor for the capacity of an oxidant stressor (i.e. blue light) to increase the development of subretinal deposits using aged C57BL/6 mice fed with a diet high in unsaturated fats (i.e. linoleic acid).(71) SubRPE deposits (BLD) were a consistent finding in these aged animals (Figure 10). These deposits were characterized by homogeneous or granular material and banded structures (Figure 11). Bruch's membrane was thickened and occasionally showed coiled, membranous or banded structures (Figure 11B and 12). Some eyes in this older group also developed changes in the choriocapillaris consistent with cellular invasion into Bruch's membrane, but without forming true lumens (Figure 12C). These observations demonstrated that aging predisposes to complicated interactions between systemic cofactors (dietary fat and lipidemia) and local ocular cofactors (environmental light and lipofuscin) to induce subRPE deposits, possibly by altering ECM turnover after oxidative injury to the RPE.

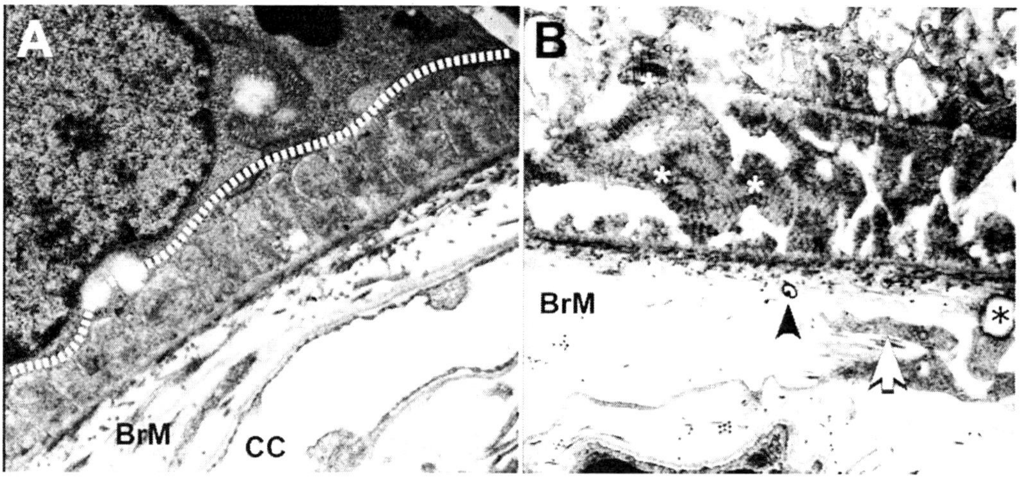

Figure 11: Transmission electron microscopy of moderate subRPE deposits in fat fed old mice exposed to blue light. A. Shows moderately thick continuous homogeneous and granular deposits (below dashed line) located between the plasma membrane of the RPE. Basal infoldings are absent. B. Shows moderately thick BLD with a palisading pattern of numerous oval-shaped banded deposits. BrM contains and empty circular profile (black arrowhead). Cellular processes from an unknown cell type within the choroid are present (white arrow) and one seems to surround an empty profile (black asterisk). RPE= Retinal pigment epithelium, BrM= Bruch's membrane, CC= Choriocapillaris, BLD= Basal laminar deposits. (Magnification: x25,000)

Using a similar mouse model to the one described above, we studied the role of gender and estrogen status.(187) Both aged male and female mice developed qualitatively similar BLD morphology, but the severity in terms of thickness, continuity and content was significantly greater in female mice (Figure 13). Aged female mice also demonstrated a trend towards more severe endothelial changes and increased BrM thickening (Figure 13A).

Middle aged mice were used to delineate the role of estrogen in the severity of subRPE deposits.(187) Ovariectomized, estrogen-deficient mice developed more severe deposits (Figure 14). In the other hand, ovariectomized mice that received high dose estrogen supplementation had thinner BrM but also developed significant deposits (Figure 15). Paradoxically, protein extracted from the RPE of these ovariectomized and estrogen supplemented mice at high doses showed decreased MMP-2 activity, which might explain the accumulation of BLD and suggests that regulation of the extracellular matrix by MMP-2 may play a role in the pathogenesis of the deposits, as explained previously. We concluded from these studies that female gender in aged mice and estrogen deficiency in middle aged mice appears to increase the severity of sub-RPE deposit formation. Hypothetically, estrogen deficiency may increase susceptibility to subRPE deposit formation by dysregulating turnover of BrM. This would contribute to collagenous thickening and endothelial changes, supporting the concept that women with early menopause appear at risk for worse AMD.(233;234). Additionally, estrogen supplementation at the high dosages used in this study does not appear to protect against sub-RPE deposit formation and might be in accordance to the more recent results of the Women Health Initiative (WHI) multicentric trials.(235;236)

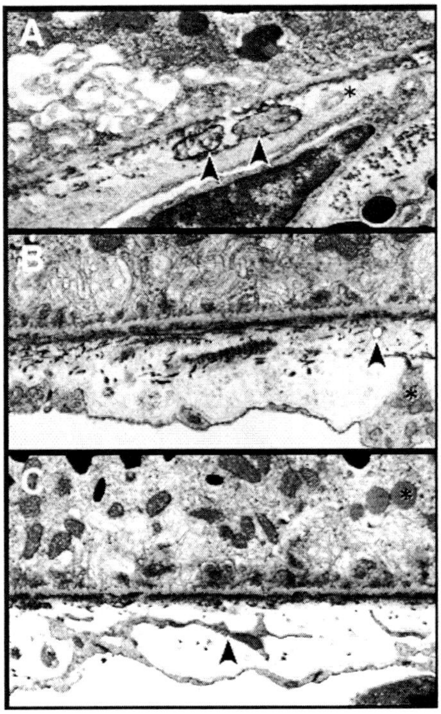

Figure 12: Transmission electron microscopy of subRPE deposits associated with significant changes in BrM in fat fed old mice exposed to blue light. A. The micrograph demonstrates mild patchy subRPE deposits overlying several membrane coated bodies within Bruch's membrane (black arrowheads), and another deposit within BrM has a coiled membranous appearance (black asterisk). B. Another specimen reveals moderately thick BLD with mostly homogeneous deposits and some banded components. BrM contains several electron dense structures and an empty circular profile (black arrowhead). A protruding cell from the choriocapillaris is present (black asterisk). C. Another eye reveals moderately thick subRPE deposits with banded structures. BrM is invaded by cellular processes from the choriocapillaris, one containing a mitochondrion (black arrowhead). Areas of small empty circular profiles are scattered throughout. BrM= Bruch's membrane, BLD= Basal laminar deposits. (Magnification: x25,000)

Our animal model has also served to test the contribution of environmental toxins in deposit formation. Some investigators have suggested that the incidence and severity of AMD has increased among populations exposed to western lifestyle and urban environments.(237-239) One possible explanation is that toxic substances associated with western lifestyle might directly contribute to the formation of drusen and late forms of AMD by an increase in oxidative stressors. Based on this idea, we reasoned that the redox molecule hydroquinone, a prevalent component of cigarette smoke, automobile exhaust and certain processed foods, might contribute to drusen pathogenesis. We evaluated the impact of oral feeding of this compound to mice and found that hydroquinone-exposed mice developed subRPE deposits (Cousins SW, et al. IOVS 2003; 44: ARVO E-Abstract 1619; Suner IJ, et al., IOVS 2004; 45: ARVO E-Abstract 1810).

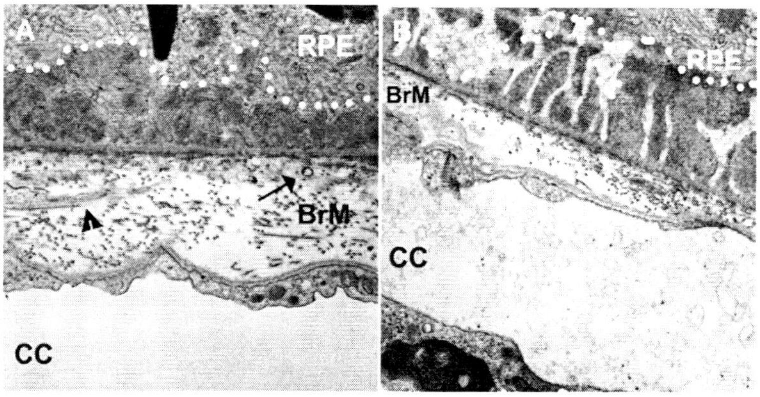

Figure 13: Transmission electron microscopy of the outer retina and choroid from old fat-fed female or male mice exposed to blue light. A. Specimen from an aged female mouse revealed moderately thick subRPE deposits (under white dotted line) containing banded structures consistent with BLDs. BrM revealed marked collagenous thickening and an empty circular profile (black arrow). Invasion by a cellular process (black arrowhead) apparently emanating from the choriocapillaris was also evident. The endothelium revealed thickening with loss of fenestrations. B. Specimen from an aged male mouse revealed continuous, moderately thick sub RPE deposits (under white dotted line) containing also banded structures in a palisading configuration. Differently from females, BrM was only mildly and irregularly thickened. The endothelial morphology appears slightly abnormal, with mild reduplication of the basement membrane but evidence of severe injury or invasion was not observed. RPE= Retinal pigment epithelium, BrM= Bruch's membrane, CC= Choriocapillaris, BLD= Basal laminar deposits. (Magnification: x25,000)

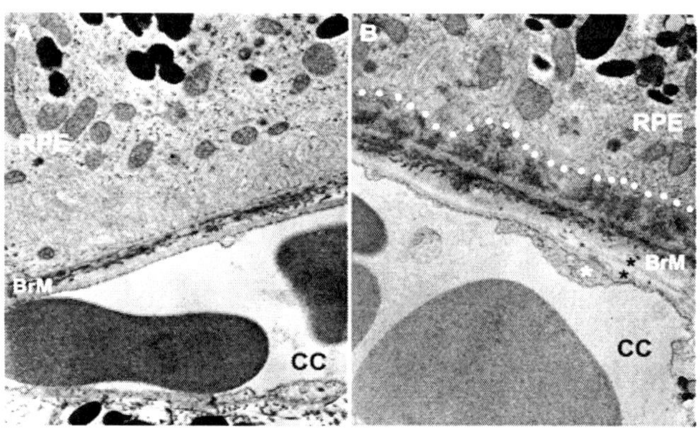

Figure 14: Transmission electron microscopy of the outer retina and choroid from a fat fed, blue light exposed middle age female mice undergoing sham surgery or ovariectomy. A. Specimen from a middle age sham-surgery (ovary intact) female mouse revealed no subRPE deposits and normal BrM and CC. B. Specimen from a middle age ovariectomized mouse revealed moderately thick continuous BLD (under white dotted line) with banded structures. Irregular thickening of BrM and hypertrophied endothelium (white asterisk) with reduplication of the basement membrane (black asterisks) is evident. RPE= Retinal pigment epithelium, BrM= Bruch's membrane, CC= Choriocapillaris, BLD= Basal laminar deposits. (Magnification: x25,000)

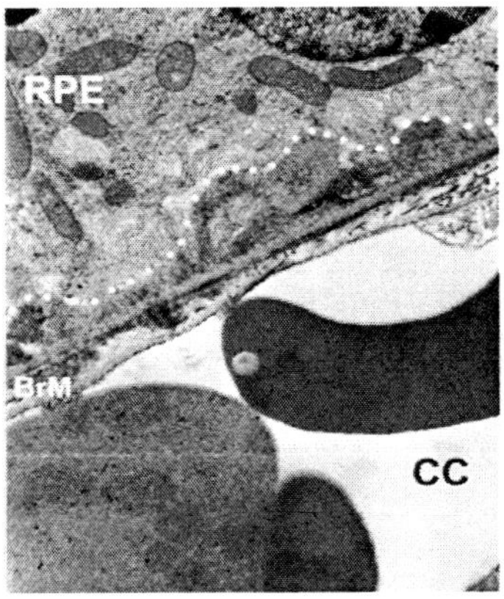

Figure 15: Transmission electron microscopy of the outer retina and choroid from a fat fed, blue light exposed middle age female mice undergoing ovariectomy with estrogen replacement. The specimen revealed moderately thick BLD (under white dotted line) of severity similar to that in the ovariectomized mouse (Figure 14B) with banded structures. However, BrM appeared to be normally compact and the endothelium was normal. RPE= Retinal pigment epithelium, BrM= Bruch's membrane, CC= Choriocapillaris, BLD= Basal laminar deposits. (Magnification: x25,000)

The subRPE changes in the hydroquinone exposed mice were similar to those of the blue light model, characterized by accumulation of moderately dense homogeneous, banded, and granular material between the RPE and its basement membrane (Figure 16). Occasional blebs were observed, BrM was thickened with coated vesicles and membranous profiles, and BLD deposits with banded structures were often present (Figure 16 and 17). These findings indicated that two different oxidant stimuli-blue light and hydroquinone can produce a common response in the RPE.

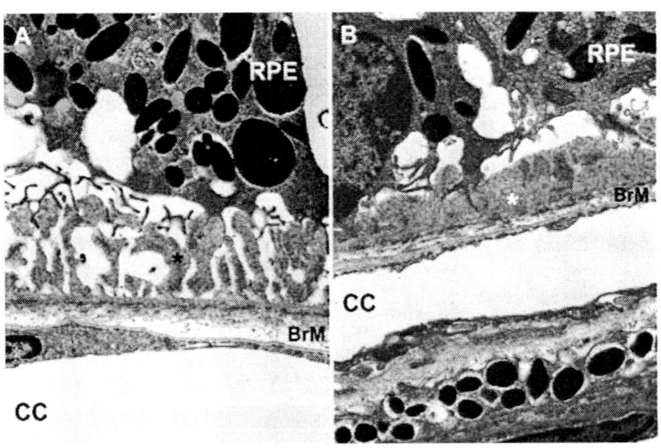

Figure 16: Transmission electron microscopy of the outer retina and choroid from hydroquinone-exposed mice. Specimens from a hydroquinone diet revealed that subRPE changes were similar to the blue light model, characterized by accumulation of moderately severe BLD with banded structures in a palisading configuration (A. black asterisk) or dense granular material between the RPE and its basement membrane (B. white asterisk). These findings indicated that different oxidant stimuli (blue light & hydroquinone) could produce a common response in the RPE. RPE= Retinal Pigment Epithelium, BrM= Bruch's Membrane, CC= Choriocapillaris, BLD= Basal laminar deposits. (Magnification, x25,000)

Finally, animal models can serve to question current hypotheses and predict outcomes of therapeutic interventions. Using young transgenic mice (C57BL/6 background) that overexpress APO B100, the major apolipoprotein in LDL cholesterol, we determined whether high fat diet and plasma lipidemia correlate with the formation of BLD.(144) Similarly to our model described previously, deposits were induced by using high fat diet and blue light. In individual affected mice, only a weak correlation was observed between deposit severity and plasma lipid concentration. None of the eyes in mice with sustained hyperlipidemia with or without BLD demonstrated obvious widespread of neutral lipids or cholesterol deposition in BLD or BrM (Figure 18 & 19). These results question the pathogenesis of the barrier hypothesis which proposes that deposit formation is secondary to a defect in transport through BrM caused by the accumulation of lipids derived from the circulation.(66-68)

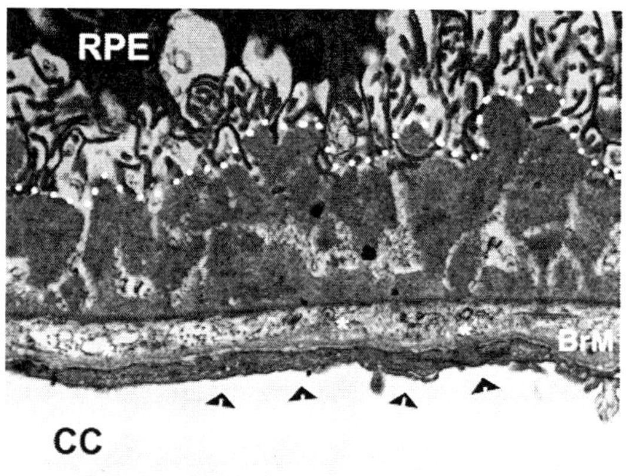

Figure 17: Transmission electron microscopy of the outer retina and choroid from hydroquinone-exposed mice. Specimens from a hydroquinone diet revealed moderately severe BLD (under white dotted line) with banded structures. BrM was irregularly thickened with empty circular profiles and coiled membranous deposits (white asterisks). The choriocapillaris endothelial cells were hypertrophied with loss of fenestrations (black arrowheads). RPE= Retinal Pigment Epithelium, BrM= Bruch's Membrane, CC= Choriocapillaris, BLD= Basal laminar deposits. (Magnification, x25,000)

Although the source of the lipids in subRPE deposits in BrM remains controversial, several authors have postulated that BrM lipids may in fact be derived from the RPE by secretion, exocitosis, or blebbing (see above). Furthermore, pretreatment with the antioxidant α-tocopherol (vitamin E) showed reduction of the severity and frequency of BLD formation suggesting an oxidative mechanism in the formation of subRPE deposits (Figure 20).(144) The Age-related Eye Disease Study (AREDS) has recently showed the effects of antioxidants (i.e. high dose vitamins C and E, beta-carotene, and zinc supplements) in preventing the progression of deposits into neovascular AMD. Estimates suggest that if patients with extensive nonexudative dry AMD or advanced AMD in the fellow eye were to take AREDS supplements, over 300,000 cases of blindness from AMD could be prevented (Reuters press release 11/11/03).

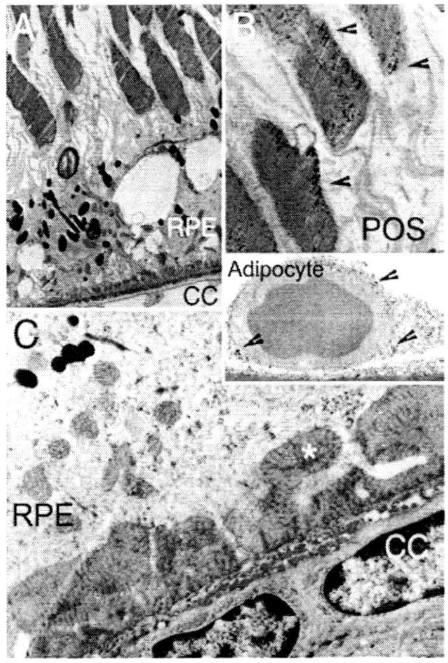

Figure 18: Filipin staining shows in low- (A) and high-(C) magnification transmission electron micrographs of the outer retina and choroid of a young fat-fed APO B100 mouse exposed to blue light. A. A low-magnification micrograph showed no filipin stain that was used to detect unesterified cholesterol in the BLD and BrM. B. Photoreceptor outer segment (POS) demonstrated significant punctuate uptake of filipin, consistent with high levels of unesterified cholesterol in the outer segments and in the intestines which we used as positive controls (black arrowheads). C. Higher magnification of another APO B100 specimen that clearly showed no filipin staining of sub RPE deposits (white asterisk). RPE= Retinal Pigment Epithelium, BrM= Bruch's Membrane, CC= Choriocapillaris, BLD= Basal laminar deposits. (Magnification: A. x7,200; B. POS: x25,000; Adipocyte: x14,500; C. x25,000)

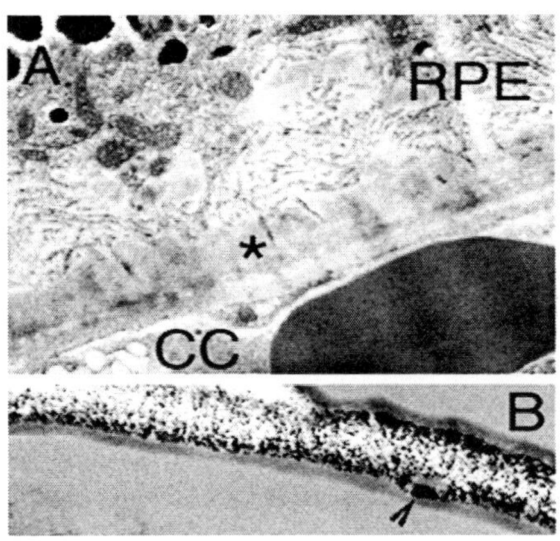

Figure 19: OTO staining of a transmission electron micrograph of the outer retina and choroid of the eye of a young APO B100 mouse exposed to blue light. A. High-magnification micrograph showed no evident OTO staining of sub RPE deposits (black asterisk). B. Mesenteric adipocytes demonstrated significant punctuate uptake of OTO stain (black arrowhead), consistent with high levels of triglycerides in the intestines used as positive control. RPE= Retinal Pigment Epithelium, CC= Choriocapillaris. (Magnification: A. x25,000; B. x18,000)

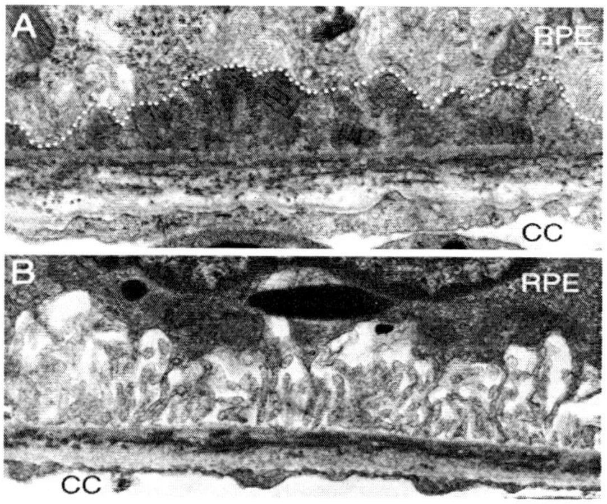

Figure 20: Transmission electron microscopy of the outer retina and choroid from a young fat fed APO B100 mice exposed to blue light and treated with vehicle (soybean) or a vitamin E supplement. A. Control APO B100 mouse showed the same changes as those described in the RPE (sub RPE deposits under white dotted line), BrM (thickening), and choriocapillaris (endothelial hypertrophy with loss of fenestrations) of transgenic mice fed a high-fat diet and exposed to blue light. B. Specimen from a young APO B100 fat-fed female mouse exposed to blue light and treated with subcutaneous vitamin E showed no abnormalities in the RPE, BrM, and CC. RPE= Retinal Pigment Epithelium, BrM= Bruch's Membrane, CC= Choriocapillaris. (Magnification, x25,000)

Future Directions and Speculation

In summary, we postulate that the early stages of dry macular degeneration are characterized by three distinct phenomena contained in our hypothetical "response to injury" paradigm (Figure 6). In the first stage, there is an injury stimulus to the RPE cells. This injury stimulus may be from oxidants derived from endogenous (i.e. metabolic processes) or exogenous sources (i.e. blue light, cigarette smoke) that will ultimately induce the formation of sub-lethal blebbing and the accumulation of subRPE deposits (BLD). These deposits are initially located in the space between the RPE cell membrane and its basement membrane. In a second stage there is a severe dysregulation of the extracellular matrix turnover. The balance between collagen synthesis and degradation by enzymes such as MMPs is lost with progression of BLD into BLinD and drusen. This stage is then characterized by progression of deposits into BrM inner collagenous layer, external to the RPE basement membrane. Risk factors such as aging, HTN, hormonal alterations, and diet among others may contribute to its severity. In a later stage, there is macrophage recruitment to sites of pathology and deposit formation. Initially these cells will be recruited to phagocyte deposits. If the initial insult does not resolve and remains chronic, these cells in turn may become activated and release oxidants, cytokines, and angiogenic factors that will ultimately maintain the vicious cycle and promote progression to the late stages (i.e. CNV) of the disease. Although this hypothetical paradigm remains to be proven, we have proposed interesting new ideas that ultimately will contribute to the understanding of the early phases of AMD pathogenesis and suggested different mechanisms by which an effective intervention might result in prevention of more severe and irreversible late stages of this dreadful disease.

Our ultimate goal is to intervene promptly in the early stages of the disease so that progression to the more severe late forms of AMD can be prevented. In this respect, macrophages are potential targets due to their pivotal role in stimulating progression of drusen into CNV by releasing cytokines like TNF-α into deposits, and by releasing factors that regulate CNV growth and severity.(31;74;75) Levels of cytokines such as TNF-α could be markers for progression of the disease and may constitute an aid to the ophthalmologic community in the management of the disease.(74;240) Drugs directed against cytokines or hormone signaling pathways in addition to antioxidants could be used successfully in the prevention of subRPE deposits formation in selected high-risk AMD patients.

ACKNOWLEDGMENTS

Supported by NEI/NIH grants: EY13318, EY014477, & EY015249.

REFERENCES

[1] Fine SL, Berger JW, Maguire MG, Ho AC. Age-related macular degeneration. *N Engl J Med* 2000; 342(7):483-492.

[2] Berger JW, Fine SL, Maguire MG. Age-related macular degeneration. *St. Louis: Mosby*, 1999.

[3] Zarbin MA. Current concepts in the pathogenesis of age-related macular degeneration. *Arch Ophthalmol* 2004; 122(4):598-614.

[4] Abdelsalam A, Del Priore L, Zarbin MA. Drusen in age-related macular degeneration: pathogenesis, natural course, and laser photocoagulation-induced regression. *Surv Ophthalmol* 1999; 44(1):1-29.

[5] Bird AC, Bressler NM, Bressler SB, Chisholm IH, Coscas G, Davis MD et al. An international classification and grading system for age-related maculopathy and age-related macular degeneration. The International ARM Epidemiological Study Group. *Surv Ophthalmol* 1995; 39(5):367-374.

[6] Gass JD. Drusen and disciform macular detachment and degeneration. *Trans Am Ophthalmol Soc* 1972; 70:409-36.:409-436.

[7] Green WR. Histopathology of age-related macular degeneration. *Mol Vis* 1999; 5:27.:27.

[8] Curcio CA, Medeiros NE, Millican CL. Photoreceptor loss in age-related macular degeneration. *Invest Ophthalmol Vis Sci* 1996; 37(7):1236-1249.

[9] Sheridan C, Williams R, Grierson I. Basement membranes and artificial substrates in cell transplantation. *Graefes Arch Clin Exp Ophthalmol* 2004; 242(1):68-75.

[10] Hiscott P, Sheridan C, Magee RM, Grierson I. Matrix and the retinal pigment epithelium in proliferative retinal disease. *Prog Retin Eye Res* 1999; 18(2):167-190.

[11] Guymer R, Luthert P, Bird A. Changes in Bruch's membrane and related structures with age. *Prog Retin Eye Res* 1999; 18(1):59-90.

[12] Inatani M, Tanihara H. Proteoglycans in retina. *Prog Retin Eye Res* 2002; 21(5): 429-447.

[13] Hewitt AT, Nakazawa K, Newsome DA. Analysis of newly synthesized Bruch's membrane proteoglycans. *Invest Ophthalmol Vis Sci* 1989; 30(3):478-486.

[14] Young RW. Pathophysiology of age-related macular degeneration. *Surv Ophthalmol* 1987; 31(5):291-306.

[15] Zarbin MA. Age-related macular degeneration: review of pathogenesis. *Eur J Ophthalmol* 1998; 8(4):199-206.

[16] van der Schaft TL, Mooy CM, de Bruijn WC, Oron FG, Mulder PG, de Jong PT. Histologic features of the early stages of age-related macular degeneration. A statistical analysis. *Ophthalmology* 1992; 99(2):278-286.

[17] Kliffen M, van der Schaft TL, Mooy CM, de Jong PT. Morphologic changes in age-related maculopathy. *Microsc Res Tech* 1997; 36(2):106-122.

[18] Hageman GS, Luthert PJ, Victor Chong NH, Johnson LV, Anderson DH, Mullins RF. An integrated hypothesis that considers drusen as biomarkers of immune-mediated processes at the RPE-Bruch's membrane interface in aging and age-related macular degeneration. *Prog Retin Eye Res* 2001; 20(6):705-732.

[19] Penfold PL, Madigan MC, Gillies MC, Provis JM. Immunological and aetiological aspects of macular degeneration. *Prog Retin Eye Res* 2001; 20(3):385-414.

[20] Hageman GS, Mullins RF. Molecular composition of drusen as related to substructural phenotype. *Mol Vis* 1999; 5:28.:28.

[21] Anderson DH, Mullins RF, Hageman GS, Johnson LV. A role for local inflammation in the formation of drusen in the aging eye. *Am J Ophthalmol* 2002; 134(3):411-431.

[22] Klein R, Peto T, Bird A, Vannewkirk MR. The epidemiology of age-related macular degeneration. *Am J Ophthalmol* 2004; 137(3):486-495.

[23] la Cour M, Kiilgaard JF, Nissen MH. Age-related macular degeneration: epidemiology and optimal treatment. *Drugs Aging* 2002; 19(2):101-133.

[24] Wang JJ, Foran S, Smith W, Mitchell P. Risk of age-related macular degeneration in eyes with macular drusen or hyperpigmentation: the Blue Mountains Eye Study cohort. *Arch Ophthalmol* 2003; 121(5):658-663.

[25] Algvere PV, Seregard S. Drusen maculopathy: a risk factor for AMD. Can we prevent visual loss? *Acta Ophthalmol Scand* 2003; 81(5):427-429.

[26] Curcio CA, Millican CL. Basal linear deposit and large drusen are specific for early age-related maculopathy. *Arch Ophthalmol* 1999; 117(3):329-339.

[27] Curcio CA, Owsley C, Jackson GR. Spare the rods, save the cones in aging and age-related maculopathy. *Invest Ophthalmol Vis Sci* 2000; 41(8):2015-2018.

[28] van der Schaft TL, Mooy CM, de Bruijn WC, Bosman FT, de Jong PT. Immunohistochemical light and electron microscopy of basal laminar deposit. *Graefes Arch Clin Exp Ophthalmol* 1994; 232(1):40-46.

[29] van der Schaft TL, de Bruijn WC, Mooy CM, de Jong PT. Basal laminar deposit in the aging peripheral human retina. *Graefes Arch Clin Exp Ophthalmol* 1993; 231(8): 470-475.

[30] Green WR, Enger C. Age-related macular degeneration histopathologic studies. The 1992 Lorenz E. Zimmerman Lecture. *Ophthalmology* 1993; 100(10):1519-1535.

[31] Grossniklaus HE, Ling JX, Wallace TM, Dithmar S, Lawson DH, Cohen C et al. Macrophage and retinal pigment epithelium expression of angiogenic cytokines in choroidal neovascularization. *Mol Vis* 2002; 8:119-26.:119-126.

[32] Tuo J, Bojanowski CM, Chan CC. Genetic factors of age-related macular degeneration. Prog Retin Eye Res 2004; 23(2):229-249.

[33] Hammond CJ, Webster AR, Snieder H, Bird AC, Gilbert CE, Spector TD. Genetic influence on early age-related maculopathy: a twin study. *Ophthalmology* 2002; 109(4):730-736.

[34] Yoshida A, Yoshida M, Yoshida S, Shiose S, Hiroishi G, Ishibashi T. Familial cases with age-related macular degeneration. *Jpn J Ophthalmol* 2000; 44(3):290-295.

[35] Klaver CC, Allikmets R. Genetics of macular dystrophies and implications for age-related macular degeneration. *Dev Ophthalmol* 2003; 37:155-69.:155-169.

[36] Gorin MB, Breitner JC, de Jong PT, Hageman GS, Klaver CC, Kuehn MH et al. The genetics of age-related macular degeneration. *Mol Vis* 1999; 5:29.:29.

[37] Felbor U, Benkwitz C, Klein ML, Greenberg J, Gregory CY, Weber BH. Sorsby fundus dystrophy: reevaluation of variable expressivity in patients carrying a TIMP3 founder mutation. *Arch Ophthalmol* 1997; 115(12):1569-1571.

[38] Zack DJ, Dean M, Molday RS, Nathans J, Redmond TM, Stone EM et al. What can we learn about age-related macular degeneration from other retinal diseases? *Mol Vis* 1999; 5:30.:30.

[39] Musarella MA. Molecular genetics of macular degeneration. *Doc Ophthalmol* 2001; 102(3):165-177.

[40] Yates JR, Moore AT. Genetic susceptibility to age related macular degeneration. *J Med Genet* 2000; 37(2):83-87.

[41] Stone EM, Braun TA, Russel SR, Kuehn MH, Lotery AJ, Moore PA, et al. Missense variations in the fibulin 5 gene and age-related macular degeneration. *N Engl J Med* 2004; 351(4):346-53.

[42] Ambati J, Ambati BK, Yoo SH, Ianchulev S, Adamis AP. Age-related macular degeneration: etiology, pathogenesis, and therapeutic strategies. *Surv Ophthalmol* 2003; 48(3):257-293.

[43] Shastry BS, Trese MT. Evaluation of the peripherin/RDS gene as a candidate gene in families with age-related macular degeneration. *Ophthalmologica* 1999; 213(3): 165-170.

[44] Hamdi HK, Kenney C. Age-related macular degeneration: a new viewpoint. *Front Biosci* 2003; 8:e305-14.:e305-e314.

[45] Chung M, Lotery AJ. Genetics update of macular diseases. *Ophthalmol Clin North Am* 2002; 15(4):459-465.

[46] Klaver CC, Kliffen M, van Duijn CM, Hofman A, Cruts M, Grobbee DE et al. Genetic association of apolipoprotein E with age-related macular degeneration. *Am J Hum Genet* 1998; 63(1):200-206.

[47] Boulton M, Dayhaw-Barker P. The role of the retinal pigment epithelium: topographical variation and ageing changes. *Eye* 2001; 15(Pt 3):384-389.

[48] Strauss O, Stumpff F, Mergler S, Wienrich M, Wiederholt M. The Royal College of Surgeons rat: an animal model for inherited retinal degeneration with a still unknown genetic defect. *Acta Anat* (Basel) 1998; 162(2-3):101-111.

[49] Beatty S, Koh H, Phil M, Henson D, Boulton M. The role of oxidative stress in the pathogenesis of age-related macular degeneration. *Surv Ophthalmol* 2000; 45(2): 115-134.

[50] Winkler BS, Boulton ME, Gottsch JD, Sternberg P. Oxidative damage and age-related macular degeneration. *Mol Vis* 1999; 5:32.:32.

[51] Dorey CK, Wu G, Ebenstein D, Garsd A, Weiter JJ. Cell loss in the aging retina. Relationship to lipofuscin accumulation and macular degeneration. *Invest Ophthalmol Vis Sci* 1989; 30(8):1691-1699.

[52] von Ruckmann A, Schmidt KG, Fitzke FW, Bird AC, Jacobi KW. [Dynamics of accumulation and degradation of lipofuscin in retinal pigment epithelium in senile macular degeneration]. *Klin Monatsbl Augenheilkd* 1998; 213(1):32-37.

[53] Szweda PA, Camouse M, Lundberg KC, Oberley TD, Szweda LI. Aging, lipofuscin formation, and free radical-mediated inhibition of cellular proteolytic systems. *Ageing Res Rev* 2003; 2(4):383-405.

[54] Brunk UT, Terman A. Lipofuscin: mechanisms of age-related accumulation and influence on cell function. *Free Radic Biol Med* 2002; 33(5):611-619.

[55] Sarks SH, Arnold JJ, Killingsworth MC, Sarks JP. Early drusen formation in the normal and aging eye and their relation to age related maculopathy: a clinicopathological study. *Br J Ophthalmol* 1999; 83(3):358-368.

[56] Feeney-Burns L, Gao CL, Tidwell M. Lysosomal enzyme cytochemistry of human RPE, Bruch's membrane and drusen. *Invest Ophthalmol Vis Sci* 1987; 28(7):1138-1147.

[57] Hollyfield JG, Salomon RG, Crabb JW. Proteomic approaches to understanding age-related macular degeneration. *Adv Exp Med Biol* 2003; 533:83-9.:83-89.

[58] Crabb JW, Miyagi M, Gu X, Shadrach K, West KA, Sakaguchi H et al. Drusen proteome analysis: an approach to the etiology of age-related macular degeneration. *Proc Natl Acad Sci* U S A 2002; 99(23):14682-14687.

[59] Ursini F, Davies KJ, Maiorino M, Parasassi T, Sevanian A. Atherosclerosis: another protein misfolding disease? *Trends Mol Med* 2002; 8(8):370-374.

[60] Lutty G, Grunwald J, Majji AB, Uyama M, Yoneya S. Changes in choriocapillaris and retinal pigment epithelium in age-related macular degeneration. *Mol Vis* 1999; 5:35.:35.

[61] Grunwald J. Choroidal Blood Flow. In: Berger JW, Fine SL, Maguire MG, editors. Age-related Macular Degeneration. *St. Louis: Mosby*, 1995: 167-172.

[62] Grunwald JE, Hariprasad SM, DuPont J. Effect of aging on foveolar choroidal circulation. *Arch Ophthalmol* 1998; 116(2):150-154.

[63] Grunwald JE, Hariprasad SM, DuPont J, Maguire MG, Fine SL, Brucker AJ et al. Foveolar choroidal blood flow in age-related macular degeneration. *Invest Ophthalmol Vis Sci* 1998; 39(2):385-390.

[64] Harris A, Chung HS, Ciulla TA, Kagemann L. Progress in measurement of ocular blood flow and relevance to our understanding of glaucoma and age-related macular degeneration. *Prog Retin Eye Res* 1999; 18(5):669-687.

[65] Giovannini A, Mariotti C, Ripa E, Scassellati SB, Tittarelli R. Choroidal filling in age-related macular degeneration: indocyanine green angiographic findings. *Ophthalmologica* 1994; 208(4):185-191.

[66] Moore DJ, Hussain AA, Marshall J. Age-related variation in the hydraulic conductivity of Bruch's membrane. *Invest Ophthalmol Vis Sci* 1995; 36(7):1290-1297.

[67] Starita C, Hussain AA, Patmore A, Marshall J. Localization of the site of major resistance to fluid transport in Bruch's membrane. *Invest Ophthalmol Vis Sci* 1997; 38(3):762-767.

[68] Starita C, Hussain AA, Pagliarini S, Marshall J. Hydrodynamics of ageing Bruch's membrane: implications for macular disease. *Exp Eye Res* 1996; 62(5):565-572.

[69] Mullins RF, Russell SR, Anderson DH, Hageman GS. Drusen associated with aging and age-related macular degeneration contain proteins common to extracellular deposits associated with atherosclerosis, elastosis, amyloidosis, and dense deposit disease. *FASEB J* 2000; 14(7):835-846.

[70] Hageman GS, Mullins RF, Russell SR, Johnson LV, Anderson DH. Vitronectin is a constituent of ocular drusen and the vitronectin gene is expressed in human retinal pigmented epithelial cells. *FASEB J* 1999; 13(3):477-484.

[71] Cousins SW, Espinosa-Heidmann DG, Alexandridou A, Sall J, Dubovy S, Csaky K. The role of aging, high fat diet and blue light exposure in an experimental mouse model for basal laminar deposit formation. *Exp Eye Res* 2002; 75(5):543-553.

[72] Strunnikova N, Baffi J, Gonzalez A, Silk W, Cousins SW, Csaky KG. Regulated heat shock protein 27 expression in human retinal pigment epithelium. *Invest Ophthalmol Vis Sci* 2001; 42(9):2130-2138.

[73] Chisolm GM, III, Hazen SL, Fox PL, Cathcart MK. The oxidation of lipoproteins by monocytes-macrophages. Biochemical and biological mechanisms. *J Biol Chem* 1999; 274(37):25959-25962.

[74] Cousins SW, Espinosa-Heidmann DG, Csaky KG. Monocyte activation in patients with age-related macular degeneration: a biomarker of risk for choroidal neovascularization? *Arch Ophthalmol* 2004; 122(7):1013-1018.

[75] Espinosa-Heidmann DG, Suner IJ, Hernandez EP, Monroy D, Csaky KG, Cousins SW. Macrophage depletion diminishes lesion size and severity in experimental choroidal neovascularization. *Invest Ophthalmol Vis Sci* 2003; 44(8):3586-3592.

[76] Cousins SW, Csaky K. *Immunology of Age-Related Macular Degeneration.* In: Lim JI, editor. Age-Related Macular Degeneration. New York: Marcel Dekker, Inc., 2002: 27-65.

[77] Nelson KC, Carlson JL, Newman ML, Sternberg P, Jr., Jones DP, Kavanagh TJ et al. Effect of dietary inducer dimethylfumarate on glutathione in cultured human retinal pigment epithelial cells. *Invest Ophthalmol Vis Sci* 1999; 40(9):1927-1935.

[78] Nelson KC, Armstrong JS, Moriarty S, Cai J, Wu MW, Sternberg P, Jr. et al. Protection of retinal pigment epithelial cells from oxidative damage by oltipraz, a cancer chemopreventive agent. *Invest Ophthalmol Vis Sci* 2002; 43(11):3550-3554.

[79] Machlin LJ, Bendich A. Free radical tissue damage: protective role of antioxidant nutrients. *FASEB J* 1987; 1(6):441-445.

[80] Florence TM. The role of free radicals in disease. *Aust N Z J Ophthalmol* 1995; 23(1): 3-7.

[81] Stohs SJ. The role of free radicals in toxicity and disease. *J Basic Clin Physiol Pharmacol* 1995; 6(3-4):205-228.

[82] Terman A, Brunk UT. Lipofuscin. *Int J Biochem Cell Biol* 2004; 36(8):1400-1404.

[83] Lamb LE, Simon JD. A2E: a component of ocular lipofuscin. *Photochem Photobiol* 2004; 79(2):127-136.

[84] Putting BJ, van Best JA, Zweypfenning RC, Vrensen GF, Oosterhuis JA. Spectral sensitivity of the blood-retinal barrier at the pigment epithelium for blue light in the 400-500 nm range. *Graefes Arch Clin Exp Ophthalmol* 1993; 231(10):600-606.

[85] Rozanowska M, Jarvis-Evans J, Korytowski W, Boulton ME, Burke JM, Sarna T. Blue light-induced reactivity of retinal age pigment. In vitro generation of oxygen-reactive species. *J Biol Chem* 1995; 270(32):18825-18830.
[86] Rozanowska M, Bober A, Burke JM, Sarna T. The role of retinal pigment epithelium melanin in photoinduced oxidation of ascorbate. *Photochem Photobiol* 1997; 65(3):472-479.
[87] Killingsworth MC, Sarks JP, Sarks SH. Macrophages related to Bruch's membrane in age-related macular degeneration. *Eye* 1990; 4(Pt 4):613-621.
[88] Grossniklaus HE, Cingle KA, Yoon YD, Ketkar N, L'Hernault N, Brown S. Correlation of histologic 2-dimensional reconstruction and confocal scanning laser microscopic imaging of choroidal neovascularization in eyes with age-related maculopathy. *Arch Ophthalmol* 2000; 118(5):625-629.
[89] Tate DJ, Miceli MV, Newsome DA. Expression of metallothionein isoforms in human chorioretinal complex. *Curr Eye Res* 2002; 24(1):12-25.
[90] Tate DJ, Jr., Miceli MV, Newsome DA. Phagocytosis and H2O2 induce catalase and metallothionein gene expression in human retinal pigment epithelial cells. *Invest Ophthalmol Vis Sci* 1995; 36(7):1271-1279.
[91] Miceli MV, Liles MR, Newsome DA. Evaluation of oxidative processes in human pigment epithelial cells associated with retinal outer segment phagocytosis. *Exp Cell Res* 1994; 214(1):242-249.
[92] Parthasarathy S, Santanam N. Mechanisms of oxidation, antioxidants, and atherosclerosis. *Curr Opin Lipidol* 1994; 5(5):371-375.
[93] St Pierre Y, Van Themsche C, Esteve PO. Emerging features in the regulation of MMP-9 gene expression for the development of novel molecular targets and therapeutic strategies. *Curr Drug Targets Inflamm Allergy* 2003; 2(3):206-215.
[94] Katsuda S, Kaji T. Atherosclerosis and extracellular matrix. *J Atheroscler Thromb* 2003; 10(5):267-274.
[95] Suner IJ, Espinosa-Heidmann DG, Marin-Castano ME, Hernandez EP, Pereira-Simon S, Cousins SW. Nicotine increases size and severity of experimental choroidal neovascularization. *Invest Ophthalmol Vis Sci* 2004; 45(1):311-317.
[96] Halliwell B. Free radicals and vascular disease: how much do we know? *BMJ* 1993; 307(6909):885-886.
[97] Pryor WA. Cigarette smoke radicals and the role of free radicals in chemical carcinogenicity. *Environ Health Perspect* 1997; 105 Suppl 4:875-82.:875-882.
[98] Winston GW, Church DF, Cueto R, Pryor WA. Oxygen consumption and oxyradical production from microsomal reduction of aqueous extracts of cigarette tar. *Arch Biochem Biophys* 1993; 304(2):371-378.
[99] Niki E, Minamisawa S, Oikawa M, Komuro E. Membrane damage from lipid oxidation induced by free radicals and cigarette smoke. *Ann N Y Acad Sci* 1993; 686:29-37; discussion 37-8.:29-37.
[100] Bolton JL, Trush MA, Penning TM, Dryhurst G, Monks TJ. Role of quinones in toxicology. *Chem Res Toxicol* 2000; 13(3):135-160.
[101] Day DA, Wiskich JT. Regulation of alternative oxidase activity in higher plants. *J Bioenerg Biomembr* 1995; 27(4):379-385.

[102] Hulbert PB, Grover PL. Chemical rearrangement of phenol-epoxide metabolites of polycyclic aromatic hydrocarbons to quinone-methides. *Biochem Biophys Res Commun* 1983; 117(1):129-134.

[103] Garbe TR, Kobayashi M, Yukawa H. Indole-inducible proteins in bacteria suggest membrane and oxidant toxicity. *Arch Microbiol* 2000; 173(1):78-82.

[104] Lenaz G. Quinone specificity of complex I. *Biochim Biophys Acta* 1998; 1364(2): 207-221.

[105] Kari FW, Bucher J, Eustis SL, Haseman JK, Huff JE. Toxicity and carcinogenicity of hydroquinone in F344/N rats and B6C3F1 mice. *Food Chem Toxicol* 1992; 30(9): 737-747.

[106] Degli EM. Inhibitors of NADH-ubiquinone reductase: an overview. *Biochim Biophys Acta* 1998; 1364(2):222-235.

[107] McCue JM, Link KL, Eaton SS, Freed BM. Exposure to cigarette tar inhibits ribonucleotide reductase and blocks lymphocyte proliferation. *J Immunol* 2000; 165(12):6771-6775.

[108] Cadet J, Bellon S, Douki T, Frelon S, Gasparutto D, Muller E et al. Radiation-induced DNA damage: formation, measurement, and biochemical features. *J Environ Pathol Toxicol Oncol* 2004; 23(1):33-43.

[109] Cribier S, Morrot G, Zachowski A. Dynamics of the membrane lipid phase. *Prostaglandins Leukot Essent Fatty Acids* 1993; 48(1):27-32.

[110] Wilhelm J. Metabolic aspects of membrane lipid peroxidation. *Acta Univ Carol Med Monogr* 1990; 137:1-53.:1-53.

[111] Bezard J, Blond JP, Bernard A, Clouet P. The metabolism and availability of essential fatty acids in animal and human tissues. *Reprod Nutr Dev* 1994; 34(6):539-568.

[112] Blokhina O, Virolainen E, Fagerstedt KV. Antioxidants, oxidative damage and oxygen deprivation stress: a review. *Ann Bot* (Lond) 2003; 91 Spec No:179-94.:179-194.

[113] Iwai K. An ubiquitin ligase recognizing a protein oxidized by iron: implications for the turnover of oxidatively damaged proteins. *J Biochem* (Tokyo) 2003; 134(2):175-182.

[114] Zhang C, Baffi J, Cousins SW, Csaky KG. Oxidant-induced cell death in retinal pigment epithelium cells mediated through the release of apoptosis-inducing factor. *J Cell Sci* 2003; 116(Pt 10):1915-1923.

[115] Malorni W, Donelli G. Cell death. General features and morphological aspects. *Ann N Y Acad Sci* 1992; 663:218-33.:218-233.

[116] Li Y, Liu J, Zhan X. Tyrosine phosphorylation of cortactin is required for H2O2-mediated injury of human endothelial cells. *J Biol Chem* 2000; 275(47):37187-37193.

[117] Hagmann J, Burger MM, Dagan D. Regulation of plasma membrane blebbing by the cytoskeleton. *J Cell Biochem* 1999; 73(4):488-499.

[118] Khan SA, Ghosh S, Wickstrom M, Miller LA, Hess R, Haschek WM et al. Comparative pathology of microcystin-LR in cultured hepatocytes, fibroblasts, and renal epithelial cells. *Nat Toxins* 1995; 3(3):119-128.

[119] Malorni W, Iosi F, Mirabelli F, Bellomo G. Cytoskeleton as a target in menadione-induced oxidative stress in cultured mammalian cells: alterations underlying surface bleb formation. *Chem Biol Interact* 1991; 80(2):217-236.

[120] Gerthoffer WT, Gunst SJ. Invited review: focal adhesion and small heat shock proteins in the regulation of actin remodeling and contractility in smooth muscle. *J Appl Physiol* 2001; 91(2):963-972.

[121] Smoyer WE, Ransom RF. Hsp27 regulates podocyte cytoskeletal changes in an in vitro model of podocyte process retraction. *FASEB J* 2002; 16(3):315-326.

[122] Tauchi T, Nakajima A, Sashida G, Shimamoto T, Ohyashiki JH, Abe K et al. Inhibition of human telomerase enhances the effect of the tyrosine kinase inhibitor, imatinib, in BCR-ABL-positive leukemia cells. *Clin Cancer Res* 2002; 8(11):3341-3347.

[123] Misawa M, Tauchi T, Sashida G, Nakajima A, Abe K, Ohyashiki JH et al. Inhibition of human telomerase enhances the effect of chemotherapeutic agents in lung cancer cells. *Int J Oncol* 2002; 21(5):1087-1092.

[124] Gao XD, Albert S. A role for exocytosis in the spatial regulation of actin organization. *ScientificWorldJournal* 2003; 3:1359-62.:1359-1362.

[125] Oliver JM, Berlin RD. Microtubules, microfilaments and the regulation of membrane functions. *Symp Soc Exp Biol* 1979; 33:277-98.:277-298.

[126] Henson PM. Secretion of lysosomal enzymes induced by immune complexes and complement. *Front Biol* 1976; 45:99-126.:99-126.

[127] Allison AC, Davies P. Mechanisms of endocytosis and exocytosis. *Symp Soc Exp Biol* 1974;(28):419-446.

[128] Brunk UT, Zhang H, Dalen H, Ollinger K. Exposure of cells to nonlethal concentrations of hydrogen peroxide induces degeneration-repair mechanisms involving lysosomal destabilization. *Free Radic Biol Med* 1995; 19(6):813-822.

[129] Dalle-Donne I, Rossi R, Milzani A, Di Simplicio P, Colombo R. The actin cytoskeleton response to oxidants: from small heat shock protein phosphorylation to changes in the redox state of actin itself. *Free Radic Biol Med* 2001; 31(12):1624-1632.

[130] Chen WP, Tan SK, Chen A, Lin CY. Intrarenal infusion of supernatant from cytokine-activated human mesangial cells may cause glomerular damage. Zhonghua Yi Xue Za Zhi (Taipei) 1999; 62(10):657-665.

[131] Okamoto K, Mizuno M, Nakahara N, Natsume A, Yoshida J, Mori T et al. Process of apoptosis induced by TNF-alpha in murine fibroblast Ltk-cells: continuous observation with video enhanced contrast microscopy. *Apoptosis* 2002; 7(1):77-86.

[132] Ashwood-Smith MJ, Morris GW, Fowler R, Appleton TC, Ashorn R. Physical factors are involved in the destruction of embryos and oocytes during freezing and thawing procedures. *Hum Reprod* 1988; 3(6):795-802.

[133] Hinshaw DB, Sklar LA, Bohl B, Schraufstatter IU, Hyslop PA, Rossi MW et al. Cytoskeletal and morphologic impact of cellular oxidant injury. *Am J Pathol* 1986; 123(3):454-464.

[134] Malorni W, Donelli G, Straface E, Santini MT, Paradisi S, Giacomoni PU. Both UVA and UVB induce cytoskeleton-dependent surface blebbing in epidermoid cells. *J Photochem Photobiol B* 1994; 26(3):265-270.

[135] Burns RP, Feeney-Burns L. Clinico-morphologic correlations of drusen of Bruch's membrane. *Trans Am Ophthalmol Soc* 1980; 78:206-25.:206-225.

[136] Ishibashi T, Sorgente N, Patterson R, Ryan SJ. Pathogenesis of drusen in the primate. *Invest Ophthalmol Vis Sci* 1986; 27(2):184-193.

[137] Ishibashi T, Patterson R, Ohnishi Y, Inomata H, Ryan SJ. Formation of drusen in the human eye. *Am J Ophthalmol* 1986; 101(3):342-353.

[138] Zhu ZR, Goodnight R, Nishimura T, Sorgente N, Ogden TE, Ryan SJ. Experimental changes resembling the pathology of drusen in Bruch's membrane in the rabbit. *Curr Eye Res* 1988; 7(6):581-592.

[139] Hancock JF, Magee AI, Childs JE, Marshall CJ. All ras proteins are polyisoprenylated but only some are palmitoylated. *Cell* 1989; 57(7):1167-1177.

[140] Hancock JF, Paterson H, Marshall CJ. A polybasic domain or palmitoylation is required in addition to the CAAX motif to localize p21ras to the plasma membrane. *Cell* 1990; 63(1):133-139.

[141] Lowe DG, Capon DJ, Delwart E, Sakaguchi AY, Naylor SL, Goeddel DV. Structure of the human and murine R-ras genes, novel genes closely related to ras proto-oncogenes. *Cell* 1987; 48(1):137-146.

[142] Gubin AN, Reddy B, Njoroge JM, Miller JL. Long-term, stable expression of green fluorescent protein in mammalian cells. *Biochem Biophys Res Commun* 1997; 236(2):347-350.

[143] Fillmore HL, Shurm J, Furqueron P, Prabhu SS, Gillies GT, Broaddus WC. An in vivo rat model for visualizing glioma tumor cell invasion using stable persistent expression of the green fluorescent protein. *Cancer Lett* 1999; 141(1-2):9-19.

[144] Espinosa-Heidmann DG, Sall J, Hernandez EP, Cousins SW. Basal laminar deposit formation in APO B100 transgenic mice: complex interactions between dietary fat, blue light, and vitamin E. *Invest Ophthalmol Vis Sci* 2004; 45(1):260-266.

[145] Lanzetti L, Di Fiore PP, Scita G. Pathways linking endocytosis and actin cytoskeleton in mammalian cells. *Exp Cell Res* 2001; 271(1):45-56.

[146] Taunton J. Actin filament nucleation by endosomes, lysosomes and secretory vesicles. *Curr Opin Cell Biol* 2001; 13(1):85-91.

[147] Rao A, Craig AM. Signaling between the actin cytoskeleton and the postsynaptic density of dendritic spines. *Hippocampus* 2000; 10(5):527-541.

[148] Kaibuchi K, Kuroda S, Amano M. Regulation of the cytoskeleton and cell adhesion by the Rho family GTPases in mammalian cells. *Annu Rev Biochem* 1999; 68:459-86: 459-486.

[149] Valentijn K, Valentijn JA, Jamieson JD. Role of actin in regulated exocytosis and compensatory membrane retrieval: insights from an old acquaintance. *Biochem Biophys Res Commun* 1999; 266(3):652-661.

[150] Downey GP. Mechanisms of leukocyte motility and chemotaxis. *Curr Opin Immunol* 1994; 6(1):113-124.

[151] Hirokawa N. Axonal transport and the cytoskeleton. *Curr Opin Neurobiol* 1993; 3(5):724-731.

[152] Weed SA, Parsons JT. Cortactin: coupling membrane dynamics to cortical actin assembly. *Oncogene* 2001; 20(44):6418-6434.

[153] Rodriguez OC, Schaefer AW, Mandato CA, Forscher P, Bement WM, Waterman-Storer CM. Conserved microtubule-actin interactions in cell movement and morphogenesis. *Nat Cell Biol* 2003; 5(7):599-609.

[154] Milzani A, DalleDonne I, Colombo R. Prolonged oxidative stress on actin. *Arch Biochem Biophys* 1997; 339(2):267-274.

[155] Huot J, Houle F, Rousseau S, Deschesnes RG, Shah GM, Landry J. SAPK2/p38-dependent F-actin reorganization regulates early membrane blebbing during stress-induced apoptosis. *J Cell Biol* 1998; 143(5):1361-1373.

[156] Concannon CG, Gorman AM, Samali A. On the role of Hsp27 in regulating apoptosis. *Apoptosis* 2003; 8(1):61-70.

[157] Delogu G, Signore M, Mechelli A, Famularo G. Heat shock proteins and their role in heart injury. *Curr Opin Crit Care* 2002; 8(5):411-416.
[158] Haslbeck M. sHsps and their role in the chaperone network. *Cell Mol Life Sci* 2002; 59(10):1649-1657.
[159] Constantin B, Meerschaert K, Vandekerckhove J, Gettemans J. Disruption of the actin cytoskeleton of mammalian cells by the capping complex actin-fragmin is inhibited by actin phosphorylation and regulated by Ca2+ ions. *J Cell Sci* 1998; 111(Pt 12): 1695-1706.
[160] Schneider GB, Hamano H, Cooper LF. In vivo evaluation of hsp27 as an inhibitor of actin polymerization: hsp27 limits actin stress fiber and focal adhesion formation after heat shock. *J Cell Physiol* 1998; 177(4):575-584.
[161] Ganea E. Chaperone-like activity of alpha-crystallin and other small heat shock proteins. *Curr Protein Pept Sci* 2001; 2(3):205-225.
[162] Mehlen P, Mehlen A, Guillet D, Preville X, Arrigo AP. Tumor necrosis factor-alpha induces changes in the phosphorylation, cellular localization, and oligomerization of human hsp27, a stress protein that confers cellular resistance to this cytokine. *J Cell Biochem* 1995; 58(2):248-259.
[163] Preville X, Schultz H, Knauf U, Gaestel M, Arrigo AP. Analysis of the role of Hsp25 phosphorylation reveals the importance of the oligomerization state of this small heat shock protein in its protective function against TNFalpha- and hydrogen peroxide-induced cell death. *J Cell Biochem* 1998; 69(4):436-452.
[164] Martin JL, Mestril R, Hilal-Dandan R, Brunton LL, Dillmann WH. Small heat shock proteins and protection against ischemic injury in cardiac myocytes. *Circulation* 1997; 96(12):4343-4348.
[165] Martin JL, Hickey E, Weber LA, Dillmann WH, Mestril R. Influence of phosphorylation and oligomerization on the protective role of the small heat shock protein 27 in rat adult cardiomyocytes. *Gene Expr* 1999; 7(4-6):349-355.
[166] Tezel G, Hernandez R, Wax MB. Immunostaining of heat shock proteins in the retina and optic nerve head of normal and glaucomatous eyes. *Arch Ophthalmol* 2000; 118(4):511-518.
[167] de Lanerolle P, Cole AB. Cytoskeletal proteins and gene regulation: form, function, and signal transduction in the nucleus. *Sci STKE* 2002; 2002(139):E30.
[168] Landry J, Huot J. Modulation of actin dynamics during stress and physiological stimulation by a signaling pathway involving p38 MAP kinase and heat-shock protein 27. Biochem *Cell Biol* 1995; 73(9-10):703-707.
[169] Stokoe D, Engel K, Campbell DG, Cohen P, Gaestel M. Identification of MAPKAP kinase 2 as a major enzyme responsible for the phosphorylation of the small mammalian heat shock proteins. *FEBS Lett* 1992; 313(3):307-313.
[170] Aumailley M, Gayraud B. Structure and biological activity of the extracellular matrix. *J Mol Med* 1998; 76(3-4):253-265.
[171] Jacot TA, Striker GE, Stetler-Stevenson M, Striker LJ. Mesangial cells from transgenic mice with progressive glomerulosclerosis exhibit stable, phenotypic changes including undetectable MMP-9 and increased type IV collagen. *Lab Invest* 1996; 75(6):791-799.
[172] Peten EP, Garcia-Perez A, Terada Y, Woodrow D, Martin BM, Striker GE et al. Age-related changes in alpha 1- and alpha 2-chain type IV collagen mRNAs in adult mouse glomeruli: competitive PCR. *Am J Physiol* 1992; 263(5 Pt 2):F951-F957.

[173] Belkhiri A, Richards C, Whaley M, McQueen SA, Orr FW. Increased expression of activated matrix metalloproteinase-2 by human endothelial cells after sublethal H2O2 exposure. *Lab Invest* 1997; 77(5):533-539.

[174] Schroen DJ, Brinckerhoff CE. Nuclear hormone receptors inhibit matrix metalloproteinase (MMP) gene expression through diverse mechanisms. *Gene Expr* 1996; 6(4):197-207.

[175] Ries C, Petrides PE. Cytokine regulation of matrix metalloproteinase activity and its regulatory dysfunction in disease. Biol Chem Hoppe Seyler 1995; 376(6):345-355.

[176] Ohbayashi H. Matrix metalloproteinases in lung diseases. *Curr Protein Pept Sci* 2002; 3(4):409-421.

[177] Kuzuya M, Iguchi A. Role of matrix metalloproteinases in vascular remodeling. *J Atheroscler Thromb* 2003; 10(5):275-282.

[178] Mattana J, Margiloff L, Chaplia L. Oxidation of extracellular matrix modulates susceptibility to degradation by the mesangial matrix metalloproteinase-2. *Free Radic Biol Med* 1999; 27(3-4):315-321.

[179] Hirai Y, Migita K, Honda S, Ueki Y, Yamasaki S, Urayama S et al. Effects of nitric oxide on matrix metalloproteinase-2 production by rheumatoid synovial cells. *Life Sci* 2001; 68(8):913-920.

[180] Kinnula VL, Linnala A, Viitala E, Linnainmaa K, Virtanen I. Tenascin and fibronectin expression in human mesothelial cells and pleural mesothelioma cell-line cells. *Am J Respir Cell Mol Biol* 1998; 19(3):445-452.

[181] Lee HB, Yu MR, Yang Y, Jiang Z, Ha H. Reactive oxygen species-regulated signaling pathways in diabetic nephropathy. *J Am Soc Nephrol* 2003; 14(8 Suppl 3):S241-S245.

[182] Ha H, Lee HB. Reactive oxygen species as glucose signaling molecules in mesangial cells cultured under high glucose. Kidney *Int Suppl* 2000; 77:S19-25.:S19-S25.

[183] Marin-Castano ME, Elliot SJ, Potier M, Karl M, Striker LJ, Striker GE et al. Regulation of estrogen receptors and MMP-2 expression by estrogens in human retinal pigment epithelium. *Invest Ophthalmol Vis Sci* 2003; 44(1):50-59.

[184] Eichler W, Friedrichs U, Thies A, Tratz C, Wiedemann P. Modulation of matrix metalloproteinase and TIMP-1 expression by cytokines in human RPE cells. *Invest Ophthalmol Vis Sci* 2002; 43(8):2767-2773.

[185] Padgett LC, Lui GM, Werb Z, LaVail MM. Matrix metalloproteinase-2 and tissue inhibitor of metalloproteinase-1 in the retinal pigment epithelium and interphotoreceptor matrix: vectorial secretion and regulation. *Exp Eye Res* 1997; 64(6):927-938.

[186] Alexander JP, Bradley JM, Gabourel JD, Acott TS. Expression of matrix metalloproteinases and inhibitor by human retinal pigment epithelium. *Invest Ophthalmol Vis Sci* 1990; 31(12):2520-2528.

[187] Cousins SW, Marin-Castano ME, Espinosa-Heidmann DG, Alexandridou A, Striker L, Elliot S. Female gender, estrogen loss, and Sub-RPE deposit formation in aged mice. *Invest Ophthalmol Vis Sci* 2003; 44(3):1221-1229.

[188] Sato T, Ito A, Mori Y, Yamashita K, Hayakawa T, Nagase H. Hormonal regulation of collagenolysis in uterine cervical fibroblasts. Modulation of synthesis of procollagenase, prostromelysin and tissue inhibitor of metalloproteinases (TIMP) by progesterone and oestradiol-17 beta. *Biochem J* 1991; 275(Pt 3):645-650.

[189] Puistola U, Westerlund A, Kauppila A, Turpeenniemi-Hujanen T. Regulation of 72-kd type IV collagenase-matrix metalloproteinase-2 by estradiol and gonadotropin-releasing hormone agonist in human granulosa-lutein cells. *Fertil Steril* 1995; 64(1):81-87.
[190] Lei J, Silbiger S, Ziyadeh FN, Neugarten J. Serum-stimulated alpha 1 type IV collagen gene transcription is mediated by TGF-beta and inhibited by estradiol. *Am J Physiol* 1998; 274(2 Pt 2):F252-F258.
[191] Silbiger S, Lei J, Neugarten J. Estradiol suppresses type I collagen synthesis in mesangial cells via activation of activator protein-1. *Kidney Int* 1999; 55(4):1268-1276.
[192] Potier M, Elliot SJ, Tack I, Lenz O, Striker GE, Striker LJ et al. Expression and regulation of estrogen receptors in mesangial cells: influence on matrix metalloproteinase-9. *J Am Soc Nephrol* 2001; 12(2):241-251.
[193] Deryugina EI, Bourdon MA, Reisfeld RA, Strongin A. Remodeling of collagen matrix by human tumor cells requires activation and cell surface association of matrix metalloproteinase-2. *Cancer Res* 1998; 58(16):3743-3750.
[194] Zhuge Y, Xu J. Rac1 mediates type I collagen-dependent MMP-2 activation. role in cell invasion across collagen barrier. *J Biol Chem* 2001; 276(19):16248-16256.
[195] Atkinson SJ, Patterson ML, Butler MJ, Murphy G. Membrane type 1 matrix metalloproteinase and gelatinase A synergistically degrade type 1 collagen in a cell model. *FEBS Lett* 2001; 491(3):222-226.
[196] Dinh DT, Frauman AG, Johnston CI, Fabiani ME. Angiotensin receptors: distribution, signalling and function. *Clin Sci* (Lond) 2001; 100(5):481-492.
[197] Rhinehart K, Handelsman CA, Silldorff EP, Pallone TL. ANG II AT2 receptor modulates AT1 receptor-mediated descending vasa recta endothelial Ca2+ signaling. *Am J Physiol Heart Circ Physiol* 2003; 284(3):H779-H789.
[198] Luft FC, Mervaala E, Muller DN, Gross V, Schmidt F, Park JK et al. Hypertension-induced end-organ damage : A new transgenic approach to an old problem. *Hypertension* 1999; 33(1 Pt 2):212-218.
[199] Ungar A, Castellani S, Di Serio C, Cantini C, Cristofari C, Vallotti B et al. Changes in renal autacoids and hemodynamics associated with aging and isolated systolic hypertension. *Prostaglandins Other Lipid Mediat* 2000; 62(2):117-133.
[200] Wheeler-Schilling TH, Kohler K, Sautter M, Guenther E. Angiotensin II receptor subtype gene expression and cellular localization in the retina and non-neuronal ocular tissues of the rat. *Eur J Neurosci* 1999; 11(10):3387-3394.
[201] Jaimes EA, Galceran JM, Raij L. Angiotensin II induces superoxide anion production by mesangial cells. Kidney Int 1998; 54(3):775-784.
[202] Inagami T, Guo DF, Kitami Y. Molecular biology of angiotensin II receptors: an overview. *J Hypertens Suppl* 1994; 12(10):S83-S94.
[203] Hannken T, Schroeder R, Stahl RA, Wolf G. Angiotensin II-mediated expression of p27Kip1 and induction of cellular hypertrophy in renal tubular cells depend on the generation of oxygen radicals. *Kidney Int* 1998; 54(6):1923-1933.
[204] Chiu T, Santiskulvong C, Rozengurt E. ANG II stimulates PKC-dependent ERK activation, DNA synthesis, and cell division in intestinal epithelial cells. *Am J Physiol Gastrointest Liver Physiol* 2003; 285(1):G1-11.
[205] Heitzer T, Wenzel U, Hink U, Krollner D, Skatchkov M, Stahl RA et al. Increased NAD(P)H oxidase-mediated superoxide production in renovascular hypertension: evidence for an involvement of protein kinase C. *Kidney Int* 1999; 55(1):252-260.

[206] Griendling KK, Minieri CA, Ollerenshaw JD, Alexander RW. Angiotensin II stimulates NADH and NADPH oxidase activity in cultured vascular smooth muscle cells. *Circ Res* 1994; 74(6):1141-1148.

[207] Hughes AD. Molecular and cellular mechanisms of action of angiotensin II (AT1) receptors in vascular smooth muscle. *J Hum Hypertens* 1998; 12(5):275-281.

[208] Pueyo ME, Michel JB. Angiotensin II receptors in endothelial cells. *Gen Pharmacol* 1997; 29(5):691-696.

[209] Inagami T, Eguchi S, Numaguchi K, Motley ED, Tang H, Matsumoto T et al. Cross-talk between angiotensin II receptors and the tyrosine kinases and phosphatases. *J Am Soc Nephrol* 1999; 10 Suppl 11:S57-61.:S57-S61.

[210] Brechler V, Levens NR, De Gasparo M, Bottari SP. Angiotensin AT2 receptor mediated inhibition of particulate guanylate cyclase: a link with protein tyrosine phosphatase stimulation? *Receptors Channels* 1994; 2(2):79-87.

[211] Hyman L, Neborsky R. Risk factors for age-related macular degeneration: an update. *Curr Opin Ophthalmol* 2002; 13(3):171-175.

[212] Risk factors associated with age-related macular degeneration. A case-control study in the age-related eye disease study: Age-Related Eye Disease Study Report Number 3. *Ophthalmology* 2000; 107(12):2224-2232.

[213] Chaine G, Hullo A, Sahel J, Soubrane G, Espinasse-Berrod MA, Schutz D et al. Case-control study of the risk factors for age related macular degeneration. France-DMLA Study Group. *Br J Ophthalmol* 1998; 82(9):996-1002.

[214] Hyman L, Schachat AP, He Q, Leske MC. Hypertension, cardiovascular disease, and age-related macular degeneration. Age-Related Macular Degeneration Risk Factors Study Group. *Arch Ophthalmol* 2000; 118(3):351-358.

[215] Jonas JB, Hayreh SS, Martus P. Influence of arterial hypertension and diet-induced atherosclerosis on macular drusen. *Graefes Arch Clin Exp Ophthalmol* 2003; 241(2):125-134.

[216] Hinton DR, He S, Lopez PF. Apoptosis in surgically excised choroidal neovascular membranes in age-related macular degeneration. *Arch Ophthalmol* 1998; 116(2): 203-209.

[217] Penfold PL, Killingsworth MC, Sarks SH. Senile macular degeneration: the involvement of immunocompetent cells. *Graefes Arch Clin Exp Ophthalmol* 1985; 223(2):69-76.

[218] Penfold P, Killingsworth M, Sarks S. An ultrastructural study of the role of leucocytes and fibroblasts in the breakdown of Bruch's membrane. *Aust J Ophthalmol* 1984; 12(1):23-31.

[219] Lopez PF, Grossniklaus HE, Lambert HM, Aaberg TM, Capone A, Jr., Sternberg P, Jr. et al. Pathologic features of surgically excised subretinal neovascular membranes in age-related macular degeneration. *Am J Ophthalmol* 1991; 112(6):647-656.

[220] Oh H, Takagi H, Takagi C, Suzuma K, Otani A, Ishida K et al. The potential angiogenic role of macrophages in the formation of choroidal neovascular membranes. *Invest Ophthalmol Vis Sci* 1999; 40(9):1891-1898.

[221] Espinosa-Heidmann DG, Caicedo A, Hernandez EP, Csaky KG, Cousins SW. Bone marrow-derived progenitor cells contribute to experimental choroidal neovascularization. *Invest Ophthalmol Vis Sci* 2003; 44(11):4914-4919.

[222] Gottsch JD, Bynoe LA, Harlan JB, Rencs EV, Green WR. Light-induced deposits in Bruch's membrane of protoporphyric mice. *Arch Ophthalmol* 1993; 111(1):126-129.

[223] Dithmar S, Curcio CA, Le NA, Brown S, Grossniklaus HE. Ultrastructural changes in Bruch's membrane of apolipoprotein E-deficient mice. *Invest Ophthalmol Vis Sci* 2000; 41(8):2035-2042.

[224] Kliffen M, Lutgens E, Daemen MJ, de Muinck ED, Mooy CM, de Jong PT. The APO(*)E3-Leiden mouse as an animal model for basal laminar deposit. *Br J Ophthalmol* 2000; 84(12):1415-1419.

[225] Mahley RW, Rall SC, Jr. Apolipoprotein E: far more than a lipid transport protein. *Annu Rev Genomics Hum Genet* 2000; 1:507-37.:507-537.

[226] Ashavaid TF, Todur SP, Nair KG. Apolipoprotein E polymorphism and coronary heart disease. *J Assoc Physicians India* 2003; 51:784-8.:784-788.

[227] Shuvaev VV, Laffont I, Siest G. Kinetics of apolipoprotein E isoforms-binding to the major glycosaminoglycans of the extracellular matrix. *FEBS Lett* 1999; 459(3): 353-357.

[228] Rakoczy PE, Zhang D, Robertson T, Barnett NL, Papadimitriou J, Constable IJ et al. Progressive age-related changes similar to age-related macular degeneration in a transgenic mouse model. *Am J Pathol* 2002; 161(4):1515-1524.

[229] Ambati J, Anand A, Fernandez S, Sakurai E, Lynn BC, Kuziel WA et al. An animal model of age-related macular degeneration in senescent Ccl-2- or Ccr-2-deficient mice. *Nat Med* 2003; 9(11):1390-1397.

[230] Hahn P, Qian Y, Dentchev T, Chen L, Beard J, Harris ZL et al. Disruption of ceruloplasmin and hephaestin in mice causes retinal iron overload and retinal degeneration with features of age-related macular degeneration. *Proc Natl Acad Sci U S A* 2004; 101(38):13850-13855.

[231] Hahn P, Milam AH, Dunaief JL. Maculas affected by age-related macular degeneration contain increased chelatable iron in the retinal pigment epithelium and Bruch's membrane. *Arch Ophthalmol* 2003; 121(8):1099-1105.

[232] Dithmar S, Sharara NA, Curcio CA, Le NA, Zhang Y, Brown S et al. Murine high-fat diet and laser photochemical model of basal deposits in Bruch membrane. *Arch Ophthalmol* 2001; 119(11):1643-1649.

[233] Klein BE, Klein R, Lee KE. Reproductive exposures, incident age-related cataracts, and age-related maculopathy in women: the beaver dam eye study. *Am J Ophthalmol* 2000; 130(3):322-326.

[234] Vingerling JR, Dielemans I, Witteman JC, Hofman A, Grobbee DE, de Jong PT. Macular degeneration and early menopause: a case-control study. *BMJ* 1995; 310(6994):1570-1571.

[235] Post-menopausal hormone replacement therapy (cont'd): risk-benefit balance in the hot seat. *Prescrire Int* 2004; 13(71):106-109.

[236] Warren MP. A comparative review of the risks and benefits of hormone replacement therapy regimens. *Am J Obstet Gynecol* 2004; 190(4):1141-1167.

[237] McCarty CA, Mukesh BN, Fu CL, Mitchell P, Wang JJ, Taylor HR. Risk factors for age-related maculopathy: the Visual Impairment Project. *Arch Ophthalmol* 2001; 119(10):1455-1462.

[238] Smith W, Mitchell P, Leeder SR. Smoking and age-related maculopathy. The Blue Mountains Eye Study. *Arch Ophthalmol* 1996; 114(12):1518-1523.

[239] Evans JR. Risk factors for age-related macular degeneration. *Prog Retin Eye Res* 2001; 20(2):227-253.

[240] Seddon JM, Gensler G, Milton RC, Klein ML, Rifai N. Association between C-reactive protein and age-related macular degeneration. *JAMA* 2004; 291(6):704-710.

In: Focus on Eye Research
Editor: O.R. Ioseliani, pp. 81-90
ISBN: 1-59454-434-4

Chapter 3

DEFLAZACORT TREATMENT OF CYSTOID MACULAR EDEMA IN PATIENTS AFFECTED BY RETINITIS PIGMENTOSA. A PILOT STUDY

Cristiano Giusti**, Renato Forte and Enzo Maria Vingolo
Institute of Ophthalmology, University "La Sapienza" Rome, Italy

ABSTRACT

Background: To investigate the efficacy of a long-term treatment with Deflazacort (DFZ), a third generation synthetic glucocorticoid, in patients affected by retinitis pigmentosa (RP) complicated by cystoid macular edema (CME). Methods: A randomized group of 10 RP subjects were selected for this pilot study and treated with DFZ for one year according to a standard protocol. Far and near best corrected visual acuity (BCVA), fluorescein angiography (Heidelberg Retina Angiograph) and computerized perimetry (Humphrey Visual Field Analyzer) were statistically assessed. Results: Near visual acuities, fluorescein angiographic findings and perimetric data improved significantly ($p<0.01$) while far BCVA varied only slightly ($p<0.05$). No ocular or systemic side effects were recorded. Conclusions: Further case-control studies, also involving a larger number of patients, are required to confirm these preliminary results. However, the present investigation seem to suggest that DFZ could be effective in reducing fluorescein angiographic findings and improving perimetric data and near visual acuities in RP patients, even though the pathogenesis of CME remains poorly understood.

Keywords: Cystoid macular edema – Deflazacort – Heidelberg Retina Angiograph - Humphrey Visual Field Analyzer - Retina – Retinitis Pigmentosa.

*Correspondence concerning this article should be addressed to Dr. Cristiano Giusti, Via Palestrina 21, I-00189 Rome, Italy. Phone/fax: +39 06 30361612; E-mail address: c.giusti@unicampus.it.

INTRODUCTION

Retinitis Pigmentosa (RP) is one of the most common forms of hereditary retinal degeneration, occurring in about 1 in 5.000 individuals worldwide [1, 2]. Patients affected by the typical form of RP often complain of faulty adaptation to light or darkness, photophobia, nightblindness as well as peripheral and midperipheral field defects; central vision is usually preserved in the early stages of the disease. The symptoms tend to appear at about 20 years of age but can occur later or even earlier, depending on the genetic defect and/or the pedigree. As the disease progresses, not only visual filed narrows but also central vision deteriorates, mainly due to the onset of posterior subcapsular cataract and cystoid macular edema (CME). In particular, the persistence of CME over prolonged periods of time may lead to a legal blindness due to chronic foveal cysts, retinal pigment epithelium (RPE) atrophy and lamellar macular holes [1, 2].

Carbonic anhydrase inhibitors have been found to be helpful in reducing CME and improving visual acuity in RP patients [3, 4]. Although a rebound of macular edema with a prolonged use of methazolamide has been observed [5], acetazolamide and methazolamide, orally taken, are the only drugs that have a proven beneficial effect at this time. On the contrary, no measurable improvement in visual acuity was observed with the topical use of dorzolamide hydrochloride [6].

Given the main role played by autoimmunity and apoptosis in RP, already postulated by several studies [7-10], we decided some years ago to test the efficacy of Deflazacort (DFZ) as a novel therapy of macular edema in RP patients [11]. This drug, an oxazolinic derivative of prednisolone with fewer side effects and a prolonged immunomodulating and anti-inflammatory activity, has already been used, with excellent results, in the treatment of chronic affections characterized by an impairement of the immune system: e.g., Duchenne muscular dystrophy [12], renal transplantation in childhood [13], autoimmune hepatitis [14].

However, despite the positive clinical effects on CME that we found in our first preclinical trial [11], no other studies are, to our knowledge, available in the ophthalmic literature at this time. It was therefore the purpose of this paper to present the final results of a one-year DFZ treatment of macular edema in patients affected by RP.

SUBJECTS AND METHODS

10 RP subjects (4 M and 6 F; mean age: 42.7 ± 12.6 years) were randomly selected from our patient population in order to avoid interference by selection bias and, thereafter, studied during a one-year period.

The diagnosis of RP was based on the clinical, genetic and instrumental criteria established some years ago by Marmor et al.[15]. Only patients whose inheritance pattern was clearly identified were selected for this study: autosomal dominant, autosomal recessive or X-linked forms were considered. In all patients, electroretinographic and clinical data were consistent with a typical rod-cone degenerative disorder (inclusion criteria). Patients who showed a definite cone-rod pattern or were affected by RP syndromic forms (i.e., Usher or Laurence-Moon-Bardet-Biedl) were not included in this study (exclusion criteria). Other therapies in progress (e.g. systemic corticosteroids, thiazide diuretics, digitalis, nonsteroidal anti-inflammatory agents, anticoagulants) as well as age-related macular degeneration, diabetes, amblyopia, smoking (> 10 cigarettes daily), pregnancy, cataract, aphakia or pseudophakia, intraocular pressure > 22 mmHg, refractive error > ±4 D, history of vitreoretinal surgery, previous retinal occlusive disorders or other systemic diseases (e.g. tyroid pathologies; cancer; vasculitis; obliterating peripheral arteriopathies) were also exclusion criteria.

All necessary ethical approvals were obtained by the University Commitee and the study itself was conducted in compliance with the Declaration of Helsinki. The drugs used for this pilot study were supplied by the University of Rome "La Sapienza" (Azienda Policlinico "Umberto I") and were prescribed in accordance with the manufacturer's instructions. Regarding to this matter, the authors wish to clarify that they had no financial interests in this research.

Before starting the therapeutic protocol, all patients were fully informed about DFZ's risks and benefits and, thereafter, undersigned their consent. The chance to stop therapy was guaranteed to any subject at any time. After a baseline examination (T0), repeated thereafter at every modification of therapy, patients were orally treated with DFZ (FLANTADIN® – Gruppo Lepetit SpA, Lainate (MI), Italy) for one year as follows: 30 mg/die for a week (T1); 15 mg/die for two weeks (T2); 6 mg/die for one month (T3); 6 mg every other day for two months (T4); 6 mg/die every three days for four months (T5); 6 mg/die every three days for four more months (T6). This schedule was assessed some years ago in a preclinical trial in which the better treatment interval, in order to avoid both DFZ's adverse effects and decrease in retinal activity due to long-term suspension of therapy, was assessed [11].

Far and near best corrected visual acuity (BCVA), Amsler grid test, color vision testing (Ishihara pseudoisochromatic plates) and retinal biomicroscopy, using high positive power precorneal lenses (Super Field and +78D Volk Lenses), were performed at baseline (T0) and before any modification of therapy was made (T1→T6). As previously done by Fishman et al [3-5], the Early Treatment Diabetic Retinopathy Study (ETDRS) chart was used for assessing far BCVA whereas near BCVA was measured by means of a special chart following ICAO (International Civil Aviation Organization) recommendations. Fluorescein angiography (Heidelberg Retina Angiograph) and computerized perimetry (Humphrey Visual Field Analyzer, 10-2 threshold program), on the contrary, were performed at baseline (T0) and, thereafter, every four months only. In order to determine the correct area of CME to be graded, we decided to follow the ETDRS classification of clinically significant macular edema [16]: therefore, the area considered was that within one disc diameter (DD) from the center of the fovea, i.e., within a circle two DD in diameter concentric with the macula. Inside this area, all angiograms were graded by one examiner only (E.M.V.) according to the previously published Fishman's classification of macular edema in RP [3]. Any leakage from radial peripapillary vessels seen along the temporal vascular arcades was not included in the grading.

At all visits, subjects were also asked if there was any subjective difference in vision between their current visual acuity and that at baseline and/or that at the previous visit. The response was graded as a large, moderate or small improvement; no change; worse; unsure.

Data were expressed as mean ± standard deviation (SD) and statistically analyzed by means of Student *t* test (Apple Macintosh, StatView II program). Statistical significance was expressed in terms of *p* values at 0.01 or less.

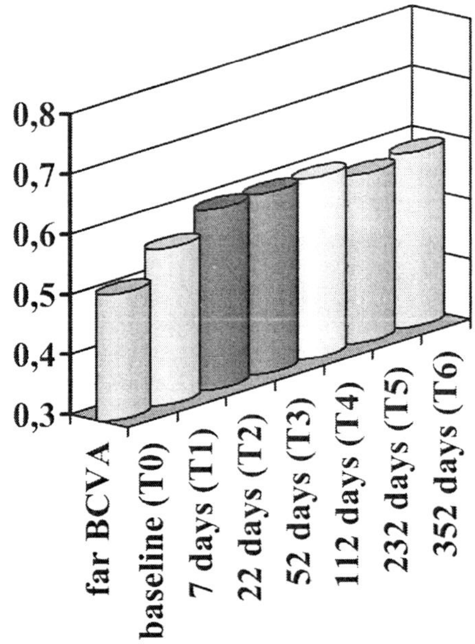

Figure 1. Modification of far best corrected visual acuity (BCVA) during the study (decimal values; *n* = mean).

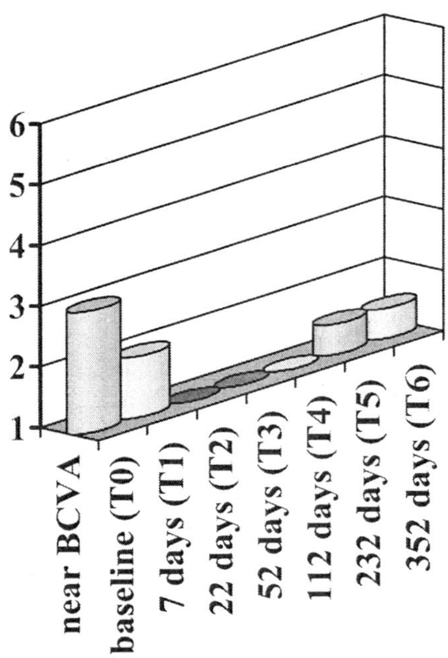

Figure 2. Modification of near best corrected visual acuity (BCVA) during the study (size print, being N1 the smallest and N6 the largest one; *n* = mean).

RESULTS

Far BCVA varied only slightly ($p < 0.05$) (Figure 1) while near visual acuity improved significantly during the whole follow-up period, even though DFZ showed a greater efficacy during the first three weeks of treatment ($p < 0.01$) (Figure 2). Amsler grid test demonstrated insufficient sensibility in detecting variations of CME, resulting statistically insignificant in this study ($p > 0.05$). Despite the clinically evident improvement of near vision, a slight degree of metamorphopsia and color vision impairement persisted in many subjects. A small subjective improvement from baseline examination was reported by most patients after the first three weeks of treatment only.

A remarkable angiographic reduction of macular edema (Figures 3-5) was observed during the study, even though a full and long lasting resorption of CME was not obtained (Figures 4-5). These data were more evident after the first four months of treatment, when all patients showed a significant reduction of fluorescein leakage compared to the baseline angiograms (Figure 3). Thereafter, as already reported in RP patients during methazolamide therapy [5], a slight rebound of macular edema was observed and persisted during the whole follow-up period. Nevertheless, at the end of the study, a reduction of fluorescein leakage, compared to the baseline angiograms, was still present in about 47% of subjects (Figure 3).

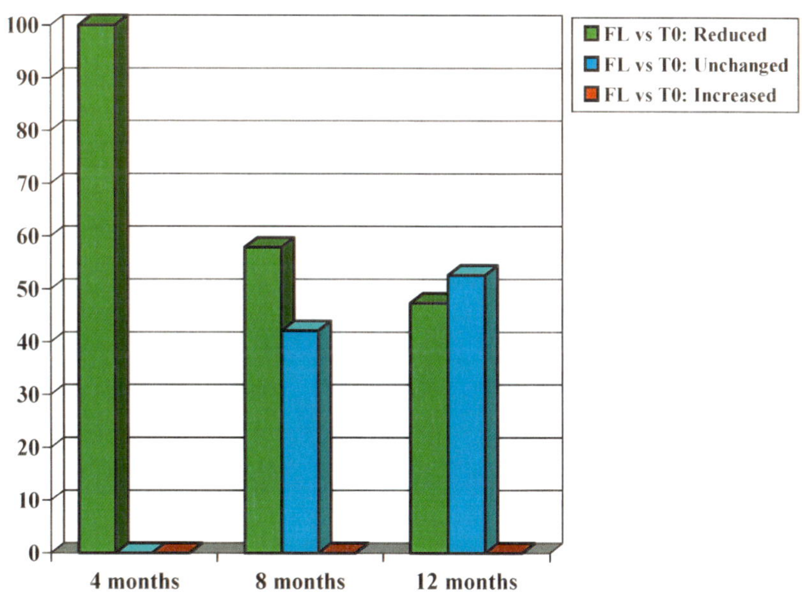

Figure 3. Modification of fluorescein leakage (FL) during the study compared to the baseline examination (percentages of patients).

A marked perimetric increase of the retinal central sensitivity (10° around the fixation point) was found ($p < 0.01$) (Figure 6). In particular, it was characterized not only by a higher mean retinal sensitivity and a lower mean defect (compared to the baseline examinations), but also by a parallel reduction of the short fluctuation value, an important parameter that indicates a reduced and more stable defect after treatment. Similarly to what observed on fluorescein angiograms, also the improvement of perimetric data was particularly evident after the first four months of therapy, correponding to the increase in far and near visual acuity. All patients were fully trained in computerized visual field testing and, therefore, the potential beneficial effect due to the so called "learning effect" is meaningless.

Regarding to the response to therapy, no ocular or systemic side effects were recorded and the patient compliance was good during the whole study.

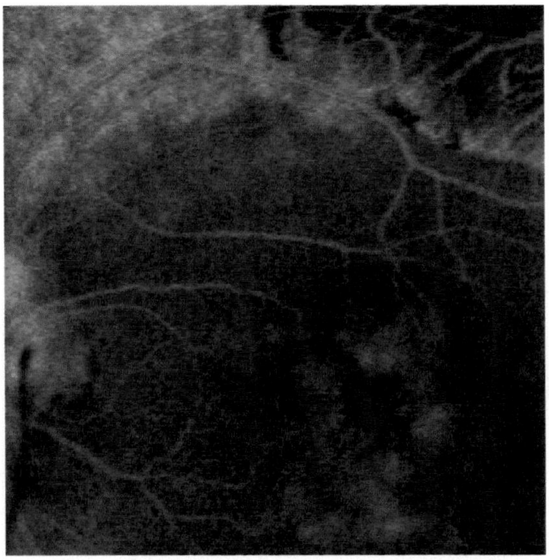

Figure 4. Case report: angiographic findings at baseline (T0) (late phase).

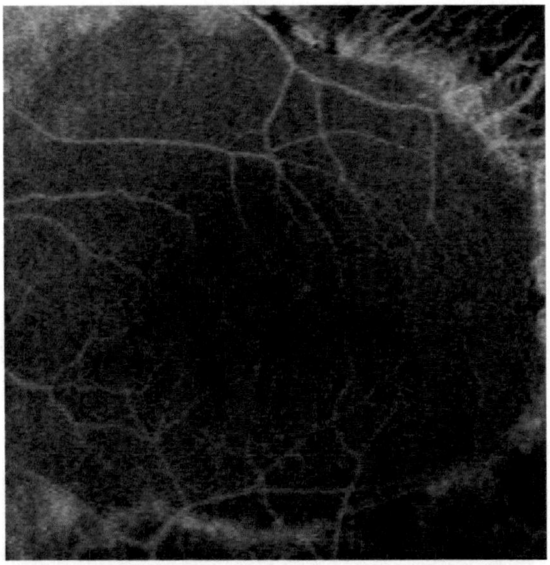

Figure 5. Case report: angiographic findings after therapy (T6) (late phase).

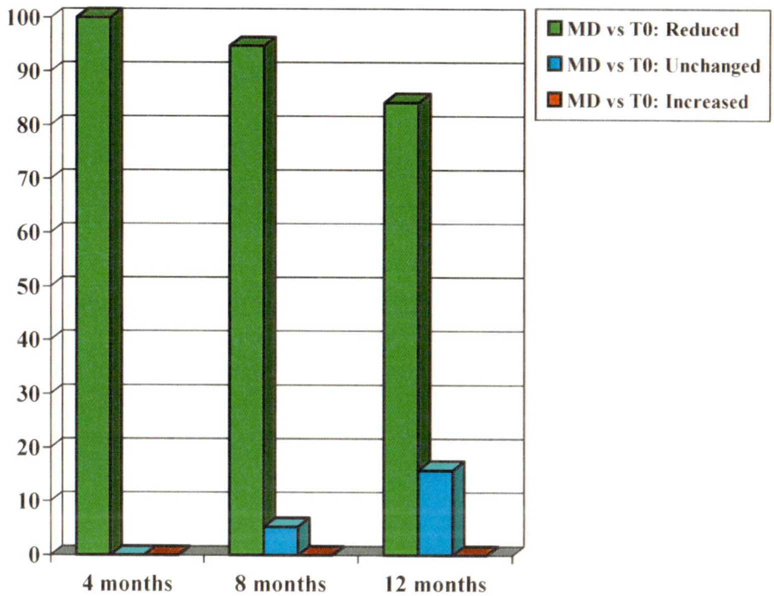

Figure 6. Modification of the visual field parameter "mean defect" (MD) during the study compared to the baseline examination (percentages of patients).

Discussion

Despite the remarkable clinical impact on visual function of this frequent complication of RP (about 10%-15% of cases according to Gass [17] and Fishman [4] respectively), the exact pathogenesis of CME is still poorly understood.

There should be no doubts that a main role is probably played by a specific loss of the perifoveal capillary vascular integrity with the consequent pooling of fluid into the foveal region [1]. At the same time, however, a disruption of the constant transport of fluid outward from the retina to the choroid through a damaged RPE could also lead to a lack of the normal relative deturgescence of the outer retinal extracellular space and, consequently, to the characteristic "honeycombed" biomicroscopic appearance and the "flower-petal" angiographic pattern of the foveal retina (Figure 7) [2]. In fact, Gass already reported several years ago that the extravascular staining observed in the degenerative areas of the retina seemed to originate both from the retinal perifoveal vessels (inner retina) and the RPE-photoreceptor complex (outer retina) [17]. Moreover, as already hypothesized in the pathogenesis of diabetic maculopathy [18], the vitreous should also play some unknown role in determining CME, as vitreal alterations are a common feature in RP subjects [7].

At present, still exists a genuine controversy regarding the precise location of the tissues from which the cystic spaces arise in CME. The "intracellular" theory holds that the cysts develop from edematous Müller cells, whereas the "extracellular" theory, accepted by most Authors, proposes that the cysts originate from spaces within the outer plexiform and inner nuclear layers of the macula [2].

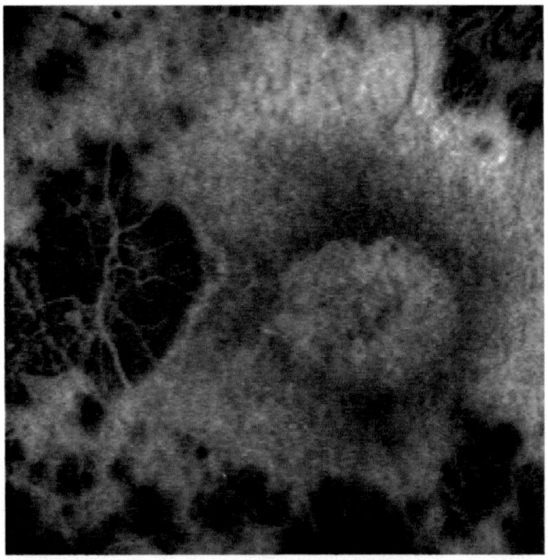

Figure 7. A typical example of cystoid macular edema in retinitis pigmentosa with the characteristic "flower-petal" angiographic pattern of the foveal retina.

The potential implication of autoimmunity and apoptosis in RP, in determining the immune-related RPE alterations and the correlated photoreceptor death, has already been postulated by several studies [7-10]. Given these experimental data as well as the reported DFZ therapeutical effects on RPE and blood cells (reduced expression of interleukin (IL) receptor and HLA-DR antigen by RPE; reduced chemoattractants plasma levels; increased monocyte-mediated expression of cytokines, IL, growth factors and activin by RPE; inhibited HLA class II antigen expression by activated T-cells and macrophages; inhibited antibody-dependent cellular cytotoxicity and natural killer activity; inhibited proliferation and response of T and B lymphocytes) [11-14], the novel therapy of CME proposed in this paper could successfully interfer, in theory, with the RP natural history, slowing the degenerative progress itself and improving the clinical impact of CME on visual function.

Observations from this pilot study seem to suggest that DFZ could be effective in the treatment of macular edema in RP patients, being able to determine a significant reduction of fluorescein leakage and an improvement of both perimetric data and near visual acuities compared to the baseline examinations. According to us, these positive clinical findings could not only be explained by an effective removal of the retinal edema across the RPE but also by a partially restored integrity of the RPE-photoreceptor complex itself that allows a better macular function.

In summary, our investigation may not be considered conclusive, because of the small number of patients involved, the open design with absence of a control group and the relatively short follow-up, but only as a personal contribution for finding a valid medical approach to CME. However, even though further studies are required to determine the exact mechanism of action of DFZ in RP subjects, these preliminary results seem to suggest that this drug could be useful in the treatment of these patients, even though the pathogenesis of CME remains poorly understood.

References

[1] Albert DM, Jakobiec FA. *Principles and practice of ophthalmology*. Philadelphia: Saunders, 1994

[2] Federman JL, Gouras P, Schubert H, Slusher MM, Vrabec TR. *Retina and vitreous. Textbook of Ophthalmology*, vol. 9. London: Mosby, 1994

[3] Fishman GA, Gilbert LD, Fiscella RG, Kimura AE, Jampol LM. Acetazolamide for treatment of chronic macular edema in retinitis pigmentosa. *Arch Ophthalmol* 1989; 107: 1445-1452.

[4] Fishman GA, Gilbert LD, Anderson RJ, Marmor MF, Weleberg RG, Viana MA. Effect of methazolamide on chronic macular edema in patients with retinitis pigmentosa. *Ophthalmology* 1994; 101: 687-693.

[5] Fishman GA, Glenn AM, Gilbert LD. Rebound of macular edema with continued use of methazolamide in patients with retinitis pigmentosa. *Arch Ophthalmol* 1993; 111: 1640-1646.

[6] Grover S, Fishman GA, Fiscella RG, Adelman AE. Efficacy of dorzolamide hydrochloride in the management of chronic cystoid macular edema in patients with retinitis pigmentosa. *Retina* 1997; 17: 222-231.

[7] Vingolo EM, Giusti C, Forte R, Onori P. Vitreal alterations in retinitis pigmentosa: biomicroscopic appearance and statistical evaluation. *Ophthalmologica* 1996; 210: 104-107.

[8] Portera-Calliau C, Sung CH, Nathans J, Adler R. Apoptosis photoreceptor cell death in mouse models of retinitis pigmentosa. *Proc Natl Acad USA* 1994; 91: 974-978.

[9] Dryja TP, Berson EL. Retinitis Pigmentosa: the Friedenwald Lecture. *Invest Ophthalmol Vis Sci* 1995; 36: 1197-1200.

[10] Adler R. Mechanisms of photoreceptor death in retinal degenerations. *Arch Ophthalmol* 1996; 114: 79-83.

[11] Forte R, Iacobelli L, Grenga P, Volante V, Vingolo EM. Cystoid macular edema in retinitis pigmentosa: treatment with Deflazacort. Clinical and functional investigations [ARVO Abstract]. *Invest Ophthalmol Vis Sci* 1998; 39(4): S969. Abstract nr 4477.

[12] Biggar WD, Gingras M, Fehlings DL, Harris VA, Steele CA. Deflazacort treatment of Duchenne muscular dystrophy. *J Pediatr* 2001; 138: 45-50.

[13] Ferraris JR, Pasqualini T, Legal S, et al. Effect of Deflazacort versus methylprednisone on growth, body composition, lipid profile and bone mass after renal transplantation. The Deflazacort Study Group. *Pediatr Nephrol* 2000; 14: 682-688.

[14] Rebollo Bernandez J, Cifuentes Mimoso C, Pinar Moreno A, et al. Deflazacort for long-term maintenance of remission in type 1 autoimmune hepatitis. *Rev Esp Enferm Dig* 1999; 91: 630-638.

[15] Marmor MF, Aguirre G, Arden G, Berson EL. Retinitis Pigmentosa symposium on terminology and methods of examination. *Ophthalmology* 1983; 90: 126-131.

[16] Diabetic Retinopathy Study Research Group. Report 7. A modification of the Airlie House classification of diabetic retinopathy. *Invest Ophthalmol Vis Sci* 1981; 21: 210-226.

[17] Gass JDM. Stereoscopic atlas of macular diseases. *Diagnosis and treatment*. St. Louis: C.V. Mosby Company, 1987

[18] Nasrallah FP, Jalkh AE, Van Coppenolle F. The role of the vitreous in diabetic macular edema. *Ophthalmology* 1988; 95: 1335-1339.

In: Focus on Eye Research
Editor: O.R. Ioseliani, pp. 91-115

ISBN: 1-59454-434-4

Chapter 4

SPECIES VARIATIONS IN THE REFRACTIVE INDEX OF THE EYE LENS AND PATTERNS OF CHANGE WITH AGEING

Barbara K. Pierscionek*

Department of Biomedical Sciences, University of Ulster, Cromore Road, County Londonderry, Northern Ireland, U.K.

ABSTRACT

The eye lens contains no vasculature and has no direct innervation. Its simple arrangement of long thin fibre-like cells, containing proteins and water, is organised to maintain transparency, which is retained for the greater part of life. This may be considered unusual in a structure believed to possess short-range order and one which contains a mixture of proteins with irregular shapes and varying physical and immunochemical properties. Any change in protein concentration that is sufficient to cause light to scatter rather than to refract, will cause opacification, the clinical manifestation of which is cataract. A uniform concentration of protein, however, is not the optimum design for a lens that needs to contribute a certain amount of refractive power to focus light onto the retina as well as to alter its shape to meet varying visual demands. Refraction occurs when light passes through a curved surface or across an interface between media of varying refractive index. In a lens with a uniform protein concentration and hence a constant refractive index, all refraction would take place at the lens surface. This would require a high protein concentration and/or a very curved lens in order to meet focussing requirements and would not allow for any change in lens shape. The distribution patterns of the various protein classes create a gradual change in refractive index across the lens, ensuring that functional demands are met without any detrimental effects to transparency of the tissue. Variations in the refractive index distribution exist in lenses from different species and some change in refractive index occurs with age. This paper discusses the contribution of the structural proteins to the functional requirements of the lens and presents comparative results of refractive index variations in human and animal lenses as well as showing how the refractive index may alter with age in the human lens.

*Correspondence concerning this article should be addressed to Professor Barbara K. Pierscionek. Department of Biomedical Sciences, University of Ulster, Cromore Road, Coleraine, Co. Londonderry, Northern Ireland BT52 1SA UK. E-mail address: b.pierscionek@ulster.ac.uk

Keywords: eye lens, refractive index, optics, proteins, structure/function.

INTRODUCTION

The most common approach to the study of the laws of Nature is to investigate order and change: order in structure from the micromolecular level to the vast universal organisation and change to this order as well as adaptation to change with time. Any correlations from which an empirical law or formula can be derived, present an efficient way of describing a relationship and/or predicting characteristics or behaviour of the factors or variables involved. The laws of Nature, however, are often not easily expressed in a formulaic way or as simple calculations and, even when this does appear feasible, it may only be applicable within a restricted range of conditions.

An increasingly more popular way of examining the patterns and order of Nature in the body is by investigating structure/function relationships; change to that order with time is studied by considering alterations that occur with ageing. The structure/function relationship is one that does not necessarily require a formulaic representation, but provides an understanding of how a system works by studying its components and their organisation. This is particularly applicable to the eye, the structure of which is biological and the function of which is, largely, optical.

From a comparative consideration, the structure of the eye lens is one of the simplest of body organs. It contains no vasculature and has no innervation. This is to ensure that the passage of light is not obstructed by the presence of blood vessels or nerves. The simple lenticular arrangement of long, thin fibre-like cells, filled with proteins and water, is organised to maintain transparency, which is retained for the greater part of life. Transparency may be considered unusual in a structure believed to possess short-range order (defined as a structure in which the distance between atoms can be described by a probability function and is therefore not one with regular spacing) and which contains a mixture of proteins with irregular shapes and varying physical and immunochemical properties. Although transparency is found in amorphous structures that lack long-range order, notably glass, transparency in such cases is believed to be because of the high density and very tight packing of molecules. The tight molecular packing that is found in glass cannot occur in the lens, the consistency of which is gel-like and which has a composition of around 35% protein and 65% water (in humans and in some animal lenses). Nevertheless, short-range spatial order is believed to be sufficient for maintaining lenticular transparency (Trokel, 1962; Benedek, 1971), although it has been pointed out that transparency does not depend solely on the degree of spatial order, but also on the interactions between the lens proteins and water (Zhao and Bettelheim, 1995). There are no results to show how densely packed the proteins are; the concentration of proteins is simply taken as an indication of density. This varies widely across species, from the protein-rich rodent lenses to their comparatively dilute avian counterparts; yet all lenses (when healthy) are transparent. The suggestion of long-range order in the lens would appear to be implausible, given the nature of the structural entities: proteins with complex configurations distributed in varying concentrations throughout the tissue. Long-range order is found in structures such as crystals in which there is a highly regular and repeated arrangement of atoms in planes separated by fixed spacings within and between planes. Quartz and calcite are good examples of long-range order. Such structures are optically anisotropic: when light travels through them, the velocities of the traversing light rays vary depending on their direction of travel. If the velocity differences are sufficiently large, as they are in calcite, an object viewed through such a structure will be seen as a double image and the structure is said to be birefringent. In addition to double imagery, when birefringent structures are placed between polarizing filters, with filter axes orthogonal to one another, characteristic patterns of concentric coloured rings can be seen when looking along the optic axis (or axes) of the crystal. These rings (isochromatics) are believed to be caused by phase differences created by rays travelling at different velocities. When the phase difference for a particular wavelength is 180°, there is destructive interference and this wavelength is 'subtracted' from the light and produces the complementary or interference colour. This explanation for the formation of isochromatics assumes a regularity of structure that does not exist in the eye lens.

This notwithstanding, it has been shown that when the lens is dehydrated, following a step-wise controlled procedure, it exhibits the characteristic patterns found in structures with long-range order (Pierscionek, 1994). These patterns are not seen with fresh or hydrated lenses. This would suggest that the protein 'back-bone' may indeed be highly organised (or that it may become highly organised when dehydrated) but that such organisation is masked by the presence of water. Furthermore, the colour and thickness of the isochromatics were found to differ in every species tested (Pierscionek, 1994) suggesting that the arrangement of the protein back-bone may vary from species to species. The finding of isochromatics in dehydrated lenses is counterintuitive: removal of a major constituent may be expected to disrupt structural organisation rather than to induce a higher level of order. No explanation for an analogous finding of a biological structure that manifests long-range order when water is removed but short-range order when hydrated, has, to the author's knowledge, been reported.

Evidence supporting short-range order in the hydrated lens was produced by Delaye and Tardieu (1983) and supported in subsequent studies (Cooper, Aquilina, Truscott and Carver, 1994). The parameters governing transparency in a structure such as the lens have been outlined (Veretout, Delaye and Tardieu, 1989, Tardieu, 1998). The structural features of α-crystallin, the largest and most abundant class of lens proteins, are thought to play a particular role in the maintenance of lens transparency (Derham and Harding, 1999).

The broad classification into α, β and γ-crystallins is based on physical and chemical properties of the protein classes (Morner, 1894; Woods and Burky, 1927; Burky and Woods, 1928). This early categorisation of the water-soluble crystallins still applies to a number of vertebrate lenses although, since it was first proposed, a number of sub-classifications, similarities between groups (β/γ superfamily) and new species-specific crystallins have been reported (Yu, East, Chang and Kuck, 1977; Tomarev, Zinovieva, Dolgilevich, Luchin, Krayev, Skryabin, Gause, 1984; Stapel. Zweers, Dodemont, Kan, de Jong, 1985; Williams, Ding, Horwitz. and Piatigorsky, 1985; Wistow, Mulders, and de Jong, 1987; Huang, Russell, Stone, Zigler, 1987; Chiou, Chang and Lai, 1989; Chiou, S.H., Lo, C.H., Chang, C.Y., Itoh, T., Kaji, H., Samejima, T. 1991; Garland, Rao, Del Corso, Mura, Zigler, 1991; van Rheede, Amons, Stewart and de Jong, 2003; Voorter, Wintjes, Heinstra, Bloemendal and De Jong, 1993).

The crystalline classes vary in proportion across the tissue (Pierscionek and Augusteyn, 1988; 1991). Variation in distribution patterns and indeed, any variations in proportion across the lens, are gradual to avoid marked differences in density as these would result in sufficiently high refractive index fluctuations causing light to scatter. It has been suggested that the degree of spatial order required for transparency may also vary across the lens, with a greater degree in the outer, cortical region than in the nucleus (Michael, van Marle, Vrensen and van den Berg, 2003). This suggestion was made on the basis of the considerable difference between the refractive index of the cortical cytoplasm and cortical fibre cell membranes. Without a certain degree of spatial order, such a difference in refractive index would result in light scatter causing opacification and cataract formation.

While marked variations in protein concentration are detrimental to sight, a uniform concentration of protein is not the optimum design for a lens the shape and size of which is restricted by the space available within the eyeball. This is because the lens requires a certain amount of refractive power to focus light onto the retina and this depends on the shape of the lens, its refractive index (determined by the concentration of proteins) and the refractive index of the surround (the ocular humors). A lens with a uniform protein concentration would need to have a greater curvature and/or higher protein concentration to produce the requisite amount of refractive power. The space such a lens would need to occupy and the density of its tissue would prevent it from changing shape in accordance with functional demands. A gradation of refractive index contributes to refractive power allowing for a less curved, less dense lens. The distribution patterns of the various protein classes create this gradual change in refractive index without causing any detrimental effects to the transparency of the tissue.

Transparency is preserved in the eye lens for a remarkably long time. Remarkable because the lens does not shed any cells and so material laid down during gestation remains in the lens throughout life. Age-related changes to the structural proteins that may cause structural breakdown leading to opacification and cataract, are countered by highly efficient repair mechanisms (Vrensen, 1995). The rate of development of senile cataract varies greatly but it is uncommon to have advanced, before the sixth decade of life, to a level so detrimental to vision that it requires removal and replacement of the lens. The function of transparency is therefore protected. Such protection is not afforded to the other function of the lens, accommodation: that of changing the refractive power of the eye to allow it to focus clearly over a range of distances. Accommodation decreases progressively and measurably with age and, unlike senile cataract, this loss of accommodation, termed presbyopia, affects everyone. It manifests as early as the fifth decade of life and presents as difficulties with focussing on near objects, most notably on reading material.

Structure/function relationships in the lens can be looked at in more than one way. When dealing with transparency, the relationship is concerned with the organisation and order of the proteins and how these may be related to the maintenance of transparency. In studies on presbyopia, the structure/function relationship has been investigated by looking at how ageing changes in the optical and rheological properties of the tissue may be related to the loss of accommodative function. Regardless of how the structure/function relationship is studied, the crystallin proteins, their arrangements and interactions underlie all aspects of structure. However, trying to establish how the crystallin proteins may be linked to the function is not easy; the difficulty is largely one of methodology. In order to determine the protein distribution patterns, the lens must be divided into sections and each section analysed for protein proportions. The process requires a step-wise structural breakdown from fractionation of the tissue, to chromatographic separation of proteins and characterisation of individual classes. This cannot produce any information about the structures, arrangements or interactions of the proteins within the intact tissue. Proteins have very elaborate and complex structures: the primary sequence of amino acids is twisted and bent into secondary, tertiary and quaternary structures that are characteristic of the particular protein and related to its properties, the way in which it may interact with other proteins and consequently to the arrangement of proteins within the lens.

When investigations about the nature of a relationship are constrained by the inability to directly measure or observe one of the aspects of that relationship, an indirect means or another factor, which can be related to one or both aspects, may prove very useful. In the case of the eye lens, the refractive index serves this purpose. The refractive index distribution is part of the optical design of the lens and is therefore related to the optical function. The magnitude of the refractive index depends on the protein concentration and hence is also related to the biological organisation ie to the distribution and properties of the crystallin proteins. It is known that lens has a variable refractive index that increases in magnitude into the centre, and it has been suggested that the colloid osmotic behaviour of the crystallins may, at least partly, contribute to the construction of the refractive index gradations (Veretout and Tardieu, 1989; Magid, Kenworthy, McIntosh, 1992). How the distributions of the proteins may be related to the refractive index gradient was the subject of research some years ago (Pierscionek and Augusteyn, 1991). While a direct, quantitative relationship between the optical parameter and any of the protein classes was not found, there is some suggestion that γ-crystallin may make a greater contribution to refractive index that the other protein classes (Pierscionek, Smith and Augusteyn, 1987).

Unlike the protein distributions, the refractive index can be measured on whole lenses. This has been most frequently done using ray tracing and calculating the refractive index from ray trace parameters (Campbell and Hughes, 1981; Campbell, 1984; Pierscionek, Chan, Ennis, Smith. and Augusteyn, 1988; Axelrod, Lerner and Sands, 1988; Pierscionek, 1989; Pierscionek and Chan, 1989; Pierscionek, 1990; Jagger, 1992; Kroger, Campbell, Munger and Fernald, 1994; Pierscionek and Augusteyn, 1995). The mathematics used in ray tracing relies on assumptions about the outer shape of the lens and the contours of refractive index within the tissue. Another method of measuring the refractive index directly with an optic fibre probe, has been developed (Pierscionek, 1995a, 1995b, 1997). This provides the advantage of direct, localised measurement with no necessity for underlying assumptions. The method is invasive, but any tissue rupture is of such low degree that repeat measurements are reproducible to within the range of measurement error (Pierscionek, 1995a).

This paper presents studies on the refractive index of the lens as measured with the optic fibre probe. The first section looks at how the refractive index varies in different species; the second part is concerned with the refractive index in the human lens and how this may alter with age to explain the loss of accommodative function.

I. Species Variability in Refractive Index

The refractive power of the eye depends on the combined contributions of the two optical components: the lens and the cornea. For both of these components, shape or curvature as well as refractive index are important determinants of power. Among species, there is a great deal of variation in the curvature and size of the eye lens which is not related to the size of the animal nor even to the size of the eye. There are also variations in the distribution and magnitude of refractive index.

Methods

Refractive index variations were measured in lenses from the eyes of four species: human, cow, gibbon and guinea pig. The human (*Homo sapien*) lens (47 year old) was obtained from the Lions Eye Bank of the Royal Victorian Eye and Ear Hospital in Melbourne, the bovine (*Bos taurus*) lenses from a local abattoir, the gibbon (*Hylobates lar*) lens from the National Vision Research Institute, Melbourne and the guinea pig (*Cavia porcellus*) lens from Professor A. Sinclair (Royal Melbourne Institute of Technology).

All lenses were used within 24 of death and were weighed before and after experimentation. Refractive index was measured using a reflectometric optic fibre sensor; the instrument and method has been described in detail in previous publications (Pierscionek, 1995a, 1995b). The sensor comprises a coupler (Amphenol: 50:50 for 670nm and made of single mode Flexcor fibre (125 microns in diameter with a core diameter of 4 microns)) that acts as a beam splitter. It is made up of 2 optic fibres joined over small sections of their lengths to enable light transfer from one to the other. One arm of the coupler is attached to a 670nm, 1mW diode laser (Fibrenet Glotracr) and another to a detector (Anritsu, MA9412A) and power meter (Anritsu, MA9001A). The flattened end of the third arm (the probe) is housed in a 26 gauge needle (Terumo syringe needle) with a polished, flattened end. The probe makes contact with the sample and part of the reflected light from the sample/fibre interface is directed to the detector that sends signals to the power meter. The refractive index is calculated from the amount of light reflected at the fibre/sample interface, according to Fresnel reflectance theory taking into account losses and spurious components (Pierscionek, 1995a, 1995b). Readings were collected on a Macintosh PowerBook 140 using the data acquisition program SuperScope (GW Instruments, Somerville, MA 02143, U.S.A.). The probe is attached to a three-way translation stage with manual micrometer adjustment, allowing accurate localisation of measurement position within the tissue.

After the initial weighing, the width of each lens in the sagittal plane (the plane within which the optic axis is found) was measured against a millimetre scale. The lens was then immobilized, equatorial plane (orthogonal to the sagittal plane) horizontal, partially submerged in a physiologically balanced gel medium (Pierscionek, Ennis, Chan, Smith and Augusteyn, 1988) within a square cell, with millimetre markings around its borders. The equatorial diameter was determined by measuring the distance moved by the probe as it traversed from one end of the lens to the other. Measurements were made along the optic axis; alignment of the fibre optic probe with the correct axes of the sample has been described previously (Pierscionek, 1995b). Immediately prior to measurement, the capsule was gently pierced with a 22 gauge needle (Terumo syringe needle) and a reading was taken in air. The probe was moved to the surface where a measurement was made in duplicate. Each measurement was the average of 40 readings collected within seconds by the data acquisition program. Subsequent (duplicate) measurements were made at intervals of 0.5mm through the human, gibbon and guinea pig lenses and at 1mm intervals through the bovine lens. In the human, gibbon and bovine lenses, measurements were made over the entire sagittal width; for the guinea pig lens only half of the profile was measured as the centre of the lens was quite hard and there was concern that this core may be 'pushed' by the needle before it could be penetrated properly and hence would distort the other half of the profile.

Post-experimentation weights were always lower than pre-experimentation weights, by up to 10 % of the latter in the human, bovine and guinea pig lenses and up to 15% in the gibbon lens. In all cases, removal of the lens from the gel after experimentation resulted in capsular damage and some tissue loss, which would explain any decrease in weight. The error in reading the micrometer scale was ±0.001mm. The error in refractive index was ±0.002.

Results

The refractive index variations along the optic axes of four lenses: human, gibbon, bovine and guinea pig, are shown in Figure 1. In the human and bovine lenses, refractive index was measured from the anterior to the posterior poles (entry and exit points for light rays travelling along the optic axis) but it was not possible to differentiate between anterior and posterior sections in the gibbon and guinea pig lenses because these lenses were symmetrical in shape.

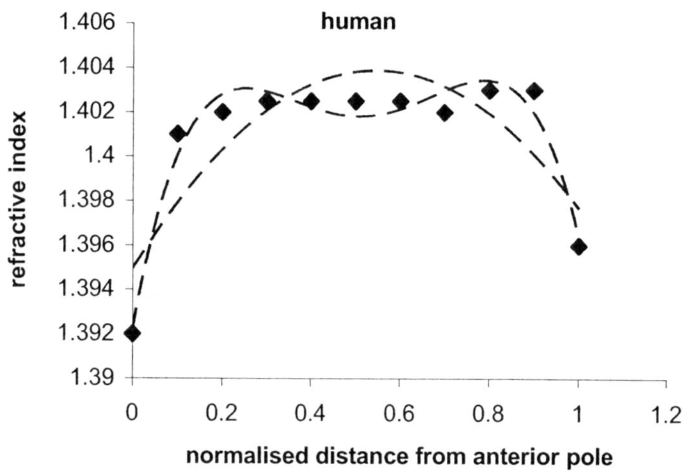

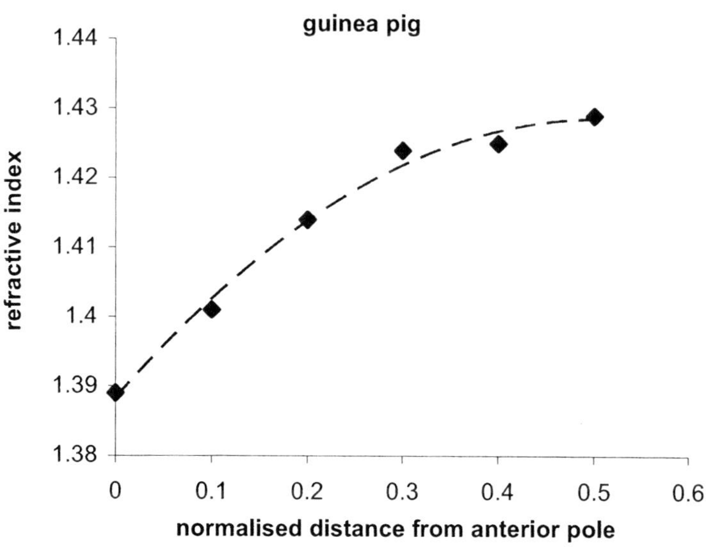

Figure 1 continued on next page

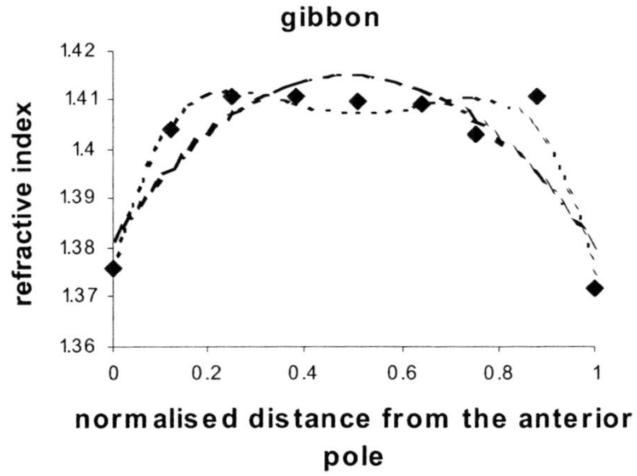

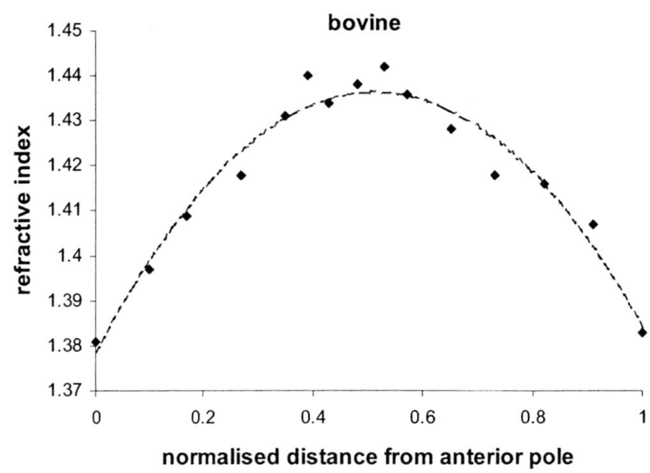

Figure 1. Variations in refractive index (for 670nm) along the optic axes of human, guinea pig, gibbon and bovine lenses plotted against the normalised distance from the anterior pole.

The results fall into two sets: the refractive index profiles from the human and gibbon lenses are quite different from those of the bovine or the guinea pig. The former set have a gradient only in the periphery, whilst retaining a constant value over the inner region of each lens. This is not seen in the profiles of the bovine or guinea pig lenses in which the index values continue to rise towards the centre. The shapes of these latter two profiles closely approximate parabolae and can be fitted with second order polynomials, with significance levels $p<<0.005$, (Table 1). Second order polynomials could also be fitted to the primate lens profiles with a high degree of statistical significance but the correlation coefficients are substantially lower than for the bovine and guinea pig lenses and the theoretical curves for the primate lenses do not fit the experimental data well. Higher order polynomials, of 4th order, provide more predictable fits.

Table 1. Polynomial fits of second order (A) and fourth order (B) made to refractive index profiles shown in figure 1.

A.

Lens	Equation	r^2	p
Human	$y=-0.030x^2+0.033x+1.395$	0.688	<0.005
Gibbon	$y=-0.138x^2+0.136x+1.382$	0.743	<0.005
Bovine	$y=-0.219x^2+0.225x+1.379$	0.957	<<0.005
Guinea pig	$y=-0.157x^2+0.159x+1.388$	0.991	<<0.005

B.

Human	$y=-0.278x^4+0.576x^3-0.406x^2$ $+0.113x+1.392$	0.962	<<0.005
Gibbon	$y=-1.029x^4+2.067x^3-1.432x^2$ $+0.392x+1.375$	0.932	<<0.005

The maximum index values in the primate lenses are 1.402-1.403 and 1.411-1.412 in the centres of the human and gibbon lenses respectively, both substantially lower than the maximum of 1.429 for the guinea pig lens and 1.440-1.442 for the bovine lens. In the edge values, however, the human lens edge index at 1.392-1.396 is closer to the value at the edge of the guinea pig index profile (1.389) than it is to the gibbon edge index value of 1.372-1.376. For the bovine lens, the edge index value is 1.381-1.383.

Although the general form of the refractive index profile does not change, the magnitude of refractive index has been shown to increase with age in the bovine (Pierscionek, 1989) and, slightly, in the cortical part of the human lens (Pierscionek, 1990). Index magnitude therefore needs to take account of age of the animal. Although it is not always possible to obtain information about age, it has been shown that age of the animal can be derived from the weight of the lens (Hockwin, 1971). Unfortunately, Hockwin did not include the gibbon or guinea pig among the species studied and no other work, relating age to lens weight for these species, has been found. It was therefore not possible to determine whether the lenses used in this study came from animals at comparable stages in their respective life spans and hence no conclusions could be drawn from an inter-species comparison of refractive index magnitudes. All that can be said is that the animals were adult and no lenses showed signs of opacification or yellowing (which can be an indication of advanced age).

The refractive index and dimensions of the four lenses can be used to calculate an approximate value of total protein. The sagittal distance (t), (thickness of the lenses from pole to pole), the equatorial radius (ρ), the lens weights (before experimentation) (W) and the estimated volume (V) (Table 2) are used to calculate volume, according to the following formula:

$$V= (2/3)\pi\rho^2 t \tag{1}$$

The final column in Table 2 shows the approximate total protein content (g), determined from the refractive index using the Gladstone-Dale formula (Appendix A).

Table 2. Dimensions of the lenses: sagittal width (t), equatorial radius (ρ), weight (W), calculated volume (V), calculated protein weight (P).

Lens	t(mm)	ρ(mm)	W(g)	V(cm^{-3})	P(g)
Human	4.70	4.88	0.2298	0.234	0.089
Gibbon	4.00	4.57	0.1738	0.175	0.064
Bovine	11.60	8.99	2.1810	1.966	0.750
Guinea pig	5.00	2.72	0.0802	0.077	0.038

Discussion

From the data in this paper, comparing a rodent (guinea pig), ungulate (bovine) and two primate (gibbon and human) lenses, the latter have the flatter profiles and the lower index maxima, with the human lens having the lowest value. Apart from the observation that in the gibbon lens the edge index value is lower than that of its human counterpart and that it rises to a slightly higher index maximum, there is little difference in the shapes of the primate lens index profiles. In both, the gradation only occurs in the outer 20% of the distance along the optic axes, unlike the bovine and guinea pig lenses in which the index gradients continue to rise into the very centres. The human and bovine lens results support previously measured refractive index profiles for these species (Pierscionek, 1995a; 1995b) as well as water (human: Bours, Fodisch and Hockwin, 1987; Huizinga, Bot, de Mul, Vrensen and Greve, 1989; Siebinga, Vrensen, de Mul and Greve, 1991; bovine Castoro and Bettelheim, 1987) and protein concentration gradients (human: Bours, Fodisch and Hockwin, 1987; Fagerholm, Philipson and Lindstrom, 1981; Hockwin, Ahrend and Bours, 1986) which can be directly related to refractive index. The closest comparison to previous studies that can be made for the guinea pig data is to refractive index profiles measured for the rat lens (Campbell, 1984). The shapes of both guinea pig and rat profiles can be fitted with second order polynomials but the guinea pig lens does not have as steep an index gradient or as high an index magnitude as does the rat lens.

All of the profiles can be fitted with second order polynomials but while the bovine and guinea pig profiles are approximately parabolic, this cannot be said of the primate lenses. In spite of the deceptively high statistically significant correlation found with second order polynomials, the human and gibbon index profiles are more realistically described by higher order functions.

The flatter the index profile, the less is its contribution to the refractive power of the lens because refraction of light occurs when there are differences in refractive index: the steeper the index gradient, the greater the amount of refraction. However, another source of refraction comes from the refractive index differences between the surrounding media and the surface of the lens. Within the eye, the lens is surrounded by the humours, the refractive indices of which are closely approximated to that of water (1.333). The difference between the refractive index of the ocular humours and the surface of the lens is far greater than the gradual changes in refractive index found within any of the lenses. The surface or edge index value of the human lens (1.392-1.396) is highest of all the lenses and its distribution is the least varying. The human lens, of the four lenses examined, is therefore most reliant on surface refraction and least reliant on the refractive contribution from internal index variations.

The other contribution to surface refractive power comes from the lens shape: the rounder the lens the greater is its capacity to refract light. Of the four lenses in this work, the guinea pig lens has the greatest curvature. It also has the second highest edge index value (after the human lens) and the second highest maximum index (after the bovine lens). This lens would provide the greatest refractive power of the four lenses. The bovine lens, which is the largest of the four lenses, is not as curved as the guinea pig lens, but more curved than the two primate lenses. It has the highest index maximum and its edge index value is slightly less than that of the guinea pig lens. The bovine lens would provide less refractive power than the lens of the guinea pig but more power than the primate lenses.

With regard to shape, there is of course the question of accommodation, and the recognition that a lens in vitro only represents a single state of accommodation (if that lens does indeed accommodate in situ). Since the accommodated state of the lens occurs when it is freed from zonular tension, then the in vitro lens should be at its most curved. The human lens, at least for part of its life, is able to alter its shape to cater for varying visual needs. Primate lenses also have this function, as has been shown for the rhesus monkey (Koretz, Bertasso, Neider, True-Gabelt and Kaufman, 1987) and is even more likely to apply to the gibbon as the latter belongs to the anthropoids, the primate family most closely related to humans. It is uncertain whether or not ungulates accommodate and, while it is generally believed that they do not (Blogg, 1975), this is based on the speculation of their visual needs. Better gauges of accommodative ability are the rheological and physical properties of a lens: if a lens is softer, more pliable and flatter, it is easier to deform and likely to engage in more accommodation than a denser, less malleable and rounder lens. It is, for example, readily apparent that the hard, round lens of an adult rat would have difficulty changing its shape. Its refractive index profile is very steep and reaches a high maximum value of about 1.5 (Campbell, 1984) close to a density of almost pure protein in the lens centre. Similarly the guinea pig lens, while not as hard as the lens of the rat is nevertheless very curved rendering deformation difficult.

In three of the lenses (human, gibbon and bovine), the major types of crystallins are α and β/γ superfamily whilst in the guinea pig lens ζ-crystallin is a major component (about 10% of the total soluble proteins (Huang et al, 1987)). This protein differs from the other major crystallins in its secondary structure (Huang et al, 1987; Borras and Rodokanaki, 1989) and in the way that it responds to the effects of heat and the protective action of α-crystallin (Rao, Horwitz and Zigler, 1994). The chaperone-like nature of α-crystallin acts to prevent aggregation of the other crystallins after heat denaturation (Horwitz, 1992). ζ-crystallin requires a 10-fold greater amount (w/w) of the chaperone than do β- and γ-crystallins for effective protection (Rao et al, 1994). Whilst it is difficult to relate these findings to optical properties in the healthy lens, the greater level of chaperone required by ζ-crystallin could indicate a propensity to form larger clusters and to exist in regions of relatively lower hydration/higher protein concentration. The higher protein concentration would provide a greater refractive index and, in an eye as small as that of the guinea pig, refractive power needs to be high. This, however, does not provide a complete explanation as the value of refractive index in the centre of the bovine lens is higher than that at the centre of the guinea pig lens.

Although it is not yet possible to elucidate the relationship between distributions of specific lens proteins and the refractive index, the approximate amounts of protein can be calculated from the refractive index profiles. The values obtained in this work give total protein weights as a proportion of lens weight of: 38.8%, 36.8%, 34.4% and 47.8% in the human, gibbon, bovine and guinea pig lenses respectively (Table 2).

II. Changes with Time: The Paradox of the Human Lens

The lens of the eye continues to grow throughout life and as it does so, its shape changes. Over centuries, the alteration in shape with age has attracted particular attention with respect to the human lens because it served to explain the loss of accommodative function. Since the lens loses the extra refractive power needed for near vision, it was long believed that the lens must become flatter with age. Seminal work on living lenses in the 1970s dispelled this notion and showed that with age the human lens increases in curvature (Brown, 1973; Lowe and Clark, 1973; Brown, 1974). Subsequent work has supported these findings (Koretz, Handelman and Brown, 1984; Koretz, Kaufman, Neider and Goeckner 1989; Dubbelman and Van der Heijde, 2001). [Studies on lenses that have been removed from the eye provide limited information about lens shape because they disregard the important role of the musculature and attaching ligaments].

An increase in lens curvature with age is plausible given the continual growth of the tissue within an eyeball that has a limited growth period. This leaves the lens with no space to expand in radial directions (orthogonal to the optic axis), but able to increase in thickness along the optic axis, thereby becoming more curved as it grows. However, the findings produced a dilemma in the understanding of functional changes with age, for if a lens becomes more curved, its refractive power should increase. An increase in power should lead to a more short-sighted (myopic) refractive state of the eye. Clearly, this does not occur. The human eye does not become progressively more short-sighted with age; on the contrary, the eye loses its ability to focus on near objects.

Explanations for the dilemma, or paradox (as it was termed (Brown, 1974; Koretz and Handelman, 1988)) turned to the role of refractive index, with suggestions that this may decrease with age (Koretz and Handelman, 1988; Siebinga, Vrensen, de Mul, Greve, 1991; Moffat, Atchison and Pope, 2002). Such a decrease in refractive index can only occur if there is a decrease in soluble protein or an increase in water. A loss of protein from the lens cannot happen in a healthy lens or eye. Koretz and Handelman (1988) suggested that with age some of the protein may become insoluble thereby depleting the proportion of soluble protein. The explanation was based on rings or zones (termed the zones of discontinuity) seen within the living lens when examined with a slit-lamp and the findings that, with age, an increasing amount of protein that is extracted from the lens is insoluble in water. While the suggestion sounds reasonable, the zones of discontinuity are not seen when the lens is removed from the eye and no evidence of insoluble protein layered in a manner corresponding to the zones has been found. Moreover, protein coming out of solution and forming insoluble plaques would cause refractive index fluctuations that could cause scatter and opacification. It should also be noted that insolubilisation of extracted proteins is not necessarily indicative of the protein state in vivo. Dilley (1975) has pointed out that although there is an increase, with age, in the proportion of high-molecular weight aggregates extracted, it does not relate to a decrease in transparency. This has been borne out in experimental observations: an old bovine lens from which over 80% of protein was found to be insoluble on extraction, was completely transparent before experimentation (Pierscionek, 1988; Pierscionek and Augusteyn, 1992). If the same proportion of protein had been insoluble in the intact lens, it would have been opaque. It is more likely that proteins remain soluble within the lens, but that older proteins are more vulnerable to the changing conditions imposed by extraction and that this may render them insoluble in the test-tube.

The other potential reason for a decrease in refractive index is an increase in lens water. There is no known physiological mechanism for this to occur and the notion has not been supported by studies in which protein and water proportions have been measured in lenses of varying ages (Satoh, 1972; van Heyningen, 1972; Fisher and Pettet, 1973). In a later study, an increase in lens hydration was reported, but the significance of the rise was based on lenses over the age of 50 years (Siebinga at al, 1991). This cannot counteract the increase in lens growth and curvature change that occurs throughout life. In addition, the amount of hydration was too small to significantly compensate for the increased curvature as it was found in the inner region, where the refractive index is relatively constant and contributes little to the refractive power. The fundamental oversight inherent in the suggestion of a decreased refractive index with age, was in treating the refractive index as a single entity, with any ageing change assumed to apply over its entirety.

Another resolution to the apparent paradox has been postulated: that changes in the refractive index with age, sufficient to counter-balance the changes in curvature, require only a slight alteration in the gradient of refractive index in the outer region of the lens (Pierscionek, 1990). This would not cause significant changes in protein/water proportion. The hypothesis was based on observations from ray tracing studies (Pierscionek, 1988; Pierscionek, 1990) that showed small age-related differences in the outer part of the refractive index profile. It was tested on model data and found to be feasible (Smith, Atchison and Pierscionek, 1992). Further support was shown from estimations based on clinical measurements (Hemenger, Garner and Ooi, 1995) and similar age-related differences in protein concentration profiles have been reported (Fagerholm et al, 1981). Subsequent studies have supported the notion of a compensatory process between the refractive index distribution and the curvature as an explanation for the paradox (reviewed in Brown, Koretz and Bron, 1999; Moffat et al, 2002).

The original ray tracing studies, which showed changes in the refractive index gradient, were made in the equatorial plane, because the mathematics used to calculate the refractive index from ray trace parameters, required the shape symmetry found in that plane (Pierscionek, 1988; Pierscionek, 1990). However, the equatorial plane is orthogonal to the sagittal plane within which the optic axis is contained and as such is not pertinent to vision. Direct measurement of the refractive index gradient along the optic axis, avoiding the necessity of assumptions, has been made using fibre optic sensing.

Methods

Post-mortem lenses (two 25 year old, one 47 year old, two 53 year old) were obtained from the Lions Eye Bank at the Royal Victorian Eye and Ear Hospital in Melbourne. Each lens was weighed immediately after removal from the eye and re-weighed after completion of the experiment. Pre- and post-experimentation weights varied by up to 1.5% of the original weights for the 25 year old lenses, 10% for the 47 year old lens, 5.7% and 11.4% of the original weight for the two 53 year old lenses. The instrumentation and technique used has been described in the first section

Results

The results show whole profiles from the five lenses plotted against distance along the optic axis from the anterior to the posterior poles (Figure 2). The sagittal widths of the lenses were: 4.0 mm for the 25 year old lenses; 4.5mm for the 53 year old lenses and 4.7mm for the 47 year old lens (also shown in the first section). In all five profiles there is an approximately constant index of around 1.402 in the central region and a gradient of refractive index in the outer sections. The constant index region is longer in the older lenses (over half of the sagittal width) than it is in the younger lenses (about one quarter of the sagittal width). The outer gradients rise from an edge value of 1.391-1.392 for the 25 year old lenses and 1.392-1.396 for the older lenses. Gradients from the two younger lenses differ from those of their older counterparts and the refractive index values are lower at any given point along the axis. The anterior gradients, compared in Figure 3a, show that in the younger lenses the increase from the minimum value of refractive index, at the anterior pole, reaches a maximum value at about 2.0mm from the pole. In the older lens profiles the maximum value is reached at about 1.0mm from the anterior pole. Comparing the posterior gradients (Figure 3b), the younger lenses have a smooth gradient from the posterior pole (4.0mm from the anterior pole) up to 3.0mm from the anterior pole. The data for the older lens set is more scattered, the refractive index value rising from the posterior pole (around 4.5-4.7 from the anterior pole) to about 3.0 –3.5 mm from the anterior pole. To test whether the gradients from the two sets of data were significantly different, an F test for nested regression was applied. The results indicate that there is a statistically significant difference ($p<0.01$) between the younger and older anterior gradients and a very high statistically significant difference ($p<0.001$) between the posterior gradients.

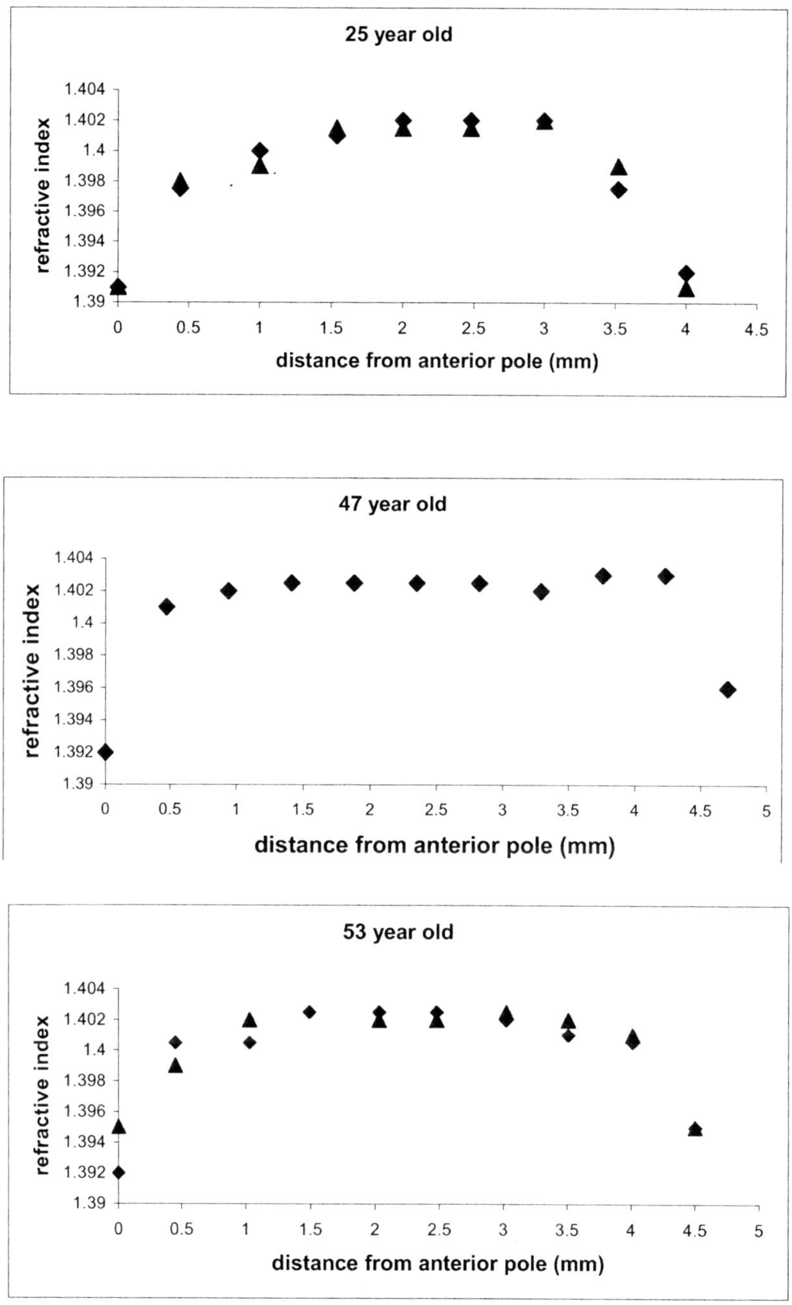

Figure 2. Refractive index variations (for 670nm) along the optic axes of two 25 year old, a 47 year old and two 53 year old lenses plotted against the distance from the anterior pole (mm).

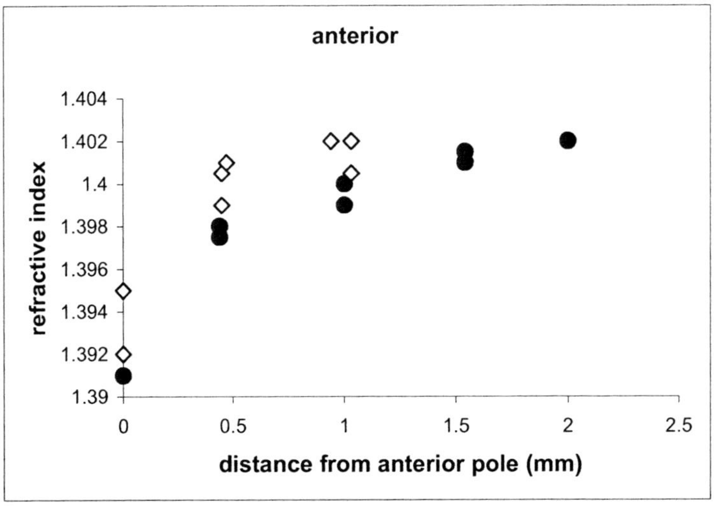

(a)

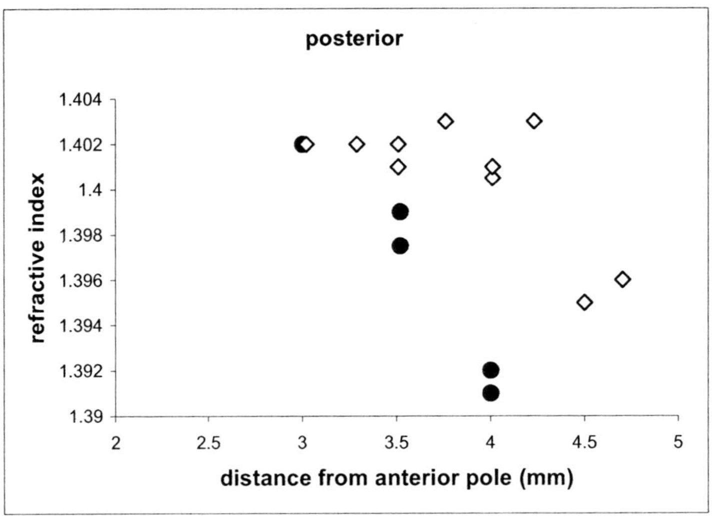

(b)

Figure 3. Refractive index gradients (for 670nm) along the optic axis in the a) anterior and b) posterior regions of younger (•) and older (◇) lenses. The younger lens set contains two 25 year old lenses, the older set contains a 47 year old and two 53 year old lenses.

Discussion

The lens is often referred to as having a 'gradient index', but the gradient is only found in the outer regions; the inner lens has a uniform refractive index as shown in the results from this study. This has been found in previous ray trace (Pierscionek and Chan, 1989) and reflectometric measurements (Pierscionek, 1995b) and is supported by studies on the distribution of lenticular water (Huizinga et al, 1989; Siebinga et al, 1991) and protein concentration profiles (Fagerholm et al, 1981).

From the results of this study, the anterior and posterior refractive index gradients are not the same and this is most evident in the older lens set in which the posterior gradient is longer. This is consistent with the shape asymmetry, as the lens is a biconvex ellipsoid, the anterior surface of which is less curved than the posterior. There is a suggestion that the growth rate of the posterior cortex may be greater than that of the anterior (Schulz, Chamberlain, de Iongh, McAvoy, 1993). The difference is thought to arise from lenticular development and growth patterns (reviewed in McAvoy and Chamberlain, 1990) and to be maintained by the differences in growth factor activity between the humors that surround the lens (Schulz, Chamberlain, de Iongh, McAvoy, 1993). The vitreous humor contains more Fibroblast Growth Factor (FGF), which induces growth and differentiation of lens fibre cells, than does the aqueous humor (Schulz et al, 1993). This may explain the inequality in width of the anterior and posterior refractive index gradients. However, such a difference was not found in the previous study on water gradients (Siebinga et al, 1991), and slit-lamp (Dubbelman et al, 2003) and Magnetic Resonance Imaging (MRI) (Strenk et al, 2004) studies have shown a greater increase in the width of the anterior cortex and in the anterior cross-sectional area, respectively, with age. These findings are difficult to explain but may be, at least in part, based on interpretations of the cortical/nuclear boundary (discussed below).

All the lenses in this study have approximately the same maximum index value but there are differences in the length of the region of constant refractive index. It is longer in the older lens set (from 1.0mm to around 3.0-3.5mm from the anterior pole) compared to the younger set (from 2.0mm to 3.0mm from the anterior pole). This is supported by calculations of refractive index from the water content determined from MRI (Moffat et al, 2002) but not by measurements of water gradients using Raman microspectroscopy which showed no change in the length of the constant region with age (Siebinga et al, 1991). It should be noted that determination of the length of the gradient cannot be exact. In this study it was taken from the edge of the lens to the first point of maximum refractive index; in the study by Siebinga et al, 1991, the inner limit of the gradient was taken at the first point of minimum water content. These minima and maxima could only be determined from points at which measurements were made and hence the extent of each cortical gradient is an estimate between measured points. The difficulty is further compounded by uncertainty about the nuclear/cortical boundary. There is no clear distinction between the cortex and the nucleus. Any separation into cortical and nuclear regions is approximate, the nucleus taken as occupying the inner two-thirds of the lens as defined by the clinical appearance of coloration in older lenses or by the zones of discontinuity observed in vivo through a slit-lamp biomicroscope. There are also differences between findings from living eyes. Some slit-lamp observations have found no change in nuclear thickness with age (Patnaik, 1963; Cook, Koretz, Pfahnl, Hyun and Kaufman, 1994) while others report an increase (Dubbelman, Van der Heijde, Weeber, Vrensen, 2003). In the later study, results were corrected for optical distortions arising from the camera system and the refractive surfaces of the eye. The differences between these studies illustrate the difficulty in ascertaining the cortical/nuclear boundary even when using similar methods. It is even more difficult to relate in vivo observations based on coloration or zones of discontinuity to measurements of refractive index gradients on lenses that have been removed from the eye and within which the zones cannot be seen. The region of uniform refractive index may not correspond exactly to the region defined as the nucleus from slit-lamp studies.

When comparing older and younger lenses in vitro, it is important to remember that lenses of different ages may not be representing the same level of accommodation. The younger lenses were able to accommodate within the living eye and, when removed from the tension imposed by the zonule and ciliary muscle, are likely to have assumed a more curved, accommodated state that the older lenses which have lost their accommodative capacity. It has been shown, from slit-lamp studies, that when the lens accommodates, only (what has been defined as) the nucleus, changes in thickness (Patnaik, 1963; Brown, 1973; Koretz, Cook and Kaufman 1997; Dubbelman et al, 2003). Although the extent of the uniform index region may not correspond exactly to the nucleus seen through the slit-lamp, an increase in the width of the nucleus with accommodation is likely to indicate an increase in the uniform index region. It is therefore possible that the difference in the lengths of the uniform index region between the older and younger lenses may have been even greater had the younger lenses been in the same (unaccommodated) state as the older lenses. It is worth noting that results obtained using MRI (Strenk, Strenk, Semmlow and de Marco, 2004) appear to show that with accommodation there is also an increase in the width of the anterior cross-sectional area of the lens. The variation in findings further demonstrates the uncertainty in defining lens regions and the differences that may arise by the use of different methods.

Differences between the young and old lens sets are particularly evident in the outer regions of the lens. Statistically significant differences between the data sets were found for both anterior and posterior gradients. This finding supports the hypothesis there is a change in the gradient portion of the refractive index distribution with age (Pierscionek, 1990). However, the results from this study suggest that the change in the cortical gradient with age may not be symmetrical: the change in the posterior gradient is greater than that for the anterior gradient. This would suggest either a change in the geometry and shape of the lens with age and/or an anterior movement of the nucleus. Previous reports and findings have shown support for both processes (Brown, 1973, 1974; Koretz et al, 1984; Koretz and Handelman, 1988; Koretz et al, 1989; Farnsworth and Shyne, 1979; Cook, Koretz, Pfahnl, Hyun and Kaufman, 1994; Koretz, Cook and Kaufman, 2001).

In terms of refractive index magnitude, for any point along the optic axis, the older lenses have higher values of refractive index in the outer regions than do the younger lenses. This would suggest some decrease, albeit small, in water content with age. From studies that have found age-related increases (Siebinga et al, 1991) and decreases in hydration (Lahm, Lee and Bettelheim, 1985) the findings have pertained only to the nucleus. It has been suggested previously that the lens undergoes compaction of existing tissue, as it is compressed by accrual of new cells on the lens surface and that this may be causal in the formation of the index gradient (Brown, 1976; Brown, Sparrow and Bron, 1988). Compaction of the outer layer cells may appear to provide an explanation for the slight increase in outer refractive index with age. However, the source of any compacting force is not known. Accruement of tissue on the lens surface as it grows, is not enough to compress the layers of cells beneath. The elastic capsule may be providing some force, but this cannot be constant; the capsular force must allow for the lens to change its shape with accommodation. To suggest that compaction and compression result in an increased refractive index, would imply that these processes have caused water to be squeezed out of the lens and through its capsule. No studies have shown evidence of such a process.

In contrast to the findings of this study, Moffat et al (2002) reported that age-related changes in the refractive index occur in the inner, uniform index region with no alteration in the gradient portion. Their results show an age-related decrease in maximum refractive index from about 1.44 in a 10 year old lens to about 1.415 in lenses over 80 years of age. Protein and water contents (Appendix B) calculated using the dimensional figures and refractive index distributions from Moffat et al (2002), indicate that an 82 year old lens had 15% more water in its central region than did a 29 year old lens. This comparatively large decrease in refractive index over the age range studied by Moffat et al (2002) suggests a significant and measurable increase in water content with age. No evidence for an increase of such magnitude has ever been found (Satoh, 1972; van Heyninghen, 1972; Fisher and Pettet, 1973; Lahm, Lee and Bettelheim, 1985; Pierscionek, 1988) and it is not plausible that it could occur without disrupting physiological processes within the cells. It is possible that Moffat et al (2002), who used MRI, were not measuring refractive index gradients but the distribution of free water (water not bound to proteins), which has been shown to increase with age (Lahm, Lee and Bettelheim, 1985).

Conclusion

The lens is composed of proteins and water, organized for the maintenance of transparency and with optical properties designed to serve, as part of the optical system of the eye, the visual needs of the animal. One can speculate on the biological differences between animals, their behaviour, their diets and how these may relate to the lens proteins and the resulting index profiles. For example, the guinea pig and cow, whose profiles are similar, are herbivorous, while the gibbon and human also feed on meat. However, there is not enough information as yet to formulate any such links and what can best be said, given the current level of knowledge, is that the optics of the eye lens is in part the consequence of its biochemistry and will be better understood as more details about the structure/function relationship are revealed. In addition to maintenance of transparency, the protein concentration may alter with age in such a way as to induce subtle changes in the refractive index gradient. These changes prevent the eye from becoming myopic.

Although the protein distributions and their arrangements within the lens cannot, as yet, be measured directly in the intact tissue, some information about structural organisation, in terms of protein concentration, can be obtained indirectly by studying the refractive index. As techniques improve, it may one day be possible to establish how each class of proteins contributes to the function of the lens.

Appendix A

Refractive index is related to protein concentration by a simple linear relationship, known as the Gladstone-Dale formula (Barer and Joseph, 1954), in which:

$$n = n_o + \Delta . C$$

where

n is the refractive index of the lens sample

n_o is the refractive index of the aqueous component of the lens

Δ is the specific refractive increment
C is the concentration

Taking a value of 1.33 for n_o and $0.19 ml/g^{-1}$ for Δ (Perry and Koenig, 1967; Pierscionek et al 1987) (refractive index and Δ vary with temperature and wavelength but for the purposes of these calculations, such variations are negligible):

$$C = (n - n_o)/\Delta$$

An estimation for the total protein content in each lens can be made by substituting n with a function which relates it to distance from lens centre. (Fourth order polynomial fits were used for the primate lenses, second order polynomials for the bovine and guinea pig lenses; sagittal profiles were transcribed to the equatorial plane assuming isoindicial contours). Hence:

$$C(r) = (n(r) - n_o)/\Delta$$

where
r is the distance from the lens centre (cm).
Since

$$\Sigma C(r) = P/V$$

where P is the cumulative weight of protein from the lens centre to the given r and V is the volume within which P is contained, then

$$P = \int_0^r C(r)A(r)dr$$

The total protein content can be calculated by integrating over small values of r and approximating the volume increments to thin ellipsoidal shells.

Appendix B

Refractive index was read from points at increments of 0.1 radial distance along the refractive index profiles shown in figures 6 and 7 (Moffat et al, 2002). Refractive index was converted to protein concentration using the Gladstone-Dale formula (Appendix A). For each increment, starting from the centre, volume was calculated using the formula for a biconvex ellipsoid, given in equation (1):

$$V = (2/3)\pi\rho^2 t$$

Values for equatorial radius and sagittal width, taken from figure 4 (Moffat et al, 2002) were used to calculate distances from the normalised values given in figures 6 and 7 (Moffat et al, 2002).

For each successive incremental step from the centre, volumes calculated for inner layers were deducted so that each volume represented only the shell for that increment. Protein content within each incremental shell was calculated by multiplying the protein concentration by the volume of the shell.

The volume of protein within each shell was obtained by multiplying the protein content by the partial specific volume of proteins (0.72ml/g) and this was deducted from the volume of the shell to give the volume of water. Water volume was converted to water weight and the total weight of water within all shells was added together.

REFERENCES

Axelrod, D. Lerner, D. and Sands, P.J. (1988) Refractive index within the lens of a goldfish eye determined from the paths of thin laser beams. *Vision Res* **28**, 57-65

Barer, R.and Joseph, S. (1954) Refractometry of living cells. Part 1. Basic principles. *Quart J Microscop Sci* **95**, 399-423

Benedek, G.B. (1971) Theory of transparency of the eye. *Applied Optics* **10**, 459-73

Blogg, J.R. (1975) The eye in veterinary practice. VC Supplies Ltd North Melbourne, 146

Borras, T. and Rodokanaki, A. (1989) Primary structure of zeta-crystallin protein from guinea pig. Its similarity to the enzyme alcohol dehydrogenase. *Lens & Eye Toxicity Research.* **6**, 795-805

Bours, J., Fodisch, H.J. and Hockwin, O. (1987) Age-related changes in water and crystallin content of the fetal and adult human lens, demonstrated by a microsectioning technique. *Ophthal Res* **19**, 235-39

Brown, N. (1973) The change in shape and internal form of the lens of the eye on accommodation. *Exp Eye Res* **15**, 441-59

Brown, N. (1974) The change in lens curvature with age. *Exp Eye Res* **19**, 175-83

Brown N. (1976) Dating the onset of cataract. *Trans Ophthal Soc UK* **96**, 18-23

Brown, N.P., Koretz, J.F. and Bron, A.J. (1999) The development and maintenance of emmetropia. *Eye* **13**, 83-92

Brown, N.A.P., Sparrow, J.M. and Bron, A.J. (1988) Central compaction in the process of lens growth as indicated by lamellar cataract. *Br J Ophthal* **72**, 538-44.

Burky, E.L. and Woods, A.C. (1928) Lens protein: the isolation of a third (gamma) crystallin. *Arch Ophthal.* **57**, 464-66

Campbell, M.C.W. (1984) Measurement of refractive index in an intact crystalline lens. *Vision Res* **24**, 409-15

Campbell, M.C.W. and Hughes, A. (1981) An analytic gradient index schematic lens and eye for the rat which predicts aberrations for finite pupil. *Vision Res* **21**, 1129-48

Castoro, J.A. and Bettelheim, F.A. (1987) Water gradients across bovine lenses. *Exp Eye Res* **45**, 191-95

Chiou, S.H., Chang, W.P. and Lai, T.A. (1989) Identification of epsilon-crystallin from swan lens as lactate dehydrogenase. *Current Eye Res* **8**, 1055-61

Chiou, S.H., Lo, C.H., Chang, C.Y., Itoh, T., Kaji, H., Samejima, T. (1991) Ostrich crystallins. Structural characterization of delta-crystallin with enzymic activity. *Biochemical J* **273**(*Pt 2)*, 295-300

Cook, C.A., Koretz, J.F., Pfahnl, A., Hyun, J. and Kaufman, P.L. (1994) Aging of the human crystalline lens and anterior segment. *Vision Res* **34**, 2945-54

Cooper, P.G., Aquilina, J.A., Truscott, R.J. and Carver, J.A. (1994) Supramolecular order within the lens: 1H NMR spectroscopic evidence for specific crystallin-crystallin interactions. *Exp Eye Res* **59**, 607-16

Delaye, M. and Tardieu, A. (1983) Short-range order of crystallin proteins accounts for eye lens transparency. *Nature* **302**, 415-7

Derham, B.K. and Harding, J.J. (1999) □-Crystallin as a molecular chaperone. *Prog Retinal Eye Res* **18**, 463-509

Dilley, K.J. (1975) The proportion of protein from the normal and cataractous human lens which exists as high molecular weight aggregates *in vitro*. *Exp Eye Res* **20**, 73-8

Dubbelman, M. and van der Heijde, G.L. (2001) The shape of the aging human lens: curvature, equivalent refractive index and the lens paradox. *Vision Res* **41**, 1867-77

Dubbelman, M., van der Heijde, G.L., Weeber, H.A. and Vrensen, G.F. (2003) Changes in the internal structure of the human crystalline lens with age and accommodation. *Vision Res* **43**, 2363-75

Fagerholm, P.P., Philipson, B.T. and Lindstrom, B. (1981) Normal human lens, the distribution of protein. *Exp Eye Res* **33**, 615-20.

Farnsworth, P.N. and Shyne, S.E. (1979) Anterior zonular shifts with age. *Exp Eye Res* **28**, 291-7

Fisher, R.F. and Pettet, B.E. (1973) Presbyopia and the water content of the human crystalline lens. *J Physiol 234*, 443-7

Garland, D., Rao, P.V., Del Corso, A., Mura, U. and Zigler, J.S. Jr. (1991) zeta-Crystallin is a major protein in the lens of Camelus dromedarius. *Archiv Biochem & Biophys* **285**, 134-6.

Hemenger, R.P., Garner, L.F. and Ooi, C.S. (1995) Change with age of the refractive index gradient of the human ocular lens. *Investig Ophthalmol & Vis Sci* **36**, 703-7

Hockwin, O. (1971) Age changes of lens metabolism, *Altern Entwickl* **1,** 95-129.

Hockwin, O., Ahrend, M.H.J. and Bours, J. (1986) Correlation of Scheimpflug photography of the anterior eye segment with biochemical analysis of the lens. Graefe's Arch. *Clin Exp Ophthalmol* **224**, 265-70.

Horwitz, J.(1992) □-crystallin can function as a molecular chaperone. *Proc Natl Acad Sci USA* **89**, 10449-53

Huang, Q.L., Russell, P., Stone, S.H. and Zigler, J.S. Jr (1987). Zeta-crystallin, a novel lens protein from the guinea pig. *Current Eye Res* **6**, 725-32

Huizinga, A, Bot, ACC, de Mul FFM, Vrensen GFJM, Greve J. (1989) Local variation in absolute water content of human and rabbit eye lenses measured by Raman microspectroscopy. *Exp Eye Res* **48**, 487-96

Jagger, W.S. (1992) The optics of the spherical fish lens. *Vision Res,* **32**, 1271-84

Kroger, R.H.H., Campbell, M.C.W., Munger, R. and Fernald, R.D. (1994) Refractive index distribution and spherical aberration in the crystalline lens of the African Cichlid fish Haplochromis burtoni. *Vision Res* **34**, 1815-22

Koretz, J.F. and Handelman, G.H. (1988) How the human eye focuses. *Sci American* **256**, 64-71

Koretz, J.F., Cook, C.A. and Kaufman, P.L. (2001) Aging of the human lens: changes in lens shape at zero-diopter accommodation. *J Opt Soc Am A Opt Image Sci Vis* **18**, 265-72

Koretz, J.F., Handelman, G.H. and Brown, N.P. (1984) Analysis of human crystalline lens curvature as a function of accommodative state and age. *Vision Res* **24**, 1141-51

Koretz, J.F., Bertasso, A.M., Neider, M.W.,True-Gabelt, B. and Kaufman, P.L. (1987) Slit-lamp studies of the rhesus monkey eye. II. Changes in crystalline lens shape, thickness and position during accommodation and aging. *Exp Eye Res* **45**, 317-26

Koretz, J.F., Kaufman, P.L., Neider, M.W. and Goeckner, P.A. (1989) Accommodation and presbyopia in the human eye – aging of the anterior segment. *Vision Res* **29**, 1685-92

Lahm, D., Lee, L.K. and Bettelheim, F.A. (1985) Age dependence of freezable and nonfreezable water content of normal human lenses. *Invest Ophthal Vis Sci* **26**, 1162-5

Lowe, R.F. and Clark, B.A.J. (1973) Radius of curvature of the anterior lens surface. Correlations in normal eyes and in eyes involved with primary angle-closure glaucoma. *Brit J Ophthal* **57**, 471-74

Magid, A.D., Kenworthy, A.K. and McIntosh, T.J. (1992) Colloid osmotic pressure of steer crystallins: implications for the origin of the refractive index gradient and transparency of the lens. *Exp Eye Res* **55**, 615-27

McAvoy, J.W. and Chamberlain, C.G. (1990) Growth factors in the eye. *Prog. Growth Factor Research* **2**, 29-43

Michael, R., van Marle, J., Vrensen, G.F. and van den Berg, T.J. (2003) Changes in the refractive index of lens fibre membranes during maturation - impact on lens transparency. *Exp Eye Res* **77**, 93-9.

Moffat, B.A., Atchison, D.A. and Pope, J.M. (2002) Age-related changes in refractive index distribution and power of the human lens as measured by magnetic resonance micro-imaging in vitro. *Vision Res* **42**, 1683-1693

Morner, C.T. (1894) Untersuchungen der protein substanzen in den leichtbrechenden Medier des Anges *Z Physiol Chem* **18**, 61-106.

Patnaik B. (1963) A photographic study of accommodative mechanisms: changes in lens nucleus during accommodation. *Invest Ophthal* **6**, 601-11

Perry, A.J. and Koenig, V.L. (1967) Some physiochemical properties of the water-soluble proteins of the bovine eye lens. *Biochem et Biophys Acta* **46**, 413-422

Pierscionek, B.K. (1988) The effects of development and ageing on the structure and function of the crystalline lens. PhD Dissertation, University of Melbourne.

Pierscionek, B.K. (1989) Growth and ageing effects on the refractive index gradient in the equatorial plane of the bovine lens. *Vision Res* **29**, 1759-66

Pierscionek, B.K. (1990) Presbyopia and the effect of refractive index. *Clin and Exp Optom* **73**, 26-36

Pierscionek, B.K. (1994) Isochromatics in eye lenses. *Exp Eye Res* **59**, 121-4

Pierscionek, B.K. (1995a) The refractive index along the optic axis of the bovine lens. *Eye* **9**, 776-82

Pierscionek, B.K.(1995b)Variations in refractive index and absorbance of 670nm light with age and cataract formation in human lenses. *Exp. Eye Res* **60**, 407-14

Pierscionek, B.K. (1997) Refractive index contours in the human lens. *Exp. Eye Res.* **64**, 887-93

Pierscionek, B. and Augusteyn, R.C. (1988) Protein distribution patterns in concentric layers from single bovine lenses: changes with development and ageing. *Current Eye Res* **7**, 11- 23

Pierscionek, B.K. and Augusteyn, R.C.(1991) Structure/function relationship between optics and biochemistry of the eye lens. *Lens and Eye Toxicology Res* **8**, 229-43

Pierscionek, B.K. and Augusteyn, R.C. (1992) Growth related changes to functional parameters in the bovine lens. *Biochim et Biophys Acta.* **1116**, 283-90

Pierscionek, B.K. and Augusteyn, R.C. (1995) The refractive index and protein distribution in the blue eye trevally lens. *J. Am Optom. Assoc* **66**, 739-43

Pierscionek, B.K. Chan, and D.Y.C. (1989) The refractive index gradient of the human lens. *Optom and Vision Sci* **66**, 822-29

Pierscionek, B.K., Smith, G. and Augusteyn, R.C. (1987) The refractive increments of bovine □,□ and □crystallins. *Vision Res* **27**,1539-41

Pierscionek, B.K., Chan, D.Y.C., Ennis, J.P. Smith, G. and Augusteyn, R.C. (1988) A non-destructive method of constructing three-dimensional gradient index models for crystalline lenses: I. Theory and Experiment. *Am. J. of Optom. and Physiol. Optics* **65**, 481-91

Rao, P.V., Horwitz, J. and Zigler, J.S.Jr (1994) Chaperone-like activity of □-crystallin. *J Biol Chemistry* **269**, 13266-72

Satoh K. (1972) Age-related changes in the structural proteins of human lens. *Exp Eye Res* **14**, 53-7

Siebinga, I., Vrensen, GFJM., de Mul, FFM. and Greve J. (1991) Age-related changes in local water and protein content of human eye lenses measured by Raman microspectroscopy. *Exp Eye Res* **53**, 233-9

Schulz, M. W., Chamberlain, C.G., de Iongh, R.U. and McAvoy, J. W. (1993) Acidic and basic FGF in ocular media and lens: implications for lens polarity and growth patterns. *Development* **118**, 117-26

Smith, G., Atchison, D.A. and Pierscionek, B.K (1992) Modelling the power of the ageing human eye. *J Opt Soc Am A* **9**, 2111-7

Smith, G., Pierscionek, B.K. and Atchison, D.A. (1991) The optical modelling of the human lens. *Ophthal Physiol Optics* **11**, 359-69

Stapel, S.O., Zweers, A., Dodemont, H.J., Kan, J.H. and de Jong, W.W. (1985) epsilon-crystallin, a novel avian and reptilian eye lens protein. *Eur J of Biochem* **147**, 129-36

Strenk, S.A., Strenk, L.M., Semmlow, J.L. and de Marco, J.K. (2004) Magnetic resonance imaging study of the effects of age and accommodation on the human lens cross-sectional area. *Investig Ophthal & Vis Sci* **45**, 539-45

Tardieu, A. (1998) □-Crystallin quaternary structure and interactive properties control eye lens transparency. *Int J Biol Macromol* **22**, 211-7

Tomarev, S.I., Zinovieva, R.D.,Dolgilevich, S.M., Luchin, S.V.,Krayev, A.S. Skryabin, K.G. and Gause, G.G.Jr. (1984) A novel type of crystallin in the frog eye lens. 35-kDa polypeptide is not homologous to any of the major classes of lens crystallins. *FEBS Letts* **171**, 297-302

Trokel, S. (1962) The physical basis for transparency of crystalline lens. *Invest Ophthalmol* **1**, 493-501

van Heyningen, R. (1972) The human lens. III. Some observations on the post-mortem lens. *Exp Eye Res* **13**, 155-60 van Rheede, T., Amons, R., Stewart, N. and de Jong, W.W. (2003) Lactate dehydrogenase A as a highly abundant eye lens protein in platypus (Ornithorhynchus anatinus): upsilon (upsilon)-crystallin. *Molecular Biol & Evolution* **20**, 994-8

Veretout, F. and Tardieu, A. (1989) The protein concentration gradient within eye lens might originate from constant osmotic pressure coupled to differential interactive properties of crystallins. *Eur Biophys J* **18**, 61-8

Veretout, F., Delaye, M. and Tardieu, A. (1989) Molecular basis of eye lens transparency. Osmotic pressure and X-ray analysis of alpha-crystallin solutions. *J Molecular Biol* **205**, 713-28

Voorter, C.E., Wintjes, L.T., Heinstra, P.W., Bloemendal, H. and De Jong, W.W. (1993) Comparison of stability properties of lactate dehydrogenase B4/epsilon-crystallin from different species. *Eur J Biochem* **211**, 643-8

Vrensen, G.F. (1995) Aging of the human eye lens-a morphological point of view. Comparative *Biochemistry & Physiology, Part A. Physiology* **111**, 519-32

Williams, L.A., Ding, L., Horwitz, J. and Piatigorsky, J. (1985). Tau-Crystallin from the turtle lens: purification and partial characterization. *Exp Eye Res.* **40**, 741-9

Wistow, G.J., Mulders, J.W. and de Jong, W.W.(1987) The enzyme lactate dehydrogenase as a structural protein in avian and crocodilian lenses. *Nature.* **326**, 622-4

Woods, A.C and Burky, E.L. (1927) Lens protein and its fractions: preparation and immunologic and chemical properties. *JAMA* **89**, 102-9

Yu, N-T., East, E.J., Chang, R.C. and Kuck, J.F. (1977) Raman spectra of bird and reptile lens proteins *Exp Eye Res* **24**, 321-334

Zhao, T. and Bettelheim, F.A. (1995) Enthalpy and entropy of hydration of bovine crystallins. *J Biol Chem* **270**, 24961-4

In: Focus on Eye Research
Editor: O.R. Ioseliani, pp. 117-132
ISBN: 1-59454-434-4

Chapter 5

The Mechanism of Accommodation at the Lens Fiber Level

J. R. Kuszak*
Departments of Ophthalmology and Pathology, Rush University Medical Center, Chicago, IL, USA
Rebecca K. Zoltoski
Department of Basic and Health Sciences, Illinois College of Optometry, Chicago, IL, USA

Abstract

In this chapter, we present the results of using a mechanical stretching device to study the mechanism of accommodative lens shape changes at the level of the fibers.

Key Words: 3D CADs, animations, accommodation, lens fibers.

Introduction

It is well documented, and generally well recognized, that in primates accommodation, the dynamic process by which the eye focuses on near objects, is primarily accomplished by changing the shape of the crystalline lens (von Helmholtz, 1909; Gullstrand, 1909; Koretz, Handelman and Brown, 1984; Piersconek, 1993; Koretz, Cook and Kaufman, 1997; Glasser and Campbell, 1998). The alterations in lens shape during accommodation are shown schematically in the computer assisted drawings (CADs) of figure 1. As the ciliary muscle contracts the diameter of the ciliary body is reduced thereby releasing zonular tension on the lens because it is enveloped by the lens capsule, to which the zonules are attached. As a result during accommodation the anterior and posterior curvatures of the lens increase while the

* Please address all correspondence to: J.R. Kuszak, Ph.D. Ophthalmology and Pathology, Rush University Medical Center, 1653 West Congress Parkway, Chicago, IL USA. Tel (312 942-5630); Fax (312 942-2371); E-mail address: jkuszak@rush.edu

equatorial diameter of the lens decreases and thus, the lens becomes rounder. When the eye focuses on distant objects, the ciliary muscle relaxes causing the diameter of the ciliary body to increase thereby creating zonular tension on the lens. As a result in the un-accommodated state, the anterior and posterior curvatures of the lens decrease while the equatorial diameter increases and thus, the lens becomes flattened.

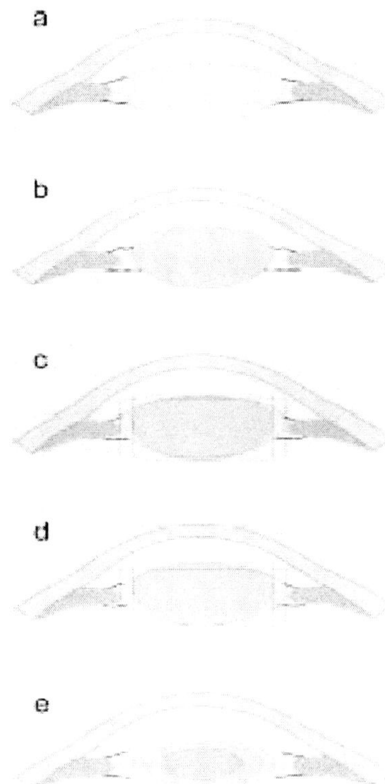

Figure 1. Scale schematic Computer assisted drawings (CADs) depicting the gross shape of an adult human lens in (a) the un-accommodated state, (b) the accommodate state, (c) incorrectly drawn as proportionate changes in lens thickness and width effected by accommodation, (d) correctly drawn as disproportionate changes in lens thickness and width effected by accommodation, and with the age-related regions (from outer to inner; the cortex, adult, juvenile and fetal nuclei) delineated. Beginning with these CADs and in all subsequent CADs and animations presented in this report, by convention we depict the un-accommodated lens in blue and the accommodated lens in green.

It is also well documented, but in general less well recognized, that in primates accommodation is not accomplished by proportionately changing the shape of the crystalline lens as shown in figures 1a - c but rather by disproportionately altering the form and dimensions of age defined regions in the lens (figure 1d & e). Specifically, slit-lamp observations of accommodating lenses in a living eye have been interpreted as revealing that the accommodative increase in lens thickness is attributable entirely to the nucleus (Koretz, Handelman and Brown, 1984; Koretz, Cook and Kaufman, 1997). During accommodation the nucleus is also displaced forward causing the anterior surface of the lens to be moved closer to the cornea thereby making the anterior chamber more shallow. The posterior surface appears to be relatively fixed in place throughout the range of focusing. In addition, the dimensions of the cortex do not appear to change during accommodation.

From a structural standpoint, it is difficult to reconcile how the mechanism (the way in which something works or is brought about) of accommodative lens shape changes can be effected at the level of the fibers without affecting lens physiology. For example, since lens thickness (antero-posterior axis) increases and lens width (equatorial axis) decreases during accommodation, the implication is that individual fiber dimensions (width, thickness and length) are altered. If this is the case, then the intercellular junctions coupling lens fibers that are essential to maintain their viability, would need to be in an almost constant state of assembly and disassembly. While this scenario is not an impossibility, it would be quite demanding especially since the terminally differentiated lens fibers lack a full complement of organelles. Another question that arises is whether or not accommodative changes in anterior surface curvature effect the form and dimensions of the overlying epithelial cells? Does the shape of these cells also vary from flatter and wider in the accommodated state to rounder and narrower in the un-accommodated state?

It is also difficult to reconcile at the lens fiber level how accommodative lens shape changes in the cortex can be effected by alterations in nuclear form. In fact, it seems more likely that the physical act of lessening tension on the capsule would be exerted first on the cortex that is immediately interior to the capsule, and then subsequently on the nucleus that is within the cortex.

Unfortunately, the mechanism of lens shape changes during accommodation at the lens fiber level cannot be ascertained by slit-lamp biomicroscopy because this type of microscope lacks the power to resolve any of the hundreds of thousands of fibers that comprise a lens. By comparison, while an electron microscope has the resolving power to examine any fiber and its substructure, this kind of microscope cannot be used to assess the mechanism of lens shape changes during accommodation at the lens fiber level because it cannot be used on the living eye. One possible way to address the issue of correlating fiber structure with dynamic focusing is to employ a mechanical device to stretch and fix a lens in the un-accommodated state and then compare its structural characteristics with those of a comparable lens fixed in the accommodated state. Such devices have been used to study gross lens shape and optical changes in the eye with age but not as yet to examine how lens shape changes are brought about at the level of fibers during accommodation. And a lens dissected free of the zonules prior to fixation, naturally assumes the accommodative configuration.

In this report, we present the results of using a mechanical stretching device to study the mechanism of accommodative lens shape changes at the level of the fibers.

Materials & Methods

Tissue

Non-paired human eyes (n = 6), from donors under 45 years of age, were obtained from the National Disease Research Interchange (NDRI, Philadelphia, PA) and the Illinois Eye Bank (Chicago, IL). These eyes had been enucleated on average within four hours of death and were either stretched or placed into the accommodated state on average within 16 hours of death. Paired baboon eyes (n = 9), from animals under 9 years of age, were obtained from the Biological Resource Center at the University of Illinois College of Medicine (Chicago,

IL). These eyes had been enucleated on average within 30 minutes of sacrifice and were either stretched or placed into the accommodated state on average within 2 hours of death.

Stretching Lenses

The mechanical lens stretching device that we used was created and provided to us by Dr. Adrian Glasser from the College of Optometry at the University of Houston (Houston, TX). It is an improved version of the one employed by Glasser and Campbell (1998) to study presbyopia and optical changes in human lenses with age. A detailed description of this type of device and the dissection protocol used to stretch lenses is given by Glasser and Campbell (1998). Therefore, we will only briefly describe the dissection protocol used to retrieve and mount a lens in the stretching device (Figure 2).

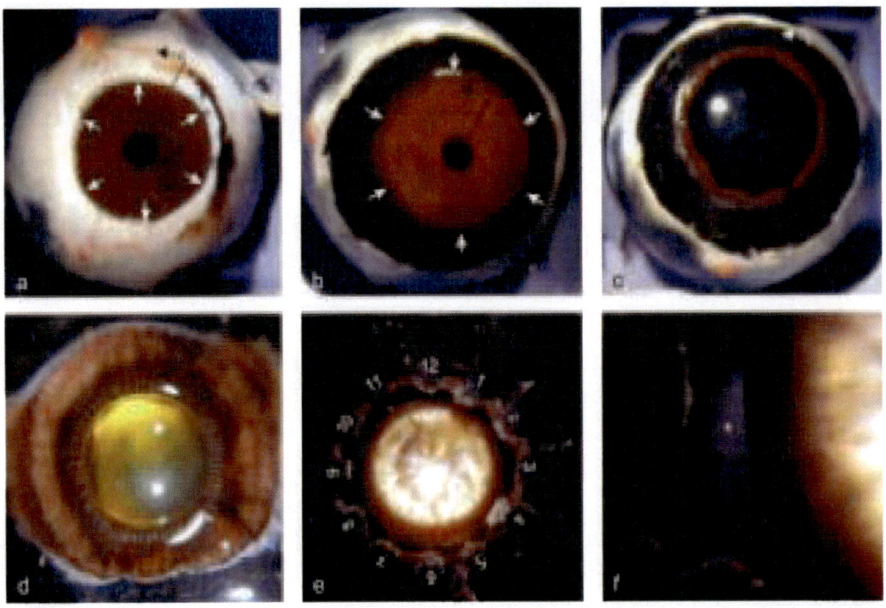

Figure 2. A series of stereo surgical microscope photos highlighting the key steps in the dissection protocol to retrieve and mount lenses in the *ex vivo* stretching apparatus. (a) Initially the cornea is removed at the corneal-scleral junction (white arrows). Then after bluntly separating the sclera from the underlying ciliary muscle and choroid, a ring of sclera is cut away (black hatched arrow) to expose the ciliary muscle and complete iris (b). Then the iris is removed by grabbing and lifting it at the pupillary margin, and then making a radial cut toward and then circumferentially along its roots. At this point the entire ciliary muscle is exposed (white arrows). (c) The lens, still attached to the ciliary muscle by the zonules, is then lifted off of the vitreous by making a circumferential cut in the choroid along the cut margin of the sclera (white hatched arrow). The lens suspended by the zonules and surrounded by a ring of choroid as seen from the posterior is shown in (d). A lens fixed in the un-accommodated state effected by stretching the ciliary muscle glued to the twelve arms of the *ex vivo* mechanical device is shown from the anterior aspect in (e). At higher magnification the taut zonules (white asterisk) applying tension to the lens capsule are apparent in (f).

First, the cornea is removed at the corneo-scleral junction (Figure 2a, white arrows). Second, the sclera just beyond the cut margin is gently separated from the underlying ciliary muscle and choroid by blunt dissection. Then after making an initial radial cut (black hatched arrow), an approximately 3- 5mm wide ring of scleral tissue is cut away from the front of the posterior globe. In this manner, the ciliary muscle (Figure 2b, white arrows) is exposed. At this point, while grasping and lifting the iris at the pupillary margin, a radial cut is made toward the root of the iris which is then continued circumferentially so as to remove the bulk of the iris without disturbing any of the zonules attached to the underlying lens (black hatched arrow). The dissection is continued as a circumferential cut is made through the choroid along the cut margin of the sclera (Figure 2c, white hatched arrow). The lens, still suspended by the zonules, the exposed ciliary muscle and the surrounding choroid are then lifted as a whole off of the vitreous (Figure 2d, posterior view). The 12 arms of the mechanical stretching device are attached to the ciliary muscle with cynoacrylate (Figure 2e). Finally, the lens is stretched and fixed in the un-accommodated state (Figure 2f).

When available, the contralateral lens is dissected free of the zonules and fixed in the accommodated state.

Structural Analysis

Detailed descriptions of the dissection and fixation protocols used to prepare lenses for scanning electron microscopic examination of fiber structure along fiber length (anterior, middle or equatorial and posterior segments) and as a function of age (cortical vs. nuclear fibers) are presented elsewhere (Sivak, Herbert, Peterson and Kuszak, 1994; Kuszak, Peterson, Herbert and Sivak, 1994). Briefly, the anterior and posterior segments cortical and nuclear fibers were examined in respectively, intact anterior and posterior suture patterns. The middle segments of fibers were examined in separate specimens.

CAD Reconstructions

Detailed descriptions of the methodology employed to reconstruct lenses in scaled computer assisted rawings (CADs) are also given elsewhere (Kuszak, Sivak, Herbert, Scheib, Garner and Graff, 2000). Briefly, the relevant axial dimensions are taken under stereo dissecting and scanning electron microscopes. These relevant parameters are then plotted onto x, y and z coordinates in a computer. The shapes and sizes of fibers are taken directly from scanning electron micrographs between 10 - 5,000x magnification.

In addition, the dynamic nature of accommodative lens shape changes can be recreated by animating a series of CADs. The CADs, representative of static SEM images taken in the accommodated and un-accommodated states, are placed on a time-line defined by a number of frames. In the case of animating the mechanism of lens accommodation, the initial frame is the lens in the stretched or un-accommodated state while the last frame is the lens in the relaxed or accommodated state. The computer "tweens" or gradually modifies the lens appearance as it transitions between the two states. This process is not to be confused with "morphing" the process whereby a computer radically transforms the shape of an object, such as a cube, into the shape of another object, such as a sphere, over time.

RESULTS

A comparison of the dimensions of a typical pair of young adult baboon lenses fixed in the stretched (un-accommodated) and un-stretched (accommodated) states is shown in figure 3. Both lenses are positioned on their posterior pole atop two concentric circles measuring 9 and 10 mm. The equatorial circumference of the accommodated lens fits into the boundary of the inner 9mm circle whilst that of the un-accommodated lens extends beyond that boundary almost to the boundary of the 10mm circle. The antero-posterior axis of a typical stretched primate lens was ~3.5mm whilst that of an un-stretched lens was ~4.0mm. Thus, the mechanical stretching device effected a gross shape change in lenses that is comparable to that observed and measured in the living eye by biomicroscopic slit-lamp analysis. Unfortunately, whether or not these changes were proportionate or disproportionate could not be ascertained because as described in the methods section, the dissection protocol used to prepare a lens for mounting in the stretching device requires the removal of both the cornea and the vitreous.

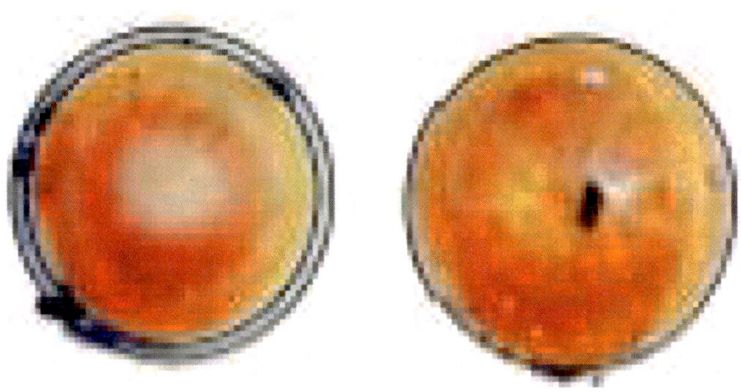

Figure 3. Surgical microscope photos of a pair of adult baboon lenses fixed in the stretched or un-accommodated state (right) and relaxed or accommodated state (left). Both lenses are placed atop 9 and 10mm concentric circles. The equator of the stretched lens extends almost to the 10mm circle while that of the relaxed lens is just inside the 9mm circle.

SEM micrographs showing the surface morphology and dimensions of the middle segment of cortical and nuclear fibers in the stretched and un-stretched states are presented in figure 4. While the more complex surface morphology of nuclear fibers in comparison to cortical fibers was readily apparent, there were neither any appreciable differences in this age-related change nor in the dimensions of fibers in the accommodated or un-accommodated states.

SEM micrographs showing the surface morphology and dimensions of the anterior and posterior end segments (the sutures) of cortical and nuclear fibers in the stretched and un-stretched states are presented in figures 5 and 6. While the surface morphology and dimensions of these segments was not dissimilar in the accommodated or un-accommodated states, the fiber-fiber organization at the sutures was different. In the un-accommodated state, the ends of the fibers were arranged end-to-end. This results in straight suture branches and an ordered confluens of branches at the poles. In contrast, in the accommodated state, the ends of fibers are interfaced. This results in slightly crooked suture branches and a less-ordered confluens of branches at the poles.

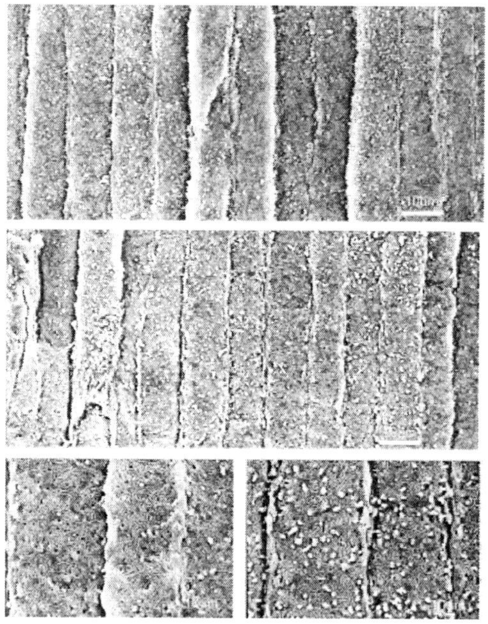

Figure 4. Scanning electron micrographs of adult human cortical (a and c) and nuclear (b and d) fibers fixed in the un-accommodated (a and b) and accommodated states (c and d). Note both fiber structure and dimensions are indistinguishable between the two states.

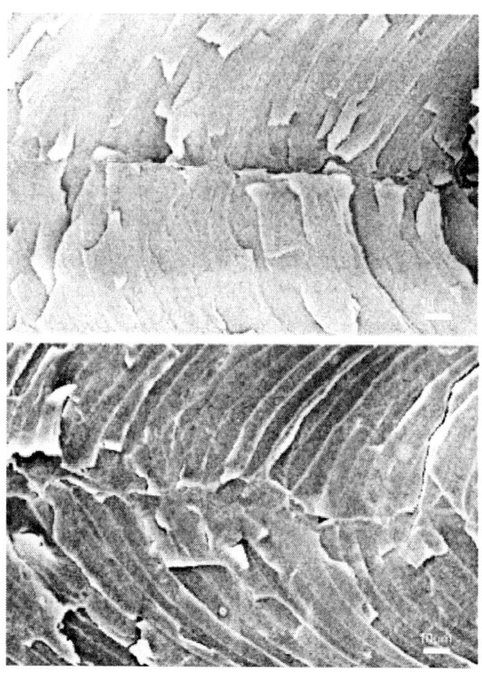

Figure 5. Scanning electron micrographs of adult human suture branches fixed in the stretched (a) and relaxed (b) states. Although some of the ends of fibers in both states were artifactually cracked off during processing, in stretched lenses intact fiber ends were consistently arranged end-to-end as straight suture branches whereas in relaxed lenses they were consistently seen to be overlain or beneath (interfaced) other fiber ends as crooked suture branches.

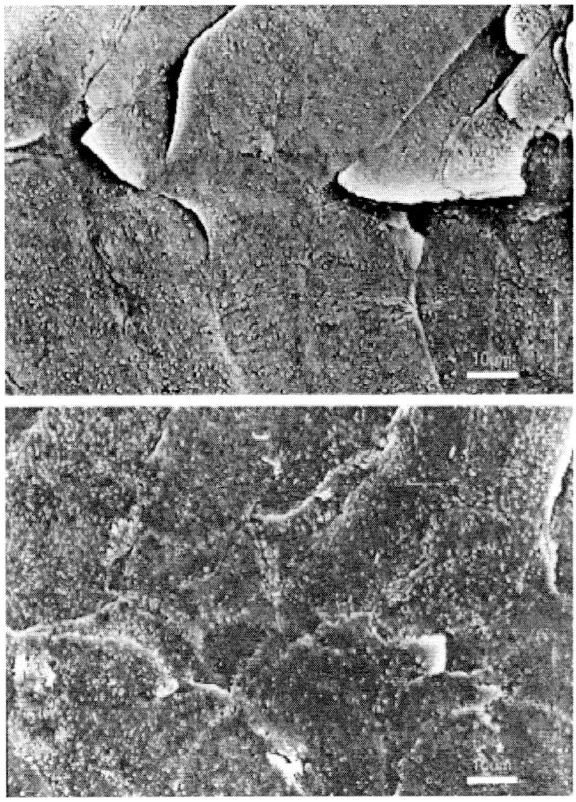

Figure 6. Higher magnification scanning electron micrographs of adult human suture branches fixed in the stretched (a) and relaxed (b) states. In some instances the interfacing of fiber ends at sutures in the accommodated state was so extreme, particularly near the distal end of suture branches, that the branch was only recognizable at lower magnification. In contrast, the straight suture branches in un-accommodated lenses were apparent at all magnifications.

DISCUSSION

The results of our comparative structural analysis of young adult primate (human and baboon) lenses in the accommodated vs. un-accommodated states show that there are neither any changes in fiber dimensions (thickness, width and/or length) nor surface morphology that occur during dynamic focusing. However, the results of this study also demonstrate that the ends of fibers are interfaced in the accommodated state but only arranged end-to-end in the un-accommodated state. When these findings are incorporated into scale schematic 3D-CAD reconstructions of dynamically focusing lenses (either in a series of static drawings [figures 7-9] or shown to greater advantage by animating these same drawings on a time line) a "novel" explanation for the mechanism of accommodative lens shape changes at the lens fiber level emerges.

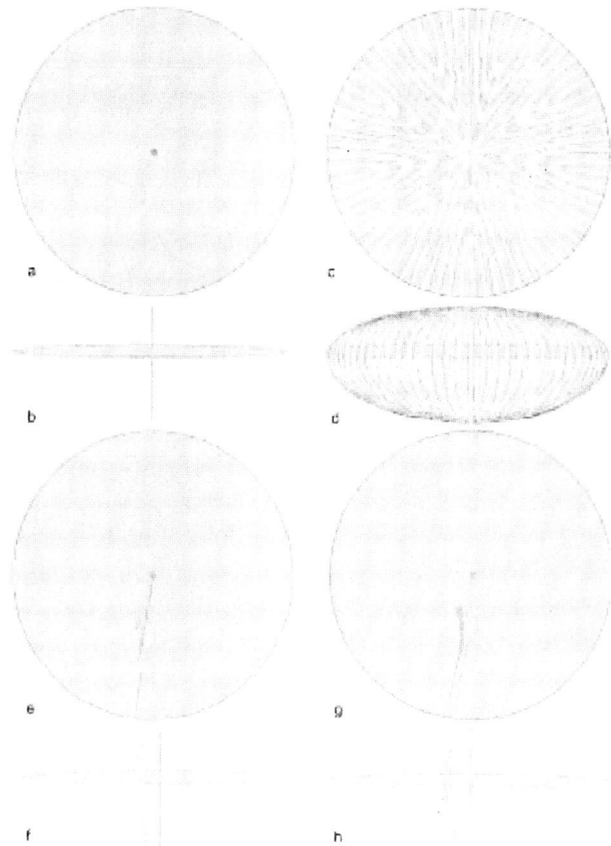

Figure 7. Static scale CADs taken from animations demonstrating the spring action mechanism of accommodation at the level of fibers: part I. (a & b) A semi-transparent equatorial plane and polar axes facilitate an appreciation of the three-dimensional shape and organization of fibers forming a nine branch star suture in adult human lens cortical growth shells (c & d). Isolating a single fiber group shows that fibers are simple springs or coils (e - h). Thus, as zonular tension is released, a fiber expands and its coil diameter decreases. To highlight accommodative fiber shape changes, fibers in the stretched or un-accommodated state are depicted in blue and fibers in the relaxed or accommodated state are depicted in green.

Figure 8. A comparison of the changes in spring shape between a complex spring and a fiber as they transition from a compressed (blue) to a relaxed (green) state.

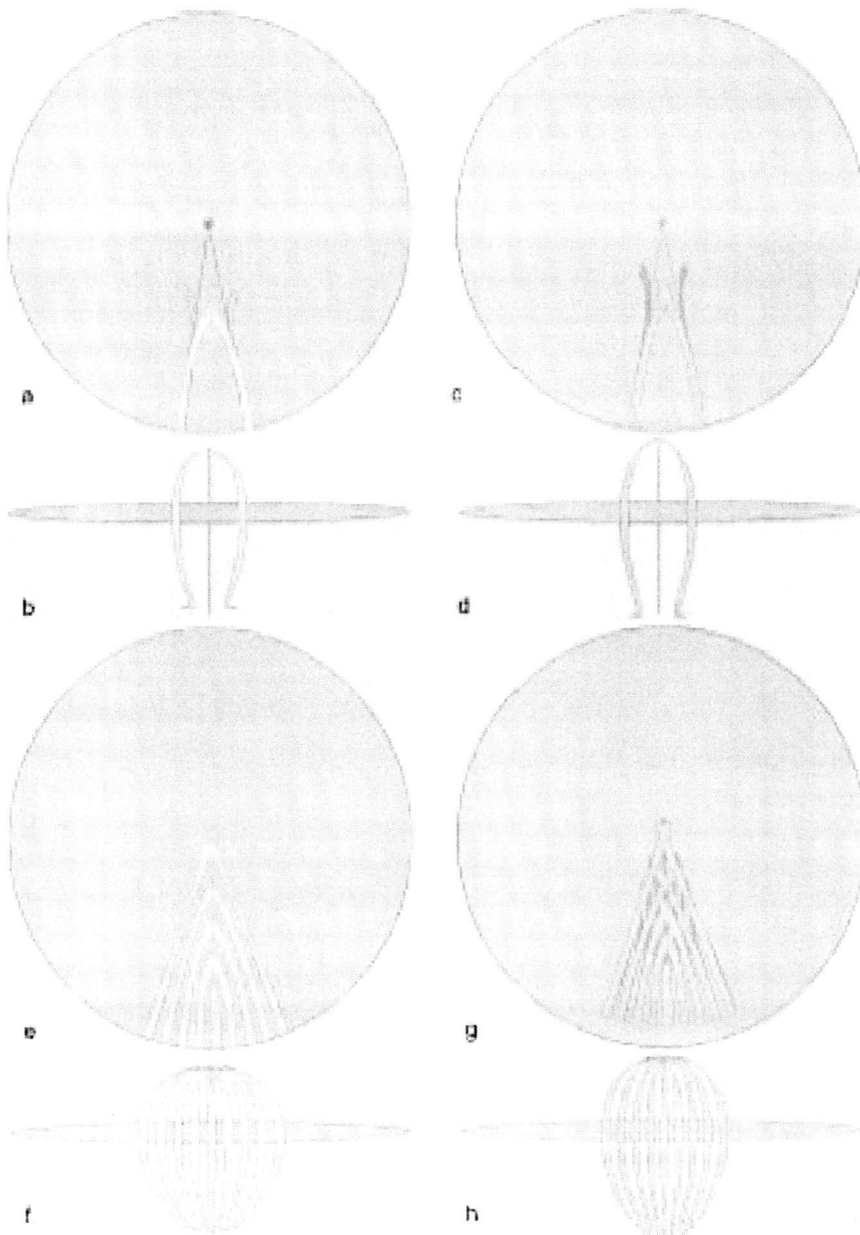

Figure 9. Static scale CADs taken from animations demonstrating the spring action mechanism of accommodation at the level of fibers: part II. In the un-accommodated state, the ends of enantiomeric fiber pairs are arranged end - to - end at suture branches (a & b and e & f). In the accommodated state, the ends of enantiomeric fiber pairs are interfaced (stacked or overlapped) at suture branches (c & d and g & h).

In figure 7 a semi-transparent equatorial plane and polar axis is represented as viewed along the equator (a) and visual axis (b). The shape and organization of fibers in a single, representative growth shell derived from SEM micrographs of a "stretched or un-accommodated" adult human lens are shown about the equator and polar axes in figures 7c & d. Each fiber shape represents a group of ~20 fibers (avg. fiber width ~10 microns). Every other group of fibers has been removed to facilitate recognition of the three dimensionality of the lens and its component fibers. Note that fibers are not meridians. That is to say that no fiber in a growth shell extends from pole - to - pole. Instead, fibers with opposite end curvature are arranged end - to - end to create suture branches and collectively suture patterns. By isolating a single fiber group (figures 7e - h) it is readily apparent why the vast majority of fibers in any growth shell have been described previously as being "S – shaped". However, because fibers are three-dimensional, a more accurate description of the shape of most fibers is that of a simple "coil or spring". As tension is released on a spring, it expands while the diameter of its coils is reduced. Both actions occur without any change in the springs dimensions (figure 8a & b). Similarly, the results of this study show that as zonular tension is released, fibers expand while their coil diameter is reduced (figures 8c & d and 7e - h). Spring action causes the ends of enantiomeric pairs of fibers to interface at the sutures (compare and contrast figures 9a - d). By extrapolation, as zonular tension is released on all of the fibers forming suture branches (figures 9g and h) and collectively suture patterns in growth shells (figure 10), their cumulative expansion along the antero-posterior axis increases lens thickness while their cumulative interfacing at sutures simultaneously decreases lens width in a manner not dissimilar to the diaphragmatic action of a camera lens. The few "straight" fibers, or fibers that lack opposite end curvature, within growth rings that define the proximal and distal ends of suture branches are "leaf springs".

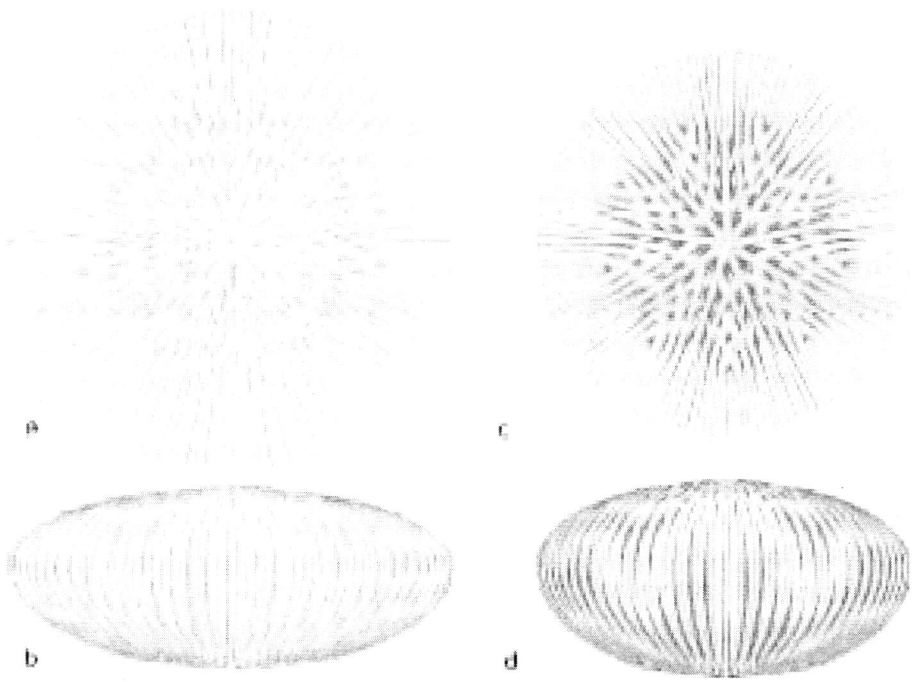

Figure 10. Static scale CADs taken from animations demonstrating the spring action mechanism of accommodation at the level of fibers: part III. The flatter and wider shape of an un-accommodated lens is the result of the cumulative compression of fibers arranged end-to-end at sutures in growth shells (a & b). The rounder and more narrow shape of an accommodated lens is the result of the cumulative expansion of fibers interfaced or stacked at sutures (c & d).

Thus, the lens is composed of simple springs, the fibers, collectively arranged so that the mechanism of accommodation at the lens fiber level is the expansion and compression of spring-like fibers as zonular tension is applied or released by contraction and relaxation of the ciliary muscle. By animating the static images of figures 7 - 10 on a time line, the spring action mechanism of accommodative lens shape changes at the lens fiber level is seen to great advantage in a simulation of dynamic focusing.

This novel explanation of the mechanism of accommodation at the lens fiber level accounts for the disproportionate lens shape changes observed during dynamic focusing by slit-lamp examination. The interfacing, overlapping or stacking of fiber end segments produces the increase in surface curvatures. The posterior increase is more pronounced because fiber thickness at the posterior ends exceeds that of the anterior ends (Kuszak, Peterson and Brown, 1996). The position of the posterior pole likely remains constant between the accommodated and un-accommodated states, in spite of the change in surface curvature, because posterior movement is constrained by the vitreous. Thus, as the posterior ends interface, not only the nucleus, but the entire lens mass is displaced forward. Furthermore, the interfacing of fiber ends to effect lens accommodative shape changes occurs beneath the lens epithelium. Thus, rather than necessitating a change in the form and dimensions of lens epithelial cells, the monolayer lens epithelium can essentially passively drape over the anterior surface of the lens as its curvature changes during accommodation.

The spring-like action of fibers to effect accommodative lens shape changes also puts into perspective previously known but unexplained structural features of lens anatomy. All vertebrate lenses are comprised of long, crescent-like fibers, arranged end-to-end in age defined growth shells (Duke-Elder, 1970; Kuszak, Alcala and Maisel, 1980; Kuszak, Peterson and Brown, 1996). But the end-to-end arrangement of fibers that define the lens sutures, are not identical in all lenses. On the basis of variable fiber shape there are four distinct types of vertebrate lenses; umbilical, line, Y and star suture lenses (Kuszak, 1995; Kuszak, Zoltoski and Tiedemann, 2004; Kuszak, Zoltoski and Sivertson, 2004). Umbilical sutures are characteristic of birds and reptiles. Rabbits and frog lenses have line sutures. The Y suture, the most common lens suture, is typical of rats, mice, cats, dogs, cows, sheep, pigs and primates at birth. After birth primates manufacture progressively more complex iterations of star sutures during infancy, adolescence and adulthood. The rationale for the different types of sutures has not yet been determined. Suture type is not a function of size because both mice and cows have Y sutures. Suture type does not appear to be a function of phylogeny because both rabbits and frogs have line sutures. The differences between the shape and organization of fibers that distinguish the different suture types is discussed in detail elsewhere. For this discussion it is sufficient to draw attention to the following facts that support the concept of suture type being a function of accommodation; birds and primates which have a broad range of accommodation, have less variation in the shape and length of fibers between and within growth shells then all other species which have a more limited range of accommodation (Kuszak, Zoltoski and Tiedemann, 2004; Kuszak, Zoltoski and Sivertson, 2004). It follows that the more uniform the shape of fibers, and the less variable the diameter or span of opposite end curvature within and between growth shells, the more evenly distributed the force and release of capsular tension will be on the lens. In addition, lenses with line and Y sutures have fiber ends that are not as flattened as is the case in lenses with umbilical and star suture. As a consequence, the ends of fibers in line and Y suture lenses are less capable of interfacing during accommodation. These arguments may also explain why primates manufacture progressively more complex iterations of star sutures during infancy, adolescence and adulthood after initially producing a Y suture lens during gestation. Thus, birds and primates produce lenses through life-long growth that support a broad range of accommodation while all other species manufacture lenses during their lifetime that are less conducive to a broad range of accommodation. It can be debated whether or not vertebrates with line and Y suture lenses accommodate poorly because they fail to produce lenses that support dynamic focusing or that they do not produce lenses that support accommodation because they do not need to focus dynamically.

It is also important to note that fibers as springs accounting for accommodative lens shape changes is supportive of lens physiology. Because all vertebrate lenses develop and grow throughout life as inverted vesicles, unlike other stratified epithelia, lenses never routinely slough off cells in their upper layers. Instead the oldest cells of the lens, the nuclear fibers, are progressively internalized with age. This is significant because the lens, like all epithelia, lacks a blood supply and its component parts, the fibers, routinely eliminate most of their organelles as a consequence of terminal differentiation so as not to interfere with the transmission of light.

How lenses maintain fiber viability, especially in consideration of the fact that life-long growth continuously moves the fibers farther away from their sources of nutrition (primarily the aqueous humor), is the subject of considerable study. Diffusion is not sufficient because it is quite slow over long distances, such that it would require several hours to move nutrients to the central fibers of the adult mammalian lens (Mathias and Rae, 2004). Instead vertebrate lenses develop an internal circulatory system consisting of intercellular communicating (gap) junctions and aquaporin water channels (Broekhuyse, Kuhlman and Stols, 1976; Goodenough, 1992; Ehring, Lagos, Zampighi and Hall, 1992; King and Agre, 1996; Benedetti, Dunia, Dufier, Yit Kim Seng and Bloemendal, 1996; Mathias, Rae and Baldo, 1997; Fotiadis, Hasler, Muller, Stahlberg, Kistler and Engel, 2000). This unique circulatory system is predicated on fluid entering lenses at the poles, or at the confluens of suture branches, into the fibers via aquaporin water channels, being transported along the length of fibers, and then between fibers toward the equator via gap junctions that primarily conjoin the middle segment of fibers (Fitzgerald, 1986; Kuszak and Costello, 2004). Gap junctions are rare between the central zone epithelial cells and the underlying elongating fibers, the epithelial-fiber interface (EFI; (Bassnett, Kuszak, Reinisch, Brown and Beebe, 1994). The concentration of gap junctions at the middle segment of fibers is established early in the fiber elongation process.

In addition, lenses are characterized by cell-to-cell fusion of fibers (Kuszak, Macsai, Bloom, Rae and Weinstein, 1985; Kuszak, Bertram and Rae, 1986; Kuszak, Peterson and Brown, 1996; Shestopalov and Bassnett, 2000a; Shestopalov and Bassnett, 2000b). Fiber fusion allows for transport between fibers above and beyond that which can pass through gap junctions. In fact, it has been proposed that fiber gap junctions, aquaporin water channels and fusion zones are so extensive, that lenses are "functional syncytiums" developed as the means to ensure that fibers remain viable throughout life.

Thus, the mechanism of accommodation cannot conflict with the placement, maintenance or functionality of fiber-fiber contacts critical for lens physiology. The spring action mechanism of accommodation meets these criteria because it is effected without any change in fiber structure or dimensions. In this manner, the structural integrity of intercellular contacts along the middle segment of fibers, and the paucity of intercellular junctions at the

EFI and between the end segments of fibers at sutures, are prime examples of form following function.

The interfacing of fiber ends as spring-like fibers expand is not consistent with the notion that accommmodative lens shape changes are entirely attributable to the lens nucleus. The reason for this discrepancy may be a question of resolution. As described earlier, though slit-lamp biomicroscopy is unparalleled as a technique to chronicle gross lens shape changes during dynamic focusing *in situ,* this method cannot distinguish individual fibers. Similarly, while this technique can distinguish the developmental and age-related zones of discontinuity (Koretz, Handelman and Brown, 1984; Koretz, Cook and Kuszak, 1994), the boundaries of these regions are neither clearly delineated nor completely consistent from lens to lens (Kuszak and Costello, 2004). For example, the embryonic nucleus is comprised solely of the original primary fibers. The fetal nucleus is comprised of the embryonic nucleus and all of the secondary fibers added throughout gestation, on average a period of six months. The juvenile nucleus consists of the fetal nucleus and all of the fibers added through infancy and early childhood a period ranging from two to four years. The adult nucleus is comprised of the juvenile nucleus and all of the fibers formed through sexual maturation a period ranging from eight to sixteen years. From that point on the adult nucleus becomes larger with increasing age. In contrast, the size of the cortex is consistent throughout life because as fibers become mature they are considered to be nuclear. Thus, it is not unreasonable to propose that the accommodative lens shape changes observed *in situ* by slit-lamp examination were attributable at least in part to cortical changes as revealed by *ex vivo* electron microscopic examination.

SUMMARY

We have utilized an *ex vivo* mechanical device to stretch and fix adult primate and baboon) lenses in the un-accommodated state. Fiber morphology and dimensional parameters (length, width and thickness) in these lenses were compared to that from contralateral and age-matched lenses fixed in the accommodated state. The purpose of this study was to assess the mechanism of accommodative lens shape changes at the lens fiber level. The results of this study demonstrate that there is no variation in fiber morphology or dimensions during dynamic focusing and that accommodative lens shape changes are attributable to the end segments of fibers interfacing at the sutures. This mechanism of accommodation is made possible by opposite end curvature transforming fibers into simple coils or springs. As spring tension is released on the lens capsule fibers within growth shells expand in unison to effect an increase in lens thickness while simultaneously reducing lens width as the diameter of the coils (fibers) decrease as fiber end segments interface at sutures. As spring tension is applied on the lens capsule fibers within growth shells are compressed in unison to effect an decrease in lens thickness while simultaneously expanding lens width as the diameter of the coils (fibers) increase as fiber end segments only abut at sutures. The spring action of fibers as the mechanism of dynamic focusing supports critical aspects of lens physiology necessary for transparency and explains at least in part, the disparity in accommodative range between primates and non-primates.

ACKNOWLEDGEMENTS

The authors recognize the expert technical assistance of Layne Novak, Kurt Peterson and Mike Mazurkiewicz. This work supported by NIH NEI grant #EY 06642 to JRK.

REFERENCES

[1] Bassnett,S., Kuszak,J.R., Reinisch,L., Brown,H.G. and Beebe,D.C. (1994). Intercellular communication between epithelial and fiber cells of the eye lens. *J.Cell Sci.*, **107** (4), 799-811.

[2] Benedetti, E. L., Dunia, I., Dufier, J. L., Yit Kim Seng, and Bloemendal, H. Plasma membrane-cytoskeleton complex in the normal and cataractous lens. Hesketh, J. E. and Pryme, I. F. *The Cytoskeleton*. **451-518**. 1996. London, JAI Press Inc.

[3] Broekhuyse,R.M., Kuhlman,E.D. and Stols,A.L. (1976). Lens membranes II. Isolation and characterization of the main intrinsic polypepetide (MIP) of bovine lens fiber membranes. *Exper.Eye Res*. **23**, 365-71.

[4] Duke-Elder, S. The refractive media: The lens. Duke-Elder, S. *Systems of Ophthalmology*. **309-324**. 1970. St. Louis, Mo., The C.V. Mosby Co.

[5] Ehring,G.R., Lagos,N., Zampighi,G.A. and Hall,J.E. (1992). Phosphorylation modulates the voltage dependence of channels reconstituted from the major intrinsic protein of the lens fiber membranes. *J.Membr.Biol*. **126**, 75-88.

[6] Fitzgerald, P. G. The main intrinsic polypeptide and intercellular communication in the ocular lens. Hilfer, R. S. and Sheffield, J. B. *Development of order in the visual system*. **9**[4], 61-96. 1986. New York, Springer-Verlag.

[7] Fotiadis,D., Hasler,L., Muller,D.J., Stahlberg,H., Kistler,J. and Engel,A. (2000). Surface tongue-and-groove contours on lens MIP faciitate cell-to-cell adherence. *J.Mol.Biol.* **300**, 779-89.

[8] Glasser,A. and Campbell,M.C. (1998). Presbyopia and the optical changes in the human crystalline lens with age. *Vision Res*. **38**, 209-29.

[9] Goodenough,D.A. (1992). The crystalline lens. A system networked by gap junctional intercellular communication. *Sem.Cell Biol*. **3**, 49-58.

[10] Gullstrand, A. Appendix. In : von Helmholtz, H.H. (1909) *Handbuch der Physiologishen Optik. Southall, J. P. C. translator*. **143-172**. 1909. New York, Dover.

[11] King,L.S. and Agre,P. (1996). Pathophysiology of the aquaporin water channels. *Annu.Rev.Physiol*. **58**, 619-48.

[12] Koretz,J.F., Cook,C.A. and Kaufman,P.L. (1997). Accommodation and presbyopia in the human eye. *Invest.Ophthalmol.Vis.Sci*. **38**, 569-78.

[13] Koretz,J.F., Cook,C.A. and Kuszak,J.R. (1994). The zones of discontinuity in the human lens: Development and distribution with age. *Vision Res*. **34**, 2955-62.

[14] Koretz,J.F., Handelman,G.H. and Brown,N.P. (1984). Analysis of human crystalline lens curvature as a function of accomodative state and age. *Vision Res*., **10**, 1141-51.

[15] Kuszak,J.R. (1995). Development of sutures in the lens. *Progress in Retinal and Eye Research* **14**, 567-91.

[16] Kuszak,J.R., Alcala,J. and Maisel,H. (1980). The surface morphology of embryonic and adult chick lens-fiber cell. *Am.J.Anat*. **159**, 395-410.

[17] Kuszak, J. R., Bertram, B. A., and Rae, J. L. The ordered structure of the crystalline lens. Hilfer, S. R. and Sheffield, J. B. Cell and developmental biology of the eye.*Development of order in the visual system.* **1**, 35-60. 1986. New York, Springer-Verlag.

[18] Kuszak, J. R. and Costello, M. J. The structure of the vertebrate lens. Lovicu, F. J. and Robinson, M. L. *Development of the Ocular Lens.* [4], 71-118. 2004. Cambridge, Cambridge University Press.

[19] Kuszak,J.R., Macsai,M.S., Bloom,K.J., Rae,J.L. and Weinstein,R.S. (1985). Cell-to-cell fusion of lens fiber cells *in situ* : correlative light,scanning electron microscopic, and freeze-fracture studies. *J.Ultrastruct.Res.*, **93**, 144-60.

[20] Kuszak,J.R., Peterson,K.L. and Brown,H.G. (1996). Electron microscopic observations of the crystalline lens. *J.Electron Microsc.Tech.* **33**, 441-79.

[21] Kuszak,J.R., Peterson,K.L., Herbert,K.L. and Sivak,J.G. (1994). The Inter-Relationship of Lens Anatomy and Optical Quality. II. *Primate Lenses. Exper.Eye Res.* **59**, 521-35.

[22] Kuszak,J.R., Sivak,J.G., Herbert,K.L., Scheib,S., Garner,W. and Graff,G. (2000). The relationship between rabbit lens optical quality and sutural anatomy after vitrectomy. *Exper.Eye Res.* **71**, 267-82.

[23] Kuszak,J.R., Zoltoski,R.K. and Sivertson,C. (2004). Fibre cell organization in crystalline lenses. *Exper.Eye Res.* **78**, 673-87.

[24] Kuszak,J.R., Zoltoski,R.K. and Tiedemann,C.E. (2004). Development of lens sutures. *International Journal of Developmental Biology* **48**, 889-902.

[25] Mathias,R.T. and Rae,J.L. (2004). The lens: local transport and global transparency. *Exper.Eye Res.* **78**, 689-98.

[26] Mathias,R.T., Rae,J.L. and Baldo,G.J. (1997). Physiological properties of the normal lens. *Physiological Rev.* **77**, 21-49.

[27] Pierscionek,B. (1993). In vitro alteration of human lens curvatures by radial stretching. *Exper.Eye Res.* **57**, 629-35.

[28] Shestopalov,V.I. and Bassnett,S. (2000a). Expression of autofluorescent protein reveals a novel protein permeable pathway between cells in the lens core. *J.Cell Sci.*, **113**, 1913-21.

[29] Shestopalov,V.I. and Bassnett,S. (2000b). Three dimensional organization of primary lens fiber cells. *Invest.Ophthal.& Vis.Sci.* **41**, 1-5.

[30] Sivak,J.G., Herbert,K.L., Peterson,K.L. and Kuszak,J.R. (1994). The Inter-Relationship of Lens Anatomy and Optical Quality. I. Non-Primate Lenses. *Exper.Eye Res.* **59**, 505-20.

[31] von Helmholtz, H. H. Handbuch der Physiologishen Optik. Southall, J. P. C. translator. *Helmholtz's Treatise on Physiological Optics* (1962). 143-172. 1909. New York, Dover.

In: Focus on Eye Research
Editor: O.R. Ioseliani, pp. 133-151

ISBN: 1-59454-434-4

Chapter 6

ROLE OF THE CYTOSKELETON IN RETINAL ENDOTHELIAL CELL BARRIER DYSFUNCTION AND DIABETIC RETINOPATHY

L. A. Linz-McGillem, and J. G. N. Garcia*

Pulmonary and Critical Care Medicine, Center for Translational Respiratory Medicine
Johns Hopkins University, Baltimore, MD

ABSTRACT

The regulation of endothelial cell permeability is essential for maintenance of the delicate physiological environment of the retina. Retinal capillary barrier dysfunction is a hallmark of multiple ocular pathologies including diabetic retinopathy and macular edema leading to severe vision loss and blindness. Several factors alter the retinal microvascular barrier including exposure to angiogenic growth factors (VEGF), angiogenic inhibitors (endostatin, angiostatin), chemokines, reactive oxygen species, platelet phospholipids (sphingosine 1-phosphate), and the class of drugs known as the statins (simvastatin). VEGF, for example, increases barrier permeability in the retina via multiple signaling pathways which include a signal cascade culminating in activation of the cytoskeletal contractile apparatus. The balance between endothelial cell contractility and forces which promote intracellular adhesion both contribute to vascular barrier regulation via dynamics of the microfilament-based cytoskeleton and associated proteins. Alterations in cell-cell adhesion proteins are also associated with barrier permeability linked to retinopathies. The retinal endothelial cell cytoskeleton represents an important therapeutic target for the amelioration of retinal vascular pathology.

Keywords: Diabetic retinopathy, hyperglycemia, edema, MLCK, cytoskeleton.

* Correspondence concerning this article should be addressed to Dr. J.G.N. Garcia, Chairman, Department of Medicine, University of Chicago, Pritzker School of Medicine, Chicago, IL 60637, 773-702-1051. E-mail address: jgarcia@medicine.bsd.uchicago.edu.

Overview of Retinal Barrier Function

Vision and ocular function is dependent on precise vascular barrier regulation, a requisite for maintenance of the highly specialized physiological environment that supports the multiple cell types within the neural retina. The retina is supplied by two sets of blood vessels, one located peripheral to the retina, but within the outer choroid layer [1] and the second, a multi-layered capillary plexus found within the retina itself. Radial peripapillary capillaries (RPCs) are found in the inner part of the ganglion cell layer [2]. A second deeper layer of capillaries are also located in the ganglion cell layer. Additional outer capillary layers anastomose with the RPC and inner capillary layer and are distributed throughout the inner nuclear layer from the inner to the outer plexiform layers [2]. Each branching retinal capillary is lined by a monolayer of endothelial cells which strictly control fluid and macromolecule flow, known as the blood retina barrier (BRB). Similar to other vascular beds, the functionality of the retinal endothelial cell monolayer is dependent on the integrity of the cell-cell adhesions and dynamics of the cytoskeleton [3].

The BRB was originally described morphologically in the late 1960's with two structural components - the endothelial layer of the retinal capillaries and the retinal pigmented epithelium [4, 5]. The function of the BRB is to maintain the microenvironment of retina by regulating the absorption of fluid and macromolecules from the vitreous and retina, and the transport of fluid from the blood to the retina [5]. Subsequent fluid and macromolecule leakage between endothelial cells, known as paracellular flow, in retinal vessels is the predominant source of retinal edema in human diabetic retinopathy and experimentally-induced diabetes [6, 7]. Retinal capillary vessels are lined with a single layer of endothelial cells (EC) surrounded by pericytes. Optimal function of the BRB is dependent on the structural integrity of the endothelial cell monolayer conveyed not only by the extensive intracellular cytoskeletal networks, but also the specialized junctional complexes which adhere adjacent cells together and to the extracellular matrix.

Multiple biochemical factors alter BRB barrier properties including growth factors, oxidative stress, abnormal pathologic leukocyte adhesion, and hyperglycemia. Increased retinal permeability results in excess fluid leakage and retinal edema which is a hallmark of multiple ocular pathologies, including diabetic retinopathy, a leading cause of blindness in adults [8]. Permeability of the vascular endothelial cell layer is the earliest clinically detectable change in diabetic retinopathy [9-12] and edema of the retina is a major cause of vision loss in diabetic patients. It is interesting to note that hyperglycemia–induced blood retinal barrier dysfunction occurs principally in venules and capillaries in the superficial inner retinal vascular tree [13]. Unfortunately, at present, effective and non-invasive therapies to alleviate retinal edema remain elusive [14].

The early stages of diabetic retinopathy (known as mild and moderate nonproliferative retinopathy) are typified by pathological alterations in the pericytes and endothelial cells comprising the retinal capillary walls causing increased vascular permeability and edema within the retina. These changes have been detected as early as 4 weeks after the onset of diabetes [15]. When edema occurs adjacent to the macula (the region of the retina responsible for central, sharp focus) the result is severely blurred vision. Weakened capillary walls are susceptible to microaneurysm development and intraretinal hemorrhages which result in ischemic regions. In the third stage of diabetic retinopathy (severe nonproliferative retinopathy) increasingly low oxygen levels in retinal tissue due to ischemia prompt intracellular signaling cascades which induce neovascularization. Finally, proliferative retinopathy (the fourth and most advanced stage of diabetic retinopathy) is characterized by the dysregulated growth of blood vessels, known as angiogenesis, out of the deeper retina to the surface or into the vitreous cavity. These nascent abnormal capillaries are often immature and leaky and result in hemorrhage into the vitreous humor thereby obscuring vision.

ROLE OF ENDOTHELIAL CYTOSKELETON IN VASCULAR BARRIER REGULATION

It has become increasingly appreciated that vascular barrier regulation is intimately linked to the endothelial cell cytoskeleton which includes actin-containing microfilaments, vimentin-containing intermediate filaments and microtubules. Each component has multiple associated proteins which regulate and modify the dynamics of these elements. For example, the actin cytoskeleton is a dynamic filamentous structure with over 80 actin-binding proteins, that undergoes rearrangement under the control of the mechanochemical motor protein known as myosin, as well as multiple actin-capping, -nucleating and -severing proteins which are involved in regulating cell morphology, motility and contractile status. The actin cytoskeleton has a critical role in regulation of endothelial cell permeability since integrity of BRB barrier function is disturbed by treatment with the actin disrupting agent, cytochalasin D, whereas actin-stabilizing agents exert a protective effect on endothelial cell barrier function[16]. Endothelial cell shape, permeability and paracellular gap formation appears to be regulated by a balance between opposing contractile forces that generate centripetal tension versus tethering forces which enhance adhesion via linkage to cell-cell and cell matrix junctions[3]. These opposing forces heavily influence the actin-based EC cytoskeletal network through coordinate action of actin-binding proteins which focally connect the network to adhesive junctions[3]. The actin network is largely responsible for generating and maintaining EC intracellular tension and relaxation via non-muscle myosin II activity that continually adjusts the extensive actomyosin network. A key event in actomyosin-based cytoskeletal alterations is the phosphorylation of the 20 kD myosin light chain (MLC) on Ser^{19} and Thr^{18} residues catalyzed by Ca^{2+}/ calmodulin (CaM)-dependent MLC kinase (MLCK) [17-19]. This event triggers myosin ATPase activity and is important for tension development, paracellular gap formation, and EC barrier dysfunction[20]. Endothelial cell MLCK (EC MLCK) activity is an important mechanism in the development of transcellular actin cables, stress fibers, intracellular tension, contraction and subsequent barrier dysfunction. EC MLCK activity is dramatically upregulated by inflammatory agonists such as histamine, VEGF and the serine protease thrombin, important agonists in coagulation, angiogenesis and inflammatory responses that induce barrier permeability[21-23]. Thrombin rapidly increases EC MLCK activity resulting in MLC phosphorylation and subsequent changes in actomyosin dynamics. Paracellular permeability *in vitro* is profoundly increased by exposure to thrombin and subsequent reorganization of the actin network is measurable by biophysical measurements such as a reduction of transcellular electrical resistance across an endothelial cell monolayer and fluorescence microscopy. Thrombin- and histamine-mediated increases in vascular permeability function can be dramatically attenuated with MLCK inhibitors [3, 24-26] (Figure1).

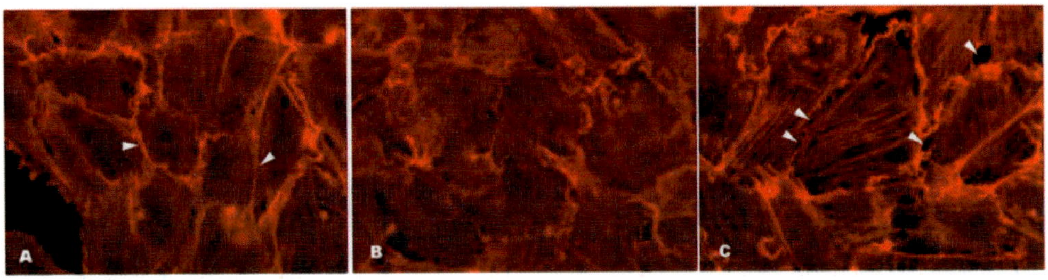

Figure 1. Retinal microvascular endothelial cell actin networks respond to barrier permeability altering agonists. Human retinal endothelial cells (EC) were plated on glass coverslips and grown to confluence. Brief incubation (5 min) with sphingosine 1-phosphate (1 uM) causes rearrangement of actin network into peripheral cortical actin rings (A, arrowheads) compared to control monolayers incubated with vehicle only (B). Retinal EC which have been incubated with thrombin (15 min) develop prominent actin-containing stress fibers and intercellular gaps (C, arrowheads).

We previously found that EC MLCK is a novel isoform consisting of 1914 amino acids displaying a higher molecular weight (214 kDa) and a novel amino terminal stretch of 922 amino acids not shared by the smooth muscle (SM) MLCK isoform[27]. Several splice variants of EC MLCK are derived from an mRNA precursor transcribed from the human MLCK gene[28]. The primary structure of one of these variants, EC MLCK 2 is identical to EC MLCK except for a deficiency of nucleotides 1428-1635 resulting from deletion of a single exon. Analysis of the unique amino terminus of EC MLCK reveals several potential regulatory motifs, including sites for $Ca^{2+/}$CaM kinase, protein kinase A, and $p60^{src}$–mediated phosphorylation, events which alter kinase activity[27, 29]. Tyrosine phosphorylation of EC MLCK1 at these sites increases MLC kinase activity indicating post-translational modification as a key element of MLCK regulation and hence, barrier regulation[29].

In addition to MLCK activity, endothelial cell barrier function appears to be regulated by multiple pathways which include small GTPases (Rho, Rac and Cdc42) and protein kinase C (PKC) isoenzymes which, via signaling cascades, transmit extracellular signals to alter actomyosin network dynamics[30]. Thick actin filament fibers, known as stress fibers, are formed by the coordinate activation of MLCK, as well as Rho through downstream effector Rho kinase activity which inhibits MLC phosphatase activity via phosphorylation and results in increased levels of MLC phosphorylation, contractile actomyosin dynamics and increased formation of stress fibers and vascular permeability[31-34]. Protein kinase C is a family of ~ 12 isoenzymes of Ca^{2+}-phospholipid- dependent serine/threonine kinases that are critical targets for lipid second messengers and are activated by diacylglycerol (DAG) [35]. The DAG-PKC signaling pathway is responsible for regulating multiple vascular functions. PKC modulates vascular permeability in a species-specific manner with PKC-dependent barrier dysfunction in bovine pulmonary EC (without changes in MLC phosphorylation), whereas activation of PKC does not increase permeability in human lung endothelium, but rather enhances monolayer integrity[24, 36-38]. Diversity among PKC isoforms may be responsible for differential effects on endothelial cell function. Increases in vascular permeability do not necessarily mandate an increase in levels of MLC phosphorylation, such as that evoked by tumor necrosis factor-α (TNF-α) and activation of p38 kinase and pertussis toxin[39, 40].

The transcytotic pathway for flux is an important pathway for protein and water movement, however, vascular permeability is largely regulated by integrity of the cell-cell junctional complexes and evolves via paracellular pathways. Endothelial cells are linked to adjacent cells primarily via two types of multi-protein complexes known as tight junctions (zona occludens) and adherens junctions[41, 42]. Adherens junctions anchor adjacent cells to one another by homotypic binding of transmembrane cadherins [43, 44] and the actin network is anchored to junctional complexes by binding to members of the catenin family which link to the cytoplasmic tail of cadherins[45]. The importance of cell type-specific vascular endothelial (VE)-cadherins to maintenance of barrier function has been demonstrated in both *in vivo* and *in vitro* experiments using VE-cadherin function blocking antibodies which increase permeability[46]. The actomyosin network is linked both directly and indirectly to multiple membrane adhesive proteins comprising the junctional complexes including transmembrane proteins, occludins, and zonula occludens 1, 2, and 3 (ZO-1, -2, -3) and members of the claudin family [47] which are mostly likely regulated by phosphorylation[48-50]. ZO-1 is expressed in all endothelial cells and its intracellular expression is altered concurrent with fluctuations in barrier permeability[51]. These junctions form diffusion barriers and regulate passage of fluid and macromolecules through the paracellular pathway with direct and critical linkage to the endothelial cell cytoskeleton thereby providing structural integrity and maintain cell morphology[52].

A variety of stimuli including VEGF[53], angiopoietins[54], CXC chemokines[55, 56], hepatocyte growth factor [57] and platelet phospholipids such as sphingosine 1-phosphate (Sph 1-P) [58, 59] alter both tight junctions and adherens junctions and thereby alter paracellular gap formation and permeability. VEGF causes a rapid phosphorylation and upregulation of occludin expression in cultured retinal endothelial cells. *In vivo*, intraocular injections of VEGF increased tyrosine phosphorylation of ZO-1[60]. This evidence suggests that retinal vascular permeability is regulated at least in part by phosphorylation of tight junction proteins. Various stimuli associated with hyperglycemia and diabetes including upregulation of growth factor expression, inflammatory factors and oxidative stress can initiate signaling pathways that alter the cytoskeleton and can result in increased contractile forces, loosened cell-cell junctions and increased vascular permeability.

Cytoskeletal Involvement in Enhanced Vascular Barrier Function

Intracellular changes in the cytoskeleton occur under the influence of a myriad of signaling cascades triggered by both receptor and non-receptor mediated protein interactions. Although platelets have roles in inflammatory response and accumulate in microthrombi in diabetic rats and humans[61], platelet-derived metabolic products such as sphingosine 1-phosphate (Sph 1-P), a complete angiogenic factor [62]also exert barrier protective effects. Sph 1-P directly induces endothelial cell activation via Edg receptor ligation and is the most potent EC chemoattractant in serum[62, 63]. Sph 1-P is highly effective at stimulating cellular proliferation, migration and changes in the cytoskeleton[58, 62, 64-67]. These critical aspects of endothelial cell barrier enhancement are regulated through Rac GTPase-dependent signaling cascades induced by ligation of the Edg receptor family. EC MLCK is essential for Sph 1-P enhancement of endothelial cell barrier integrity *in vitro* and induces rearrangement of the actin cytoskeleton to prominent cortical actin rings[59, 67-69]. The importance of Sph 1-P -induced actin rearrangement and improved vascular barrier function is underscored in diabetic rat models where BRB permeability was increased after platelet depletion, consistent with Sph 1-P as a critical component of vascular barrier maintenance and protection[70].

Additional barrier-promoting agents include oxidized phospholipids[71], HGF[57] and members of the statin family[72]. Oxidized phospholipids are bioactive components of oxidized low-density lipoproteins such as oxidized 1-palmitoyl-2-arachidonoyl-*sn*-glycero-3-phosphorylcholine (OxPAPC) which may be associated with pathological conditions and mediate multiple signaling cascades to remodel the endothelial cell cytoskeleton[73-75]. OxPAP-mediated barrier enhancement effects are linked to PKC and cAMP-dependent protein kinase (PKA) activation[76, 77]. PKA-mediated barrier enhancement effects include dampening of contractile forces within endothelial cells via multiple mechanisms including attenuation of EC MLCK activity[22, 27], phosphorylation of focal adhesion proteins which induce reduction in stress fibers[78], and downregulation of RhoA activity to stabilize the cortical actin network[79]. OxPAP does not increase MLC phosphorylation, but appears to promote actin network remodeling via phosphorylation of actin-binding and focal adhesion proteins which improves barrier function[71, 80].

Members of the statin family are inhibitors of 3-hydroxy-3-methylglutaryl-coenzyme A (HMG-CoA) reductase and are used to lower blood lipid levels, but also have direct beneficial effects on endothelial cells and vascular function[81-83]. Statins prevent prenylation reactions and reduce production of cholesterol and also appear to effect activation of Rho GTPase family members Rho and Rac. These GTPases are key molecular switches which cycle between GTP-bound (active) and GDP-bound (inactive) states to regulate cytosolic events such as actomyosin dynamics. Rho GTPase prenylation is inhibited by simvastatin, therefore MLC phosphorylation is attenuated, and actin stress fibers are reduced, along with thrombin-induced paracellular gap formation[72]. Simvastatin also appears to induce active Rac-dependent cortical actin thickening and has a barrier protective effect on endothelial cells challenged with barrier disruptive agents such as thrombin. Several intracellular pathways appear to be modified by simvastatin in order to regulate the endothelial cell cytoskeleton and improve endothelial barrier function. Simvastatin may have a role in reduction of retinal vascular inflammation associated with hyperglycemia by reducing adhesion of polymorphonuclear (PMNs) leukocyte to inner vascular walls[84]. Leukocyte adhesion via surface receptor molecules such as selectins and intracellular adhesion molecule (ICAM-1) induces paracellular gap formation to facilitate passage of the PMNs to the surrounding inflamed tissue[85]. Expression of ICAM-1 is upregulated in endothelial cells in the diabetic retina most likely stimulated by VEGF[86, 87]. Inhibition of leukocyte-endothelial cell interaction with simvastatin attenuates retinopathic vascular breakdown. Rats with experimentally-induced diabetes treated with simvastatin demonstrated suppressed expression of ICAM-1 and VEGF on endothelial cells. In addition, expression of surface CD18 diabetic leukocytes is reduced[86]. The studies suggest that members of the statin family, simvastatin in particular, may be ideal for reduction of diabetic retinopathy-induced capillary permeability.

Finally, hepatocyte growth factor (HGF) is a known angiogenic factor and endothelial cell chemoattractant [88, 89] which measurably enhances barrier integrity by regulating the EC cytoskeleton[57]. HGF increases cortical actin rearrangement and strengthens protein-protein interactions at adherens junctions, via a mechanism which appears to involve HGF stimulation of the Rac GTPase pathway and rapid actin rearrangement[57]. Other HGF effector pathways that regulate actin dynamics include Akt phosphorylation via PI-3' kinase; members of the MAP kinase family such as (ERK1/2 and p38), and PKC isoenzyme specific pathways[57].

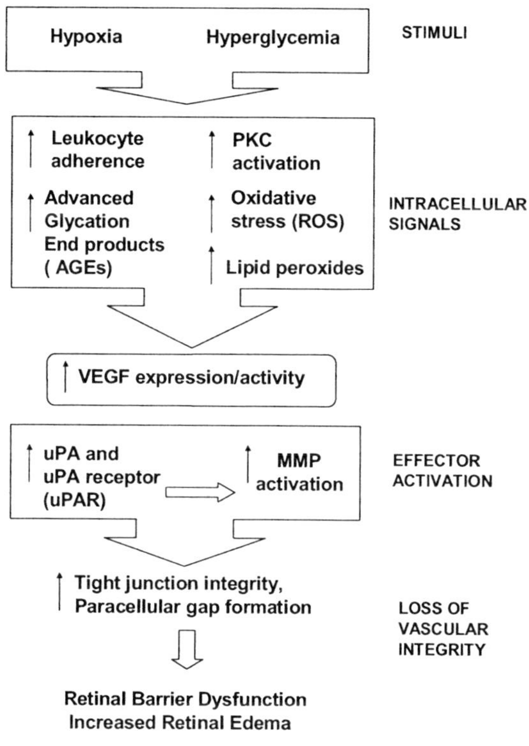

Figure 2.

SIGNALING CASCADES WHICH INDUCE DIABETIC RETINOPATHIC ASSOCIATED PERMEABILITY

Glucose levels in the diabetic retina are ~5 fold higher than in non-diabetic retinas [90] possibly due to a failure to downregulate expression of the glucose transporter GLUT-1 under hyperglycemic conditions[91]. GLUT-1 shuttles extracellular glucose inside the cell, where it is metabolized and alters multiple signaling cascades[92-94]. Hyperglycemia is correlated with changes in multiple biochemical pathways that directly impact the dynamics of the endothelial cell cytoskeleton and contribute to vascular dysfunction and breakdown of the BRB. Among these are factors that alter permeability of the retinal endothelial cell layer including upregulated expression of growth factors, increased oxidative stress, production of advanced glycation end products, PKC activation and abnormal leukocyte adhesion.

VEGF, an endothelial cell-specific potent angiogenic and vasopermeability factor[95, 96], appears to be a potent downstream effector of many of these biochemical pathways. In diabetic rodent models and humans, cells exposed to hyperglycemia, ischemia and oxidative stress, VEGF and VEGF-specific receptors Flk-1 and Flt-1 expression are upregulated and are associated with vascular barrier dysfunction[13, 97-103]. The mechanism for VEGF-induced increase in BRB permeability includes activation of urokinase plasminogen (uPA) which in turn upregulates urokinase plasminogen receptor (uPAR) expression[104]. Induction of the extracellular plasminogen cycle activates downstream matrix metalloproteinases which subsequently alters cell-cell and cell-substrate interactions[105]. Intracellularly, exposure to VEGF redistributes and reduces the expression level of the tight junction protein occludin and loosens tight junctions [104] increasing vascular permeability (Figure 2).

Role of Oxidative Stress in Glucose- induced Permeability

Oxidative stress is an important factor in development of diabetic vascular dysfunction[93, 106, 107]. Under normal physiological conditions, glucose is oxidized to produce hydrogen peroxide and hydroxyl radicals[108], whereas increased glucose levels favor the formation of reactive oxygen species including peroxides and nitric oxides[109]. Retinal microvascular cells release higher levels of exogenous superoxide than other microvascular cells and curiously demonstrate lower levels of expression and activity of antioxidant enzymes suggesting that retinal microvascular EC may be susceptible to oxidative stress under diabetic conditions[110-112]. Rats treated with the diabetogenic drug streptozotocin (STZ) show signs of barrier dysfunction concomitant with increase in reactive oxygen species such as nitric oxide (NO), superoxide (O_2^-), lipid peroxides and the peroxynitrite ($ONOO^-$) biomarker nitrotyrosine[113, 114]. Although the precise signaling cascade associated with oxidative stress and pathological permeability is not completely determined, evidence suggests that reactive oxygen species (ROS) are upstream of increases in VEGF and urokinase plasminogen receptor (uPAR) expression[113]. To underscore the role of ROS in permeability, experimental reduction in the formation of ROS inhibited VEGF and uPAR-mediated barrier dysfunction suggesting that BRB breakdown occurs as increased production of ROS induces VEGF and uPAR overexpression resulting in diabetes-induced barrier dysfunction. In combination, supraphysiological glucose levels and oxidative stress loosen tight cell-cell adhesive junctions of cells to increase BRB permeability [155].

Role of PKC Activation in Hyperglycemia-Induced Permeability

Glucose-induced activation of the PKC pathway appears to have multiple detrimental effects on retinal endothelium including increased contractility, permeability and proliferation[37, 115]. Retinal vascular cells in humans and experimentally-induced diabetic animal models demonstrate chronically increased DAG levels as well as activation of PKC which correlate with glucose levels[116, 117]. Specific PKC isoforms appear to be involved in early diabetic retinopathy vascular pathologies. Particularly, PKC α and β isoforms, are involved in endothelial cell permeability alterations induced by hyperglycemia, including capillaries in the retina[115, 116, 118, 119]. Although incompletely defined, PKC activation appears to increase retinal endothelial cell permeability by phosphorylating cytoskeletal proteins associated with junctional complexes including vinculin, talin and caldesmon resulting in cell-cell junction destabilization[37, 120-123]. PKC- β activation reduces blood flow in diabetic retinas of animals and patients inducing hypoxic conditions and leading to expression of VEGF and upregulation of VEGF activity[115]. PKC-dependent VEGF activation increases permeability that can be attenuated by treatment with PKC-β selective inhibitor[124, 125]. Inhibitors of VEGF receptor kinases and PKC also reduce retinal endothelial cell permeability produced by prostaglandin E1 (PGE1), but not cytokines such as IL-1 beta and TNF-alpha suggesting that permeability factors act in a PKC-dependent manner[126]. There is experimental evidence that hyperglycemia- induced oxidative stress can also prompt PKC activation and subsequent vascular permeability[127]. Taken together, it would appear that VEGF is an important downstream effector of PKC-related BRB dysfunction.

Role of PMN Adherence in Retinal Permeability

Another source of ROS generation and a critical event in early diabetic microvascular pathology, is the adherence of leukocytes to the endothelium lining retinal capillaries[128]. Circulating PMNs are activated by inflammatory stimuli and begin to adhere to the walls of capillary vessels (endothelial-neutrophil tethering and adhesion) in a receptor-dependent mechanism. Adhesion of PMNs increases paracellular gap formation to facilitate passage of the PMNs through the endothelium to the surrounding retinal tissue (diapedesis). A key event in leukocyte adhesion-associated paracellular gap formation surface is a significant rise in endothelial cell cytosolic Ca^{2+} levels which activate Ca^{2+}-dependent signaling cascades and regulate contraction of the EC actomyosin network by increasing Ca^{2+}/ calmodulin-dependent, MLCK-mediated MLC phosphorylation. Upregulated MLCK activity increases MLC phosphorylation and subsequently, contractility of the actin network resulting in a decrease in cell-cell junction integrity and paracellular gap formation[129, 130]. Diapedesis can be attenuated by reduction of MLCK activity[22, 131, 132]. These data underscore the importance of MLCK activity triggering actomyosin dynamics in leukocyte-induced permeability and diapedesis. Adherent leukocytes also affect barrier permeability by triggering loosening of endothelial cell-cell junctions by inducing reorganization of adherens junctional proteins such as vascular endothelial (VE)- cadherin[133]. Leukocytes abnormally and chronically bind to retinal vascular endothelium under hyperglycemic conditions followed by subsequent barrier dysfunction and onset of endothelial cell apoptosis[134, 135]. Adhesion to endothelial cells in both normal and diabetic conditions is in part mediated by selectins, vascular cell adhesion molecule (VCAM-1), and ICAM-1[86]. Under hyperglycemic conditions, increased exogenous VEGF stimulates ICAM-1 and surface integrin subunit CD18 expression in the retinal capillaries[135, 136]. Furthermore, inhibition of ICAM-1 or CD 18 in early diabetic retinopathy reduces leukocyte adhesion as well as BRB permeability[128, 134, 137].

Advanced glycation end products (AGEs) are formed by complex non-enzymatic glycation reactions that modify proteins and lipids with glucose. Induction of pro-inflammatory responses and leukocyte adhesion is related to AGE-mediated dysfunction[128]. AGEs accumulate in retinal vascular cells at a high rate in diabetics [128, 138-140] and experimental introduction of AGEs in normal animals can induce pathologies resembling diabetic retinopathies including upregulation of VEGF[141]. Transcription factor expression pathways such as NFκB are activated by accumulation of advanced glycation products which increase expression of adhesion molecules such as ICAM-1. The combination of upregulated VEGF, CD18- and ICAM-1-mediated PMN binding in the diabetic vasculature may cause a cumulative increase in BRB permeability.

Chronic leukocyte adherence is correlated with and appears to be a cause of early diabetic retinal endothelial cell injury with both necrotic and apoptotic cell death[134, 142]. Extensive retinal EC and pericyte death results in formation of acellular capillary vessels. Although the basement membrane structure of the tubes remains intact, capillary nonperfusion results in retinal ischemia[134, 143]. Leukocyte adhesion-mediated low oxygen levels trigger signaling cascades which lead to upregulation of VEGF expression and pathogenic neovascularization.

Role of Angiogenic Factors in Retinal Permeability

Angiostatin and endostatin were identified as anti-cancer agents which inhibit neovascularization and tumor growth by inhibition of endothelial cell proliferation and triggering apoptosis[144]. Angiostatin and endostatin are not members of the statin family of drugs which affect HMG CoA reductase, but represent proteolytic fragments of plasminogen [145] and collagen XVIII respectively [146] which attenuate angiogenesis by inhibiting proliferation and inducing apoptosis in endothelial cells[144, 146]. However, angiostatin treatment also reduced endothelial permeability in retinas with experimentally-induced retinopathies by streptozotocin treatment or oxygen-induced retinopathy[147, 148]. Retinas of experimental animal models of diabetic retinopathy have upregulated VEGF levels which contribute to barrier permeability. VEGF expression in diseased retinas, but not normal retinas, is significantly downregulated by angiostatin treatment[145]. Endostatin also appears to reduce levels of experimentally upregulated VEGF levels when endostatin was introduced by gene transfer[149, 150]. The mechanism of angiostatin-induced permeability inhibition may involve interaction with integrins to impact cell-matrix adhesion properties[151]. In addition, angiostatin appears to suppress activation of the p42/p44 mitogen activated protein (MAP kinase) pathway and in this way, regulate VEGF expression and reduce vascular permeability[152-154].

Summary

Increases in vascular permeability are critical features of ischemia, angiogenesis, inflammation and a key component of retinal pathobiology. Multiple signaling cascades related to hyperglycemic conditions appear to contribute to blood retinal barrier dysfunction including PKC signaling pathways, increases in oxidative stress, AGE products, angiogenic factors and pathological inflammatory responses such as chronic leukocyte diapedesis.

Several of these cascades include upregulation of VEGF expression and activity as downstream effectors that contribute to pathological changes in the integrity of the adherens and tight junctions between retinal microvascular endothelial cells. Central to the evolution of these physiological derangements is activation of the actomyosin-based endothelial cytoskeleton, an extremely dynamic cellular component responsive to receptor and non-receptor-based signaling and a critical determinant of cell-cell junctional integrity. Extracellular gaps created by contraction of the endothelial cell actomyosin network result in increased paracellular flow of fluid and macromolecules. Increased edema formation within the delicate and extremely complex structure of the retina results in blurred vision and blindness. Although currently there are no known effective non-invasive therapies for diabetic retinopathic changes within the retina, agents which reduce vascular permeability in the retina (Sph 1-P, statins and OxPAP) and alter the retinal barrier properties may attenuate retinal edema and serve as novel therapeutics to reduce visual blurring and loss.

REFERENCES

[1] Hayreh, S.S., Segmental nature of the choroidal vasculature. *B J Ophthal*, 1975. 59: p. 631-648.

[2] Zhang, H., Scanning electron-microscopic study of corrosion casts on retinal and choroidal angioarchitecture in man and animals. *Progress in Retinal and Eye Research*, 1994. 13(1): p. 243-270.

[3] Dudek, S.M. and J.G. Garcia, Cytoskeletal regulation of pulmonary vascular permeability. *J Appl Physiol*, 2001. 91(4): p. 1487-500.

[4] Cunha-Vaz, J.G., M. Shakib, and N. Ashton, Studies on the permeability of the blood-retinal barrier. I. On the existence, development, and site of a blood-retinal barrier. *Br J Ophthalmol,* 1966. 50(8): p. 441-53.

[5] Cunha-Vaz, J.G., The blood-retinal barriers system. Basic concepts and clinical evaluation. *Exp Eye Res*, 2004. 78(3): p. 715-21.

[6] Vinores, S.A., et al., Immunohistochemical localization of blood-retinal barrier breakdown in human diabetics. *Am J Pathol*, 1989. 134(2): p. 231-5.

[7] Do carmo, A., et al., Breakdown of the inner and outer blood retinal barrier in streptozotocin-induced diabetes. *Exp Eye Res*, 1998. 67(5): p. 569-75.

[8] Klein, R. and B.E. Klein, Diabetic eye disease. *Lancet*, 1997. 350(9072): p. 197-204.

[9] Cunha-Vaz, J.G., et al., Characterization of the early stages of diabetic retinopathy by vitreous fluorophotometry. *Diabetes*, 1985. 34(1): p. 53-9.

[10] Cunha-Vaz, J.G., et al., Detection of early retinal changes in diabetes by vitreous fluorophotometry. *Diabetes*, 1979. 28(1): p. 16-9.

[11] Cunha-Vaz, J.G. and M. Shakib, Ultrastructural mechanisms of breakdown of the blood-retina barrier. *J Pathol Bacteriol*, 1967. 93(2): p. 645-52.

[12] Cunha-Vaz, J.G., Studies on the permeability of the blood-retinal barrier. 3. Breakdown of the blood-retinal barrier by circulatory disturbances. *Br J Ophthalmol*, 1966. 50(9): p. 505-16.

[13] Qaum, T., et al., VEGF-initiated blood-retinal barrier breakdown in early diabetes. *Invest Ophthalmol Vis Sci*, 2001. 42(10): p. 2408-13.

[14] Moss, S.E., R. Klein, and B.E. Klein, The 14-year incidence of visual loss in a diabetic population. *Ophthalmology*, 1998. 105: p. 998-1003.
[15] Williamson, J.R., et al., Increased vascular permeability in spontaneously diabetic BB/W rats and in rats with mild versus severe streptozocin-induced diabetes. Prevention by aldose reductase inhibitors and castration. *Diabetes*, 1987. 36(7): p. 813-21.
[16] Phillips, P.G., et al., Phallacidin prevents thrombin-induced increases in endothelial permeability to albumin. *Am J Physiol*, 1989. 257(3 Pt 1): p. C562-7.
[17] Sellers, J.R. and M.D. Pato, The binding of smooth muscle myosin light chain kinase and phosphatases to actin and myosin. *J Biol Chem*, 1984. 259(12): p. 7740-6.
[18] Kamm, K.E. and J.T. Stull, The function of myosin and myosin light chain kinase phosphorylation in smooth muscle. *Annu Rev Pharmacol Toxicol*, 1985. 25: p. 593-620.
[19] Goeckeler, Z.M. and R.B. Wysolmerski, Myosin light chain kinase-regulated endothelial cell contraction: the relationship between isometric tension, actin polymerization, and myosin phosphorylation. *J Cell Biol*, 1995. 130(3): p. 613-27.
[20] Garcia, J.G., et al., Diperoxovanadate alters endothelial cell focal contacts and barrier function: role of tyrosine phosphorylation. *J Appl Physiol*, 2000. 89(6): p. 2333-43.
[21] Garcia, J.G., et al., Thrombin-induced increase in albumin permeability across the endothelium. *J Cell Physiol*, 1986. 128(1): p. 96-104.
[22] Garcia, J.G. and K.L. Schaphorst, Regulation of endothelial cell gap formation and paracellular permeability. *J Investig Med*, 1995. 43(2): p. 117-26.
[23] van Nieuw Amerongen, G.P., et al., Transient and prolonged increase in endothelial permeability induced by histamine and thrombin: role of protein kinases, calcium, and RhoA. *Circ Res*, 1998. 83(11): p. 1115-23.
[24] Garcia, J.G., H.W. Davis, and C.E. Patterson, Regulation of endothelial cell gap formation and barrier dysfunction: role of myosin light chain phosphorylation. *J Cell Physiol,* 1995. 163(3): p. 510-22.
[25] Kolodney, M.S. and R.B. Wysolmerski, Isometric contraction by fibroblasts and endothelial cells in tissue culture: a quantitative study. *J Cell Biol*, 1992. 117(1): p. 73-82.
[26] Schaphorst, K.L., et al., Thrombin-mediated focal adhesion plaque reorganization in endothelium: role of protein phosphorylation. *Am J Respir Cell Mol Biol*, 1997. 17(4): p. 443-55.
[27] Garcia, J.G., et al., Myosin light chain kinase in endothelium: molecular cloning and regulation. *Am J Respir Cell Mol Biol*, 1997. 16(5): p. 489-94.
[28] Lazar, V. and J.G. Garcia, A single human myosin light chain kinase gene (MLCK; MYLK). *Genomics*, 1999. 57(2): p. 256-67.
[29] Birukov, K.G., et al., Differential regulation of alternatively spliced endothelial cell myosin light chain kinase isoforms by p60(Src). *J Biol Chem*, 2001. 276(11): p. 8567-73.
[30] Tapon, N. and A. Hall, Rho, Rac and Cdc42 GTPases regulate the organization of the actin cytoskeleton. *Curr Opin Cell Biol,* 1997. 9(1): p. 86-92.
[31] Ridley, A.J. and A. Hall, The small GTP-binding protein rho regulates the assembly of focal adhesions and actin stress fibers in response to growth factors. *Cell,* 1992. 70(3): p. 389-99.

[32] Essler, M., et al., Thrombin inactivates myosin light chain phosphatase via Rho and its target Rho kinase in human endothelial cells. *J Biol Chem*, 1998. 273(34): p. 21867-74.
[33] Amano, M., et al., Formation of actin stress fibers and focal adhesions enhanced by Rho-kinase. *Science*, 1997. 275(5304): p. 1308-11.
[34] Kimura, K., et al., Regulation of myosin phosphatase by Rho and Rho-associated kinase (Rho-kinase). *Science*, 1996. 273(5272): p. 245-8.
[35] Dempsey, E.C., et al., Protein kinase C isozymes and the regulation of diverse cell responses. *Am J Physiol Lung Cell Mol Physiol*, 2000. 279(3): p. L429-38.
[36] Chang, Y.S., et al., Effect of vascular endothelial growth factor on cultured endothelial cell monolayer transport properties. *Microvasc Res*, 2000. 59(2): p. 265-77.
[37] Stasek, J.E., Jr., C.E. Patterson, and J.G. Garcia, Protein kinase C phosphorylates caldesmon77 and vimentin and enhances albumin permeability across cultured bovine pulmonary artery endothelial cell monolayers. *J Cell Physiol*, 1992. 153(1): p. 62-75.
[38] Chiang, E.T., et al., Sphingosine 1-phosphate enhances endothelial barrier integrity through PKC-zeta signaling. in preparation, 2005.
[39] Petrache, I., et al., Differential effect of MLC kinase in TNF-alpha-induced endothelial cell apoptosis and barrier dysfunction. *Am J Physiol Lung Cell Mol Physiol*, 2001. 280(6): p. L1168-78.
[40] Zhao, Y. and H.W. Davis, Endotoxin causes phosphorylation of MARCKS in pulmonary vascular endothelial cells. *J Cell Biochem*, 2000. 79(3): p. 496-505.
[41] Vinores, S.A., Assessment of blood-retinal barrier integrity. *Histol Histopathol*, 1995. 10(1): p. 141-54.
[42] Shakib, M. and J.G. Cunha-Vaz, Studies on the permeability of the blood-retinal barrier. IV. Junctional complexes of the retinal vessels and their role in the permeability of the blood-retinal barrier. *Exp Eye Res*, 1966. 5(3): p. 229-34.
[43] Kemler, R., Classical cadherins. *Semin Cell Biol*, 1992. 3(3): p. 149-55.
[44] Kemler, R., From cadherins to catenins: cytoplasmic protein interactions and regulation of cell adhesion. *Trends Genet*, 1993. 9(9): p. 317-21.
[45] Aberle, H., H. Schwartz, and R. Kemler, Cadherin-catenin complex: protein interactions and their implications for cadherin function. *J Cell Biochem*, 1996. 61(4): p. 514-23.
[46] Corada, M., et al., Vascular endothelial-cadherin is an important determinant of microvascular integrity in vivo. *Proc Natl Acad Sci U S A*, 1999. 96(17): p. 9815-20.
[47] Anderson, J.M. and C.M. Van Itallie, Tight junctions and the molecular basis for regulation of paracellular permeability. *Am J Physiol*, 1995. 269(4 Pt 1): p. G467-75.
[48] Mitic, L.L. and J.M. Anderson, Molecular architecture of tight junctions. *Annu Rev Physiol,* 1998. 60: p. 121-42.
[49] Kevil, C.G., et al., Vascular permeability factor/vascular endothelial cell growth factor-mediated permeability occurs through disorganization of endothelial junctional proteins. *J Biol Chem,* 1998. 273(24): p. 15099-103.
[50] Antonetti, D.A., et al., Vascular permeability in experimental diabetes is associated with reduced endothelial occludin content: vascular endothelial growth factor decreases occludin in retinal endothelial cells. Penn State Retina Research Group. *Diabetes*, 1998. 47(12): p. 1953-9.
[51] Gardner, T.W., et al., The molecular structure and function of the inner blood-retinal barrier. Penn State Retina Research Group. *Doc Ophthalmol*, 1999. 97(3-4): p. 229-37.

[52] Vestweber, D., Molecular mechanisms that control endothelial cell contacts. *J Pathol*, 2000. 190(3): p. 281-91.
[53] Kim, K.J., et al., Inhibition of vascular endothelial growth factor-induced angiogenesis suppresses tumour growth in vivo. *Nature*, 1993. 362(6423): p. 841-4.
[54] Thurston, G., et al., Leakage-resistant blood vessels in mice transgenically overexpressing angiopoietin-1. *Science*, 1999. 286(5449): p. 2511-4.
[55] Belperio, J.A., et al., CXC chemokines in angiogenesis. *J Leukoc Biol*, 2000. 68(1): p. 1-8.
[56] Strieter, R.M., J.A. Belperio, and M.P. Keane, CXC chemokines in angiogenesis related to pulmonary fibrosis. *Chest,* 2002. 122(6 Suppl): p. 298S-301S.
[57] Liu, F., et al., Hepatocyte growth factor enhances endothelial cell barrier function and cortical cytoskeletal rearrangement: Potential role of glycogen synthase kinase 3 beta. *FASEB J,* 2002. 16(9): p. 950-962.
[58] English, D., et al., Induction of endothelial cell chemotaxis by sphingosine 1-phosphate and stabilization of endothelial monolayer barrier function by lysophosphatidic acid, potential mediators of hematopoietic angiogenesis. *J Hematother Stem Cell Res*, 1999. 8(6): p. 627-34.
[59] Garcia, J.G., et al., Sphingosine 1-phosphate promotes endothelial cell barrier integrity by Edg-dependent cytoskeletal rearrangement. *J Clin Invest*, 2001. 108(5): p. 689-701.
[60] Antonetti, D.A., et al., Vascular endothelial growth factor induces rapid phosphorylation of tight junction proteins occludin and zonula occluden 1. A potential mechanism for vascular permeability in diabetic retinopathy and tumors. *J Biol Chem*, 1999. 274(33): p. 23463-7.
[61] Ishibashi, T., K. Tanaka, and Y. Taniguchi, Platelet aggregation and coagulation in the pathogenesis of diabetic retinopathy in rats. *Diabetes*, 1981. 30(7): p. 601-6.
[62] English, D., et al., Sphingosine 1-phosphate released from platelets during clotting accounts for the potent endothelial cell chemotactic activity of blood serum and provides a novel link between hemostasis and angiogenesis. *FASEB J*, 2000. 14(14): p. 2255-65.
[63] Natarajan, V., et al., Activation of endothelial cell phospholipase D by sphingosine and sphingosine-1-phosphate. *Am J Respir Cell Mol Biol*, 1994. 11(2): p. 221-9.
[64] Spiegel, S. and S. Milstien, Sphingosine-1-phosphate: signaling inside and out. *FEBS Lett,* 2000. 476(1-2): p. 55-7.
[65] Pyne, S. and N.J. Pyne, Sphingosine 1-phosphate signalling in mammalian cells. *Biochem J,* 2000. 349(Pt 2): p. 385-402.
[66] Hla, T., Sphingosine 1-phosphate receptors. *Prostaglandins Other Lipid Mediat*, 2001. 64(1-4): p. 135-42.
[67] Liu, F., et al., Differential regulation of sphingosine-1-phosphate- and VEGF-induced endothelial cell chemotaxis. Involvement of G(ialpha2)-linked Rho kinase activity. *Am J Respir Cell Mol Biol,* 2001. 24(6): p. 711-9.
[68] Wadgaonkar, R., et al., Mutation analysis of the non-muscle myosin light chain kinase (MLCK) deletion constructs on CV1 fibroblast contractile activity and proliferation. *J Cell Biochem,* 2003. 88(3): p. 623-34.
[69] Dudek, S.M., et al., Pulmonary endothelial cell barrier enhancement by sphingosine 1-phosphate: roles for cortactin and myosin light chain kinase. *J Biol Chem*, 2004. 279(23): p. 24692-700.

[70] Yamashiro, K., et al., Platelets accumulate in the diabetic retinal vasculature following endothelial death and suppress blood-retinal barrier breakdown. *Am J Pathol*, 2003. 163(1): p. 253-9.
[71] Birukov, K.G., et al., Epoxycyclopentenone-containing oxidized phospholipids restore endothelial barrier function via Cdc42 and Rac. *Circ Res*, 2004. 95(9):892-901.
[72] Jacobson, J.R., et al., Cytoskeletal activation and altered gene expression in endothelial barrier regulation by simvastatin. *Am J Respir Cell Mol Biol*, 2004. 30(5): p. 662-70.
[73] Watson, A.D., et al., Structural identification by mass spectrometry of oxidized phospholipids in minimally oxidized low density lipoprotein that induce monocyte/endothelial interactions and evidence for their presence in vivo. *J Biol Chem*, 1997. 272(21): p. 13597-607.
[74] Bochkov, V.N., et al., Protective role of phospholipid oxidation products in endotoxin-induced tissue damage. *Nature*, 2002. 419(6902): p. 77-81.
[75] Bochkov, V.N., et al., Oxidized phospholipids stimulate tissue factor expression in human endothelial cells via activation of ERK/EGR-1 and Ca(++)/NFAT. *Blood*, 2002. 99(1): p. 199-206.
[76] Harrington, E.O., et al., Role of protein kinase C isoforms in rat epididymal microvascular endothelial barrier function. *Am J Respir Cell Mol Biol*, 2003. 28(5): p. 626-36.
[77] Bogatcheva, N.V., et al., Phorbol esters increase MLC phosphorylation and actin remodeling in bovine lung endothelium without increased contraction. *Am J Physiol Lung Cell Mol Physiol*, 2003. 285(2): p. L415-26.
[78] Han, J.D. and C.S. Rubin, Regulation of cytoskeleton organization and paxillin dephosphorylation by cAMP. Studies on murine Y1 adrenal cells. *J Biol Chem*, 1996. 271(46): p. 29211-5.
[79] Lang, P., et al., Protein kinase A phosphorylation of RhoA mediates the morphological and functional effects of cyclic AMP in cytotoxic lymphocytes. *Embo J*, 1996. 15(3): p. 510-9.
[80] Birukov, K.G., et al., Signal transduction pathways activated in human pulmonary endothelial cells by OxPAPC, a bioactive component of oxidized lipoproteins. *Microvasc Res,* 2004. 67(1): p. 18-28.
[81] Scandinavian, et al., Randomised trial of cholesterol lowering in 4444 patients with coronary heart disease: the Scandinavian Simvastatin Survival Study (4S). *Lancet.*, 1994. 344: p. 1383–1389.
[82] van Nieuw Amerongen, G.P., et al., Simvastatin improves disturbed endothelial barrier function. *Circulation*, 2000. 102(23): p. 2803-9.
[83] Mueck, A.O., H. Seeger, and D. Wallwiener, Further evidence for direct vascular actions of statins: effect on endothelial nitric oxide synthase and adhesion molecules. *Exp Clin Endocrinol Diabetes*, 2001. 109(3): p. 181-3.
[84] Miyahara, S., et al., Simvastatin inhibits leukocyte accumulation and vascular permeability in the retinas of rats with streptozotocin-induced diabetes. *Am J Pathol*, 2004. 164(5): p. 1697-706.
[85] Sluiter, W., et al., Leukocyte adhesion molecules on the vascular endothelium: their role in the pathogenesis of cardiovascular disease and the mechanisms underlying their expression. *J Cardiovasc Pharmacol*, 1993. 22 Suppl 4: p. S37-44.

[86] Miyamoto, K., et al., Prevention of leukostasis and vascular leakage in streptozotocin-induced diabetic retinopathy via intercellular adhesion molecule-1 inhibition. *Proc Natl Acad Sci U S A*, 1999. 96(19): p. 10836-41.

[87] Joussen, A.M., et al., Nonsteroidal anti-inflammatory drugs prevent early diabetic retinopathy via TNF-alpha suppression. *Faseb J*, 2002. 16(3): p. 438-40.

[88] Bussolino, F., et al., Hepatocyte growth factor is a potent angiogenic factor which stimulates endothelial cell motility and growth. *J Cell Biol*, 1992. 119(3): p. 629-41.

[89] Grant, D.S., et al., Scatter factor induces blood vessel formation in vivo. *Proc Natl Acad Sci U S A*, 1993. 90(5): p. 1937-41.

[90] Puchowicz, M.A., et al., Comparison of glucose influx and blood flow in retina and brain of diabetic rats. *J Cereb Blood Flow Metab*, 2004. 24(4): p. 449-57.

[91] Rajah, T.T., A.L. Olson, and P. Grammas, Differential glucose uptake in retina- and brain-derived endothelial cells. *Microvasc Res*, 2001. 62(3): p. 236-42.

[92] King, G.L., H. Ishii, and D. Koya, Diabetic vascular dysfunctions: a model of excessive activation of protein kinase C. *Kidney Int Suppl*, 1997. 60: p. S77-85.

[93] Baynes, J.W., Role of oxidative stress in development of complications in diabetes. *Diabetes*, 1991. 40(4): p. 405-12.

[94] Kaiser, N., et al., Differential regulation of glucose transport and transporters by glucose in vascular endothelial and smooth muscle cells. *Diabetes*, 1993. 42(1): p. 80-9.

[95] Dvorak, H.F., et al., Vascular permeability factor/vascular endothelial growth factor, microvascular hyperpermeability, and angiogenesis. *Am J Pathol*, 1995. 146(5): p. 1029-39.

[96] Senger, D.R., et al., Tumor cells secrete a vascular permeability factor that promotes accumulation of ascites fluid. *Science*, 1983. 219(4587): p. 983-5.

[97] Pierce, E.A., et al., Vascular endothelial growth factor/vascular permeability factor expression in a mouse model of retinal neovascularization. *Proc Natl Acad Sci U S A*, 1995. 92(3): p. 905-9.

[98] Aiello, L.P., et al., Hypoxic regulation of vascular endothelial growth factor in retinal cells. *Arch Ophthalmol*, 1995. 113(12): p. 1538-44.

[99] Tilton, R.G., et al., Vascular dysfunction induced by elevated glucose levels in rats is mediated by vascular endothelial growth factor. *J Clin Invest*, 1997. 99(9): p. 2192-202.

[100] Kuroki, M., et al., Reactive oxygen intermediates increase vascular endothelial growth factor expression in vitro and in vivo. *J Clin Invest*, 1996. 98(7): p. 1667-75.

[101] Murata, T., et al., Vascular endothelial growth factor plays a role in hyperpermeability of diabetic retinal vessels. *Ophthalmic Res*, 1995. 27(1): p. 48-52.

[102] Vinores, S.A., et al., Upregulation of vascular endothelial growth factor in ischemic and non-ischemic human and experimental retinal disease. *Histol Histopathol*, 1997. 12(1): p. 99-109.

[103] Hammes, H.P., et al., Upregulation of the vascular endothelial growth factor/vascular endothelial growth factor receptor system in experimental background diabetic retinopathy of the rat. *Diabetes*, 1998. 47(3): p. 401-6.

[104] Behzadian, M.A., et al., VEGF-induced paracellular permeability in cultured endothelial cells involves urokinase and its receptor. *Faseb J*, 2003. 17(6): p. 752-4.

[105] Mandriota, S.J., et al., Vascular endothelial growth factor increases urokinase receptor expression in vascular endothelial cells. *J Biol Chem*, 1995. 270(17): p. 9709-16.

[106] Bierhaus, A., et al., Advanced glycation end product-induced activation of NF-kappaB is suppressed by alpha-lipoic acid in cultured endothelial cells. *Diabetes*, 1997. 46(9): p. 1481-90.

[107] Tesfamariam, B. and R.A. Cohen, Free radicals mediate endothelial cell dysfunction caused by elevated glucose. *Am J Physiol*, 1992. 263(2 Pt 2): p. H321-6.

[108] Wolff, S.P. and R.T. Dean, Glucose autoxidation and protein modification. The potential role of 'autoxidative glycosylation' in diabetes. *Biochem J*, 1987. 245(1): p. 243-50.

[109] Ido, Y., et al., Vascular dysfunction induced by AGE is mediated by VEGF via mechanisms involving reactive oxygen species, guanylate cyclase, and protein kinase C. *Microcirculation*, 2001. 8(4): p. 251-63.

[110] Grammas, P. and M. Riden, Retinal endothelial cells are more susceptible to oxidative stress and increased permeability than brain-derived endothelial cells. *Microvasc Res*, 2003. 65(1): p. 18-23.

[111] Kowluru, R.A. and A. Kennedy, Therapeutic potential of anti-oxidants and diabetic retinopathy. *Expert Opin Investig Drugs*, 2001. 10(9): p. 1665-76.

[112] Nishikawa, T., et al., Normalizing mitochondrial superoxide production blocks three pathways of hyperglycaemic damage. *Nature*, 2000. 404(6779): p. 787-90.

[113] El-Remessy, A.B., et al., Experimental diabetes causes breakdown of the blood-retina barrier by a mechanism involving tyrosine nitration and increases in expression of vascular endothelial growth factor and urokinase plasminogen activator receptor. *Am J Pathol,* 2003. 162(6): p. 1995-2004.

[114] Takeda, M., et al., Constitutive nitric oxide synthase is associated with retinal vascular permeability in early diabetic rats. *Diabetologia,* 2001. 44(8): p. 1043-50.

[115] Koya, D. and G.L. King, Protein kinase C activation and the development of diabetic complications. *Diabetes*, 1998. 47(6): p. 859-66.

[116] Shiba, T., et al., Correlation of diacylglycerol level and protein kinase C activity in rat retina to retinal circulation. *Am J Physiol*, 1993. 265(5 Pt 1): p. E783-93.

[117] Inoguchi, T., et al., Insulin's effect on protein kinase C and diacylglycerol induced by diabetes and glucose in vascular tissues. *Am J Physiol*, 1994. 267(3 Pt 1): p. E369-79.

[118] Hempel, A., et al., High glucose concentrations increase endothelial cell permeability via activation of protein kinase C alpha. *Circ Res*, 1997. 81(3): p. 363-71.

[119] Ishii, H., et al., Amelioration of vascular dysfunctions in diabetic rats by an oral PKC beta inhibitor. *Science*, 1996. 272(5262): p. 728-31.

[120] Werth, D.K., J.E. Niedel, and I. Pastan, Vinculin, a cytoskeletal substrate of protein kinase C. *J Biol Chem*, 1983. 258(19): p. 11423-6.

[121] Schliwa, M., et al., A tumor promoter induces rapid and coordinated reorganization of actin and vinculin in cultured cells. *J Cell Biol*, 1984. 99(3): p. 1045-59.

[122] Oliver, J.A., Adenylate cyclase and protein kinase C mediate opposite actions on endothelial junctions. *J Cell Physiol*, 1990. 145(3): p. 536-42.

[123] Lynch, J.J., et al., Increased endothelial albumin permeability mediated by protein kinase C activation. *J Clin Invest*, 1990. 85(6): p. 1991-8.

[124] Aiello, L.P., et al., Vascular endothelial growth factor in ocular fluid of patients with diabetic retinopathy and other retinal disorders. *N Engl J Med*, 1994. 331(22): p.1480-7.

[125] Xia, P., et al., Characterization of vascular endothelial growth factor's effect on the activation of protein kinase C, its isoforms, and endothelial cell growth. *J Clin Invest,* 1996. 98(9): p. 2018-26.
[126] Saishin, Y., et al., Inhibition of protein kinase C decreases prostaglandin-induced breakdown of the blood-retinal barrier. *J Cell Physiol*, 2003. 195(2): p. 210-9.
[127] Konishi, H., et al., Activation of protein kinase C by tyrosine phosphorylation in response to H2O2. *Proc Natl Acad Sci U S A*, 1997. 94(21): p. 11233-7.
[128] Moore, T.C., et al., The role of advanced glycation end products in retinal microvascular leukostasis. *Invest Ophthalmol Vis Sci*, 2003. 44(10): p. 4457-64.
[129] Dull, R.O. and J.G. Garcia, Leukocyte-induced microvascular permeability: how contractile tweaks lead to leaks. *Circ Res*, 2002. 90(11): p. 1143-4.
[130] Yuan, S.Y., et al., Myosin light chain phosphorylation in neutrophil-stimulated coronary microvascular leakage. *Circ Res*, 2002. 90(11): p. 1214-21.
[131] Hixenbaugh, E.A., et al., Stimulated neutrophils induce myosin light chain phosphorylation and isometric tension in endothelial cells. *Am J Physiol*, 1997. 273(2 Pt 2): p. H981-8.
[132] Saito, H., et al., Endothelial myosin light chain kinase regulates neutrophil migration across human umbilical vein endothelial cell monolayer. *J Immunol*, 1998. 161(3): p. 1533-40.
[133] Del Maschio, A., et al., Polymorphonuclear leukocyte adhesion triggers the disorganization of endothelial cell-to-cell adherens junctions. *J Cell Biol*, 1996. 135(2): p. 497-510.
[134] Joussen, A.M., et al., Leukocyte-mediated endothelial cell injury and death in the diabetic retina. *Am J Pathol*, 2001. 158(1): p. 147-52.
[135] Miyamoto, K., et al., Vascular endothelial growth factor (VEGF)-induced retinal vascular permeability is mediated by intercellular adhesion molecule-1 (ICAM-1). *Am J Pathol*, 2000. 156(5): p. 1733-9.
[136] Lu, M., et al., VEGF increases retinal vascular ICAM-1 expression in vivo. *Invest Ophthalmol Vis Sci,* 1999. 40(8): p. 1808-12.
[137] Barouch, F.C., et al., Integrin-mediated neutrophil adhesion and retinal leukostasis in diabetes. *Invest Ophthalmol Vis Sci*, 2000. 41(5): p. 1153-8.
[138] Hammes, H.P., et al., Differential accumulation of advanced glycation end products in the course of diabetic retinopathy. *Diabetologia,* 1999. 42(6): p. 728-36.
[139] Stitt, A.W., et al., Advanced glycation end products (AGEs) co-localize with AGE receptors in the retinal vasculature of diabetic and of AGE-infused rats. *Am J Pathol,* 1997. 150(2): p. 523-31.
[140] Makita, Z., et al., Hemoglobin-AGE: a circulating marker of advanced glycosylation. *Science*, 1992. 258(5082): p. 651-3.
[141] Stitt, A.W., et al., Advanced glycation end products induce blood-retinal barrier dysfunction in normoglycemic rats. *Mol Cell Biol Res Commun*, 2000. 3(6): p. 380-8.
[142] Schroder, S., W. Palinski, and G.W. Schmid-Schonbein, Activated monocytes and granulocytes, capillary nonperfusion, and neovascularization in diabetic retinopathy. *Am J Pathol,* 1991. 139(1): p. 81-100.
[143] Mizutani, M., T.S. Kern, and M. Lorenzi, Accelerated death of retinal microvascular cells in human and experimental diabetic retinopathy. *J Clin Invest*, 1996. 97(12): p. 2883-90.

[144] Claesson-Welsh, L., et al., Angiostatin induces endothelial cell apoptosis and activation of focal adhesion kinase independently of the integrin-binding motif RGD. *Proc Natl Acad Sci U S A*, 1998. 95(10): p. 5579-83.

[145] Sima, J., et al., The effect of angiostatin on vascular leakage and VEGF expression in rat retina. *FEBS Lett*, 2004. 564(1-2): p. 19-23.

[146] O'Rèilly, M.S., et al., Endostatin: an endogenous inhibitor of angiogenesis and tumor growth. *Cell,* 1997. 88(2): p. 277-85.

[147] Lai, C.C., et al., Suppression of choroidal neovascularization by adeno-associated virus vector expressing angiostatin. *Invest Ophthalmol Vis Sci*, 2001. 42(10): p. 2401-7.

[148] Meneses, P.I., et al., Recombinant angiostatin prevents retinal neovascularization in a murine proliferative retinopathy model. *Gene Ther*, 2001. 8(8): p. 646-8.

[149] Takahashi, K., et al., Intraocular expression of endostatin reduces VEGF-induced retinal vascular permeability, neovascularization, and retinal detachment. *Faseb J,* 2003. 17(8): p. 896-8.

[150] Campochiaro, P.A., Ocular neovascularisation and excessive vascular permeability. *Expert Opin Biol Ther*, 2004. 4(9): p. 1395-402.

[151] Tarui, T., L.A. Miles, and Y. Takada, Specific interaction of angiostatin with integrin alpha(v)beta(3) in endothelial cells. *J Biol Chem*, 2001. 276(43): p. 39562-8.

[152] Redlitz, A., G. Daum, and E.H. Sage, Angiostatin diminishes activation of the mitogen-activated protein kinases ERK-1 and ERK-2 in human dermal microvascular endothelial cells. *J Vasc Res*, 1999. 36(1): p. 28-34.

[153] Pages, G., et al., Signaling angiogenesis via p42/p44 MAP kinase cascade. *Ann N Y Acad Sci*, 2000. 902: p. 187-200.

[154] Milanini, J., et al., p42/p44 MAP kinase module plays a key role in the transcriptional regulation of the vascular endothelial growth factor gene in fibroblasts. *J Biol Chem*, 1998. 273(29): p. 18165-72.

[155] Ito, T., et al., Effect of glucose on intercellular junctions of cultured human peritoneal mesothelial cells. *J Am Soc Nephrol,* 2000. 11(11):1969-79.

In: Focus on Eye Research
Editor: O.R. Ioseliani, pp. 153-172
ISBN: 1-59454-434-4

Chapter 7

A NOVEL 88 KDA ACUTE PHASE PROTEIN IN INFLAMMATIONS AND ITS ANTIOXIDANT FUNCTION

S. Ramakrishnan*, M. Rajesh and K. N. Sulochana
Biochemistry Research Department, Vision Research Foundation,
Sankara Nethralaya, Chennai, India.

ABSTRACT

Identification, purification and characterization of a new protein from the serum of patients with Eales' disease is presented. The protein was purified using preparative electrophoresis and HPLC. It resolved in α_2 globulin region. The purified protein had a retention time of 9.2 min in RP-HPLC. The molecular weight as determined by gel permeation chromatography was 88 kDa. Hence the protein is referred as 88 kDa protein. Periodic acid Schiff's staining revealed it as a glycoprotein. It was completely denatured above 70° C. Its isoelectric pH was 5. The protein was present in the vitreous and epiretinal membrane of Eales' patients and the blood of patients with systemic diseases like tuberculosis, leprosy and rheumatoid arthritis, but was absent in diabetic retinopathy and healed vasculitis of Eales' disease, as in the latter there is no inflammation. Hence 88 kDa protein is an acute phase protein produced in inflammatory conditions. The protein of different sources and diseases was immunologically the same.

The N terminal amino acid sequence by automated Edman's degradation chemistry is

Ala-Asp-Asp-Pro-Asn-Ser-Leu-Ser-Pro-Ser-Ala-Phe-Ala-Glu-Ala-Leu-Ala-Leu-Leu-Arg-Asp-Ser-
A D D P N S L S P S A F A E A L A L L R D S

X-Leu-Ala-Arg-Phe-Val
X L A R F V

* Correspondence concerning this article should be addressed to Dr. S. Ramakrishnan, Biochemistry Research Department, Sankara Nethralaya, Vision Research Foundation, 18, College Road, Chennai – 600 006. E-mail address: drrk@sankaranethralaya.org. Phone: 91-44-28271616, Fax: 91-44-28254180.

Keywords: 88 kDa protein, purification, physico chemical properties, sequence of N terminal 28 amino acids and 3 internal peptides, found in serum, vitreous and epiretinal membrane in Eales' disease with inflammation, serum of other diseases like leprosy and tuberculosis with inflammation, acute phase protein, immunological identify, quenches Reactive oxygen species and Reactive Nitrogen Species, anti TBARS activity, 8% thiols, ferro oxidase, arrests Fenton's reaction, preventive and protective endogenous antioxidant, novel protein.

THE SEQUENCE OF 3 INTERNAL PEPTIDES IS AS FOLLOWS:

SKVHDSYN	K = Lysine	G = Glycine
SSGTSYAALA	H = Histidine	T = Threonine
SPSYEFEEDE	Y = Tyrosine	

As the protein is expressed in inflammatory conditions with accumulation of Reactive Oxygen Species (ROS) $O_2^{\bullet -}$, H_2O_2, $OH^{\bullet}$, it was predicated that the 88 kDa protein expressed in inflammation might have antioxidant function. Protein purified from both serum and vitreous exhibited antilipid peroxidation effect on erythrocytes when added during *in vitro* assay of thiobarbituric acid reactive substances (TBARS). The antiTBARS activity was completely inhibited by 0.1 mM concentration of para chloro mercuric benzoate (PCMB) and 5,5' dithio bis (2/nitro) benzoic acid (DTNB). Inhibition by PCMB suggested the presence of thiol groups (-SH) which may be involved in antioxidant function. On analysis, the protein was found to contain 8% thiols by mass. It also oxidized ferrous iron to ferric iron and is a ferro oxidase. As such, by removing ferrous iron, the protein could arrest the Fenton's reaction and Haber-Weiss-Fentons' reaction which produce $OH^{\bullet}$ free radical. So, it is a preventive antioxidant like ceruloplasmin which is also a ferro oxidase and arrests the Fenton's reaction and the Haber-Weiss-Fentons' reaction. By virtue of its 8% thiol content, it can also quench the oxygen free radicals directly like metallothioneins. In this respect, it could function as a protective antioxidant by removing the oxygen free radicals after their formation. i.e. protecting from oxidation by ROS and even by Reactive Nitrogen Species (RNS).

The protein and DNA data base search revealed no match to 88 kDa protein.

The molecular weight, sequence of N-terminal amino acids, functions as a preventive and protective antioxidant certify that the 88 kDa protein is a novel protein different from other antioxidant or iron-sequestering proteins like transferrin, hemopexin, haptoglobins, ceruloplasmin metallothioneins and Retinal pigment epithelial protective protein (RPP). It is expressed to offer natural defense against oxidant – assault during inflammation.

A novel 88 kDa protein was discovered in the Biochemistry Research Department, Vision Research Foundation, Sankara Nethralaya, Chennai, India, in the course of Research work done to unearth the etiology of Eales' disease (ED) (*Sulochana et al, 2001*). The disease is named after the scientist Henry Eales who described the disease in 1882 in a patient. In spite of many years of active research by different groups, the etiology of Eales' disease is not known till this date. It is an idiopathic venous occlusion that primarily affects the peripheral retina of young adults (Eales, 1880, 1882). The clinical symptoms in most cases are retinal vasculitis with inflammation within the eye that involves the retinal vessels including arterioles, recurrent vitreous hemorrhage and retinal neovascularization (*Spitzans et al., 1995*). Bleeding from neovascularization is common, usually recurrent and is one of the major causes for visual loss in such cases (*Das et al., 1994*). Vitreous hemorrhage is a prominent manifestation of the disease and is the major cause of visual impairment. In addition, the formation of epiretinal membrane imposes a tractional pull on the retina causing retinal detachment.

Timely intervention with pars plana vitrectomy, laser photocoagulation and removal of epiretinal membrane helps in the partial restoration of the vision. The treatment for ED is based on the symptoms. It includes corticosteroids, photocoagulation with or without cryoablation and vitrectomy as the case may be, depending on the clinical appraisal of the disease process (*Das et al., 1994 Biswas et al 2002*).

Vitreous hemorrhage is the prominent manifestation of the disease and is the major cause of visual impairment. Retinal vasculitis can be associated with (a) systemic disease (b) infectious disease and (c) disease exclusively affecting the eye (primary ocular disorders. ED and uveitis fall under category c i.e. primary eye disease.

ED is rare in developed countries like USA but common in the Indian subcontinent with an incidence of one in 200-250 ophthalmic patients (*Puttana, 1970*). The disease predominantly affects males in the age groups of 20-40 years and is often bilateral. The peak age of onset of symptoms is 20-30 years.

There are 2 stages in ED, the active vasculitis stage and the healed stage. The active stage is characterized with inflammation. *Rengarajan et al.* (1987) have identified and purified a 23 kDa protein from the serum of patients with ED and speculate that this protein might be involved in the pathogenesis of ED. We have found for the first time, a protein of molecular weight 88 kDa (hereafter referred to as 88 kDa protein) to be present in the sera of almost all the patients of ED with active vasculitis and inflammation. The protein was absent in healed vasculitis in which the inflammation had been cured by medical treatment.

The Protein was Identified by the Following Method

The serum samples of patients (25 µg/50 µl) with active vasculitis were run on 7.5% native polyacrylamide gel electrophoresis. After electrophoresis, the gel was stained with Coomassive brilliant blue R 250. It resolved in α_2 globulin region (figure 1). Samples showing the presence of the candidate protein were stored at – 20° C until they were used to get the purified protein. Serum samples from usually six to eight patients (1.5 gm protein / 25 ml serum) found to contain the protein were pooled and subjected to 70% ammonium sulphate precipitation. The precipitate was dialyzed against 10 mM phosphate buffer pH 7.4 for 48 hrs with frequent changes of buffer at every 4 to 6 hours interval. After dialysis, the sample was centrifuged at 5000 rpm for 30 min. at 4° C, the supernatant was subjected to further purification by preparative gel electrophoresis. During each step of purification, protein content was determined by method of *Lowry et al.* (1951). Preparative electrophoresis (Biorad 491 Hercules, CA, USA) was done on a 5% Native PAGE (NPAGE) and the proteins were eluted using 0.05 mM Tris-glycine buffer pH 8.3. Fractions of 5.0 ml were collected at a flow rate of 1.0 ml/min using continuous buffer elution system (Bio Rad Echno PumpEP1). All the fractions were screened at 280 nm using spectrophotometer (Beckman DU 640, Fullerton, CA, USA) for protein content and to asses the elution profile. They were also subjected to NPAGE and silver staining (*Morrissey, 1981*). The new protein eluted between 150-175 fractions (figure 2). The fractions positive for the protein were further subjected to anti TBARS activity. The active fractions were pooled and stored at -20°C until further purification. During every stage of purification, the presence of the protein was confirmed by performing 7.5 % NPAGE along with positive serum obtained from patients with Eales' disease.

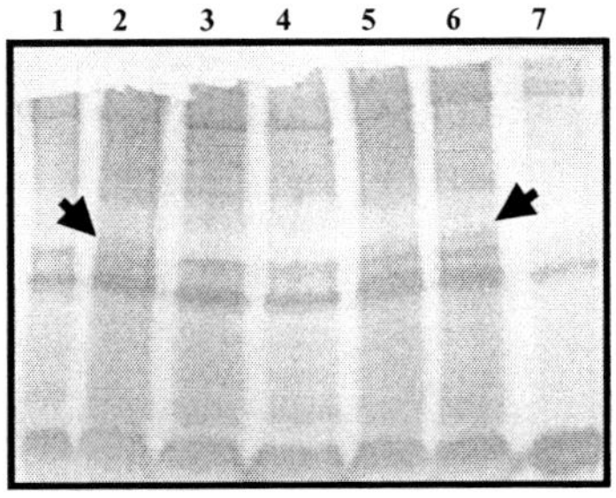

Figure 1: 7.5% native PAGE, stained by Commassie brilliant blue G250. Lane 1, and 7 serum from normal healthy volunteer, Lane 2,5 and 6 are serum from patients with Eales' disease, Lane 3 and 4 serum from patients with diabetic retinopathy. The presence of 88kDa protein in Lanes 2,5 and 6 is indicated by arrow in the photomicrograph. 20 mg of serum protein was uniformly used for protein profile.

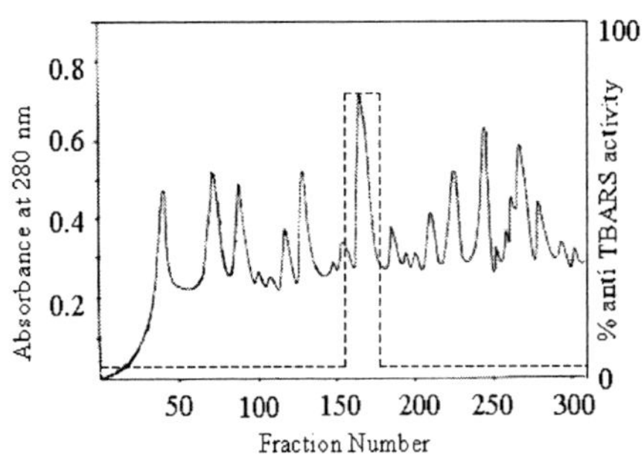

Figure 2: Elution profile of proteins from preparative cell electrophoresis system. 88 kDa protein gets eluted from 150 -175 fractions, which is represented by dashed line in the graph. Anti TBARS activity was maximum in these fractions.

Purification of the Protein: High Performance Liquid Chromatography (HPLC)

Active fractions from preparative electrophoresis were pooled and protein content was measured and then concentrated by lyophilization using Virtis freeze drier (NY, USA). The protein concentrate (50 mg) was further purified in batches using ODS reversed phase HPLC [LKB Bromma, Sweden].

Solvent A consisted of 0.05 % trifluroacetic acid (TFA) in Milli Q water (Millipore Co, MA, U.S.A). Solvent B consisted of 80 % acetonitrile and 0.05 % TFA in Milli Q water. The separation was performed using linear gradient 0.0 – 20.0 min 0.0 – 100 % B. The fractions were subjected to silver staining and anti TBARS activity. Active fractions were pooled and rechromatographed in the same conditions until the protein resolved as a homogeneous peak. In the RP-HPLC, the protein had a retention time of 9.2 min (figure 3). The purity was further checked by sodium dodecyl sulphate (SDS) PAGE electrophoresis followed by silver staining. The purified protein was dialyzed against 10 mM. N- (2 hydroxyethyl) piperazine – N'- (2 ethanesulfonic acid) [HEPES] buffer pH 7.4, and used for further characterization studies.

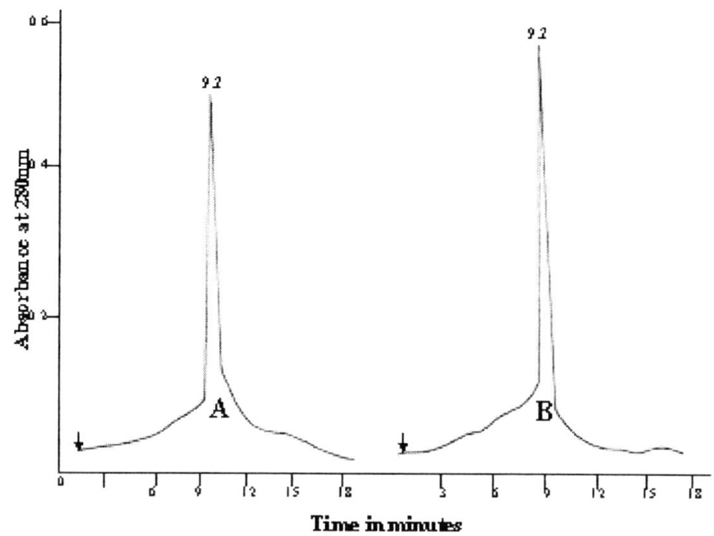

Figure 3: HPLC elution profile showing the homogeneity of the 88kDa protein from (A) serum and (B) vitreous (5 mg each) with retention time of 9.2 min. The separation was performed using RP C18 column 5 mm particle size with 300 A° pore size (Lichrosphere, Merck, Germany).

PHYSICO CHEMICAL PROPERTIES OF THE PROTEIN

Molecular Weight Determination

This was carried out using a gel permeation HPLC column (TSK 3000, Amersham Pharmacia, UK) and Sigma molecular weight markers. Along with these markers, 2 μg of purified protein was loaded to gel filtration column. The proteins were eluted with 10 mM phosphate buffer pH 7.4 containing 20 % methanol in 50 mM sodium chloride, at a flow rate of 0.2ml/min. The elution was monitored at 280 nm (LKB Bromma UV detector). Molecular weight was calculated from the graph plotted with retention time against log molecular weight (figure 4). In addition to the above, molecular weight of the purified protein was also determined by SDS PAGE (figure 5). In both the methods, the molecular weight of the new protein was found to be ~ 88 kDa.

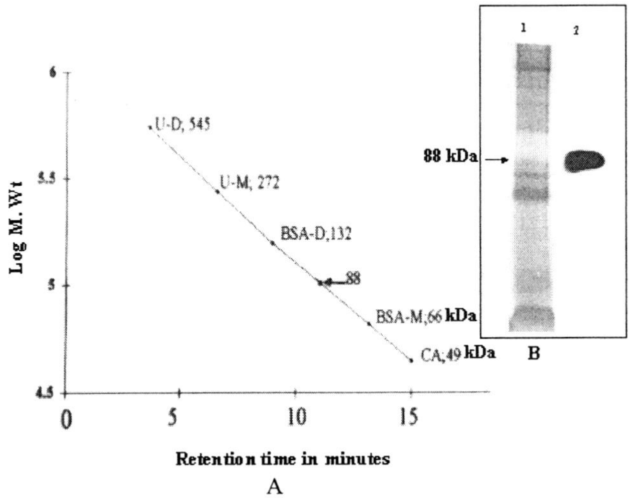

Figure 4: Molecular weight determination of the purified protein. This was done using gel filtration column (TSK 3000, Amersham Pharmacia, Sweden) using LKB Bromma HPLC system.. The gel permeation molecular weight markers used were urease dimer (545 kDa), urease monomer (272 kDa), BSA dimer (132 kDa), BSA monomer (66 kDa) and carbonic anhydrase (49 kDa). **B:** 7.5% native PAGE of purified protein stained by silver nitrate indicating its homogeneity. Lane 1, Serum (20 mg) from patient with Eales' disease, Lane 2, purified 88 kDa protein (30 mg).

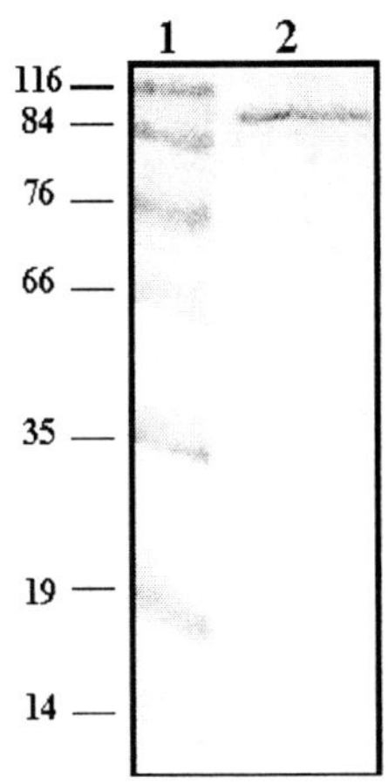

Figure 5: 12.5 % SDS PAGE gel profile for purified protein. Lane 1: molecular weight markers, Lane 2: purified protein from either serum or vitreous. The presence of homogeneous protein ~ 88 kDa was observed.

Determination of Isoelectric Point (pI)

Determination of pI of 88kDa protein was performed using Mini-Portean II tube cell apparatus (Bio Rad, U.S.A). In brief, the capillary tubes were filled with monomer solution consisting of 9.2 M urea (5.5 g), 4 % acrylamide (total monomer 1.33 ml), 20 % triton X 100 (2 ml), kaleidoscope pI marker i.e 1.6 % Bio- Lyte 5/7 ampholyte (0.4 ml) and 0.4 % Bio-

Lyte 3/10 ampholyte (0.1 ml) (Bio Rad) dH_2O, 0.01 % ammonium sulphate (10 μl) and 0.1 % TEMED (10 μL). This makes total volume of 10 ml sufficient to cast a set of 8 capillaries. The purified 88 kDa protein (5 μg/20μl) was mixed with 25 μl of sample buffer containing, 9.5 M urea, 2.0 % triton X 100, 5 % β mercaptoethanol and 1.6 % 5/7, 3/10 ampholyte markers and incubated at room temperature for 15 min. During the incubation time, the gel was pre-electrophoresed (300 V / 15 min) with the upper chamber buffer containing 100 mM NaOH and lower chamber containing 10 mM H_3PO_4. After pre-run, the buffers were discarded and the sample was loaded on to the tubes and overlaid with sample buffer 20 μl , which contained 9 M urea along with 0.8 % 5/7 ampholyte and 0.2 % 3/10 ampholyte. Then the focussing was performed by running the gels for 500V for 15 min, increasing to 750 V and continuing the run for 3.5 hrs. After the completion of the run the pI of the 88 kDa protein was determined by comparing with samples that contained standard proteins with ampholytes and with that of 88 kDa protein.

The protein had a pI at pH 5.

Thermal Stability of the 88 kDa Protein

0.5 μg 88 kDa protein /100 μl PBS pH 7.4 was incubated at various temperatures starting from 37°C - 70°C for varying time points (10 min – 60 min) and the anti TBARS activity was determined in these tubes. Results showed that 88 kDa protein was completely destroyed at 70°C when heated for more than 20 min.

88kDa protein - a Glycoprotein

Purified 88 kDa protein along with standard glycoprotein (ovalbumin) was resolved in SDS PAGE and PAS stain was performed. A positive pink staining indicated that 88 kDa is a glycoprotein (figure 6).

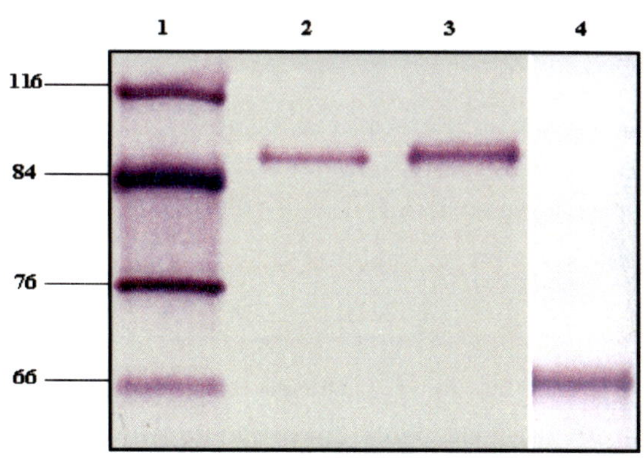

Figure 6: PAS stain for detecting glycoprotein. 12.5 % SDS PAGE gel profile, indicating the glycosylation of 88 kDa protein. Lane 1: Molecular weight markers, Lane 2: purified protein from vitreous of patients with ED, Lane 3: purified protein from serum of patients with ED. Lane 4: human albumin (monomer) was used as positive control.

Amino Terminal Sequencing of 88 kDa Protein (Matsudaria, 1987)

The purified protein was subjected to 12 % SDS PAGE electrophoresis and electrotransferred to polyvinylidine difluoride membrane (PVDF, Millipore Co., Bedford, MA, U.S.A) using Bio Rad Trans blot equipment. The electrotransfer was performed in buffer containing (3.3 g Tris base, 14.4 g glycine, 1.0 g SDS, 800 ml dH_2O and 200 ml CH_3OH) for 1hr at 100 V/400mA. The transferred protein was visualized by staining the membrane with 0.1 % ponceau S (dissolved in 1.0 % acetic acid in water). The protein band was then carefully excised, de-stained with several changes of Milli Q water. Then the PVDF membrane containing the protein was directly subjected to N terminal sequencing by using automated Edman degradation chemistry (*Matsudaria*, 1987) in Applied Biosystems 470A gas phase amino acid sequencer (Foster City, CA, USA). The derived sequence was analyzed by protein and DNA data base analysis using SWISS Prot, and NCBI programs.

Sequence of 28 amino acids from N-terminus of 88 kDa protein

^{1}Ala-Asp-Asp-Pro-Asn-Ser-Leu-Ser-Pro-Ser-Ala-Phe-Ala-Glu-Ala-Leu-Ala-Leu-Leu-Arg-Asp-Ser-
A D D P N S L S P S A F A E A L A L L R D S

X-Leu-Ala-Arg-Phe-Val ^{28}
X L A R F V

Conventional one letter symbols are used for amino acids
X - not determined

Determination of Internal Peptide Sequence

250 µg of purified protein was precipitated with 300 µl ice cold 100 % TCA, left in ice for 45 min and centrifuged at 4000 rpm at 4°C for 15 min. The supernatant was removed carefully and discarded. The precipitate was washed twice with ice-cold acetone (200 µl) by centrifuging as described above. Finally the precipitate was dissolved in 300 µl of 8 M urea solution. The solubilized protein was reduced with 10 µl of 45 mM dithiothreitol (DTT). This procedure was done in sealed ampules containing sample under nitrogen gas at 52°C for 30 min. Subsequently 10 µl of 25 mM iodoacetamide was added, after cooling the tubes to room temperature. The reaction was allowed to take place at room temperature for 15 min. To this, 150 µl of milli Q water was added. The protein was then digested with trypsin at the concentration of 0.2 mg / ml in 20mM ammonium carbonate buffer pH 8.0 for 12 – 16 hrs at 37°C. The contents were frozen rapidly in liquid nitrogen to stop the reaction and were reduced to near dryness in rotary speed vacumn concentrator (Savant Instruments, U.S.A). The residue was finally dissolved in 100 µl of Milli Q water and injected into C_8 column (Phenomax, U.S.A) and the peptides were separated using RP HPLC (Shimadzu –SLC6A, Japan). The solvents used were as follows **A**: 0.1 % TFA in water. **B**: 80 % CH_3CN in 0.75 %

TFA in water. The gradient program was: 0-5 min 0 % B, 5 – 65 min 100 % B, 65-70 min 100 % B, 80 min 0 % B. Elution was monitored at 214 nm. The major peaks were collected and used for further processing. Data collection and processing was done using C-R7A Plus software (Shimadzu Corp. Japan). The volume of the major fractions was reduced to 50 μl and then rechromatography was performed to obtain pure peptides. The chromatographic conditions were similar as described above. The fractions containing pure peptides were reduced in volume and loaded on to automated amino acid sequencer (PSQ –1, Shimadzu, Japan) to obtain the internal peptide sequence. The derived sequence was analyzed by protein and DNA data base analysis using SWISS Prot, and NCBI programs.

Internal peptide sequence derived from tryptic digestion of purified 88 kDa protein

Peak	Retention time	Sequence
12	18	S K VHDSYN
14	21	SSGTSYAALA
17	23	SPSYEFEEDE

K = Lysine G = Glycine H = Histidine
T = Threonine Y = Tyrosine

Occurrence of protein in the vitreous: The protein was found to be present in the vitreous of patients with active vasculitis. (*Sulochana et al. 2001*)

Purification of the Protein from the Vitreous

Purification of 88 kDa protein from vitreous was done by adopting the same procedure used for serum, but for the omission of ammonium sulfate precipitation. The undiluted vitreous samples (4.0 ml) from six patients were pooled, homogenized with phosphate buffered saline pH 7.4 and centrifuged at 5000 rpm for 30 minutes at 4°C. The protein content in the supernatant was measured by the method of *Lowry et al.* (1951). The supernatant (3ml) was directly subjected to 5% preparative polyacrylamide gel electrophoresis. The fractions were analyzed as for serum. The active fractions were pooled and purified further by RP-HPLC. The purified protein was dialyzed against 10 mM HEPES buffer pH 7.4 and then used for characterization. All these procedures were done in a cold room maintained at 4°C.

Protein in Epiretinal Membrane

Immuno histochemistry was performed on epiretinal membranes (ERM) obtained from ED patients. 88 kDa protein was localized in inflammatory cells and in nonvascular endothelium in ERM obtained from patients with ED (*Swami et al*, 2002). (Figure: 7)

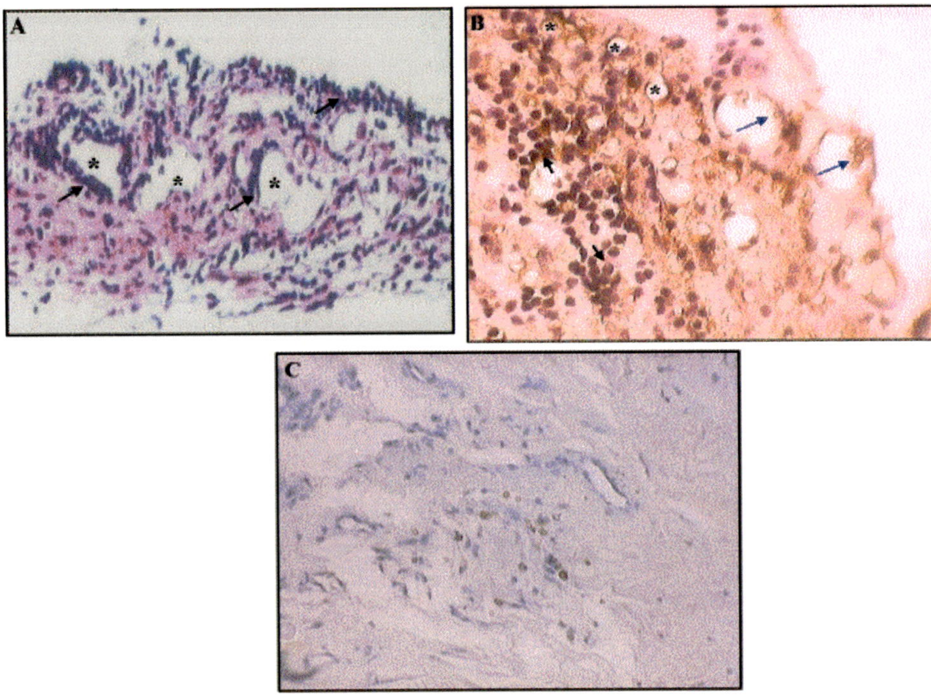

Figure 7: Immunohistochemical localization of 88 kDa protein in ERM of patients with Eales disease. **(A)** Haematoxylin and eosin staining of ERM obtained from patients with Eales disease, showing neovascular channels with dense leukocyte infiltration. Neovascular channels are indicated by black asterisks and the infiltrating leukocytes in the neovascular endothelium are represented by black arrows, X 200 magnification. **(B)** Immunolocalization for 88 kDa protein in ERM in Eales' disease. The expression of 88 kDa protein in infiltrating leukocytes are indicated by solid black arrow, while in the neovascular channels endothelium it is denoted by solid blue arrow, while the immunoreactivity of vascular endothelium for 88kDa protein is represented by black asterisks, X 400 magnification. **(C)** ERM obtained from patients with diabetic retinopathy did not reveal 88 kDa protein expression. X 200 magnification.

PRESENCE OF THE PROTEIN IN THE SERUM OF UVEITIS AND SYSTEMIC INFLAMMATORY AND OTHER DISEASES

Serum samples from healthy volunteers and from patients with ED, uveitis, pars planitis, ocular sarcoidosis, toxoplasmosis, leprosy, diabetic retinopathy, viral hepatitis, and rheumatoid arthritis were analyzed for 88 kDa protein by polyacralymide gel electrophoresis. It was detected in the serum samples obtained from patients with posterior uveitis, tuberculosis, leprosy and rheumatoid arthritis, all of which have inflammatory reaction. It was not detectable in diabetic retinopathy and proliferative diabetic retinopathy which do not have inflammatory process. *(Rajesh et al., 2003; Umamaheswari et al., 1999)*

WESTERN BLOT

The purified 88kDa protein (20µg) from serum and vitreous was subjected to 12% SDS PAGE. Then the proteins were electrotransfered to nitrocellulose membrane (Millipore Co., Bedford, MA, USA). The membrane was blocked with 5% skimmed milk in PBS pH7.4 for 1hr at room temperature in a rocking platform. The membrane was then probed with anti 88kDa antibody (goat polyclonal 1:500dilution). Mouse anti goat IgG antibody was used as secondary antibody (Sigma, St Louis, CA, USA. 1:1000 dilution) and the protein was visualized using NBT/BCIP as substrate (*Brunette, 1981*). (Figure: 8)

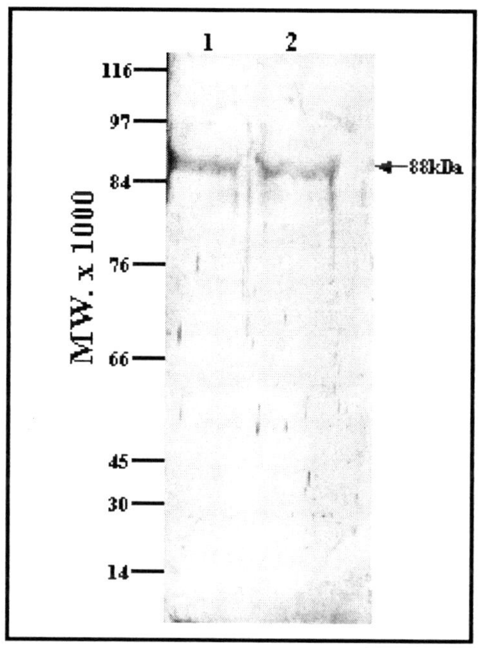

Figure 8: Western blot analysis of purified 88kDa protein. Lane 1, 30 mg purified 88kDa from serum. Lane 2, 30 mg purified 88kda from vitreous.

IMMUNOLOGICAL STUDIES ON 88 KDA PROTEIN

Partial Purification of IgG From Anti Serum:

One mg of purified 88kDa protein was used for raising polyclonal antibody in goat as described earlier (*Chase,1967*). The antibody was custom made by Chemicon Inc., (Temecula, CA, USA). Purification of IgG from polyclonal antibody was done by adopting the method described by *Talwar* (1967). This essentially involved salt fractionation using sodium sulphate (18%) followed by ion exchange chromatography on DEAE column. The immunoglobulins were eluted using 100mM phosphate buffer pH 8.0. This fraction was used for further analysis.

IMMUNOELECTROPHORESIS

Immunoelectrophoresis was performed using the method described by *Culliford* (1964) and *Lowrell* (1972). Briefly, 1% agarose was dissolved in 0.04M Veronal buffer pH 8.6. The same buffer was used as tank buffer. Electrophoresis was carried out for 2 hrs with 10mA/slide. Following electrophoresis, another horizontal trough was made in between the two antigen wells and filled with 0.1ml of partially purified antibody (1:500). The slides were then kept in a humid chamber at room temperature for 24 to 36 hrs to allow the passive diffusion of antigen and antibody. Precipitin arcs were viewed directly under dark back ground, the slides were then dried completely (60°C for 2 hrs) and subsequently stained with Coomassie brilliant blue (R250) for permanent documentation. (Figure: 9)

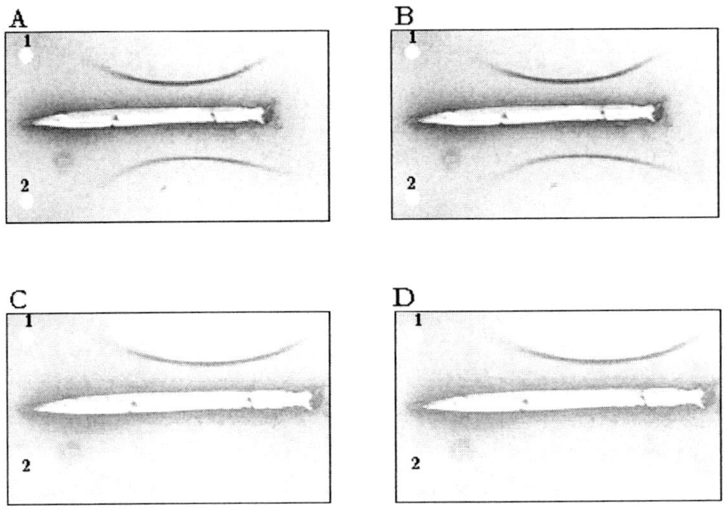

Figure 9: Immunoelectrophoresis of serum 88kDa protein with Eales' disease. **(A)** Well 1 serum (60 mg) from patient with Eales' disease, well 2 vitreous (10 mg) from patient with Eales' disease. **(B)** Purified 88kDa protein from vitreous (2 mg, well 1) and serum (2 mg, well 2) from patients with Eales' disease.**(C)** Well 1 vitreous (60 mg of protein) from a patient with Eales' disease, well 2 vitreous (10 mg of protein) from patient with diabetic retinopathy. **(D)** Well 1 serum (60 mg of protein) form patient with Eales' disease, well 2 serum (10 mg of protein) obtained from normal healthy volunteer. In all the above experiments (Fig 4A-D), the central well was probed with anti 88kDa antibody (goat polyclonal 1:500 dilution.

The immunological identify of the 88 kDa protein found in ED and in other diseases was investigated by Western blot. The 88 kDa protein found in serum from patients with ED was immunologically identical to that found in the serum of patients with uveitis, tuberculosis, leprosy, rheumatoid arthritis and the vitreous of patients with Eales' disease, all of which have inflammation. The protein was not present in diabetic retinopathy and proliferative diabetic retinopathy in which there is no inflammation. (Figure: 7)

Biological Effects

The research work done has convincingly and conclusively shown that the novel protein is produced and found in inflammatory conditions. As such, its biological effect might have something to do with inflammation. This idea gave the clue for future work.

The polymorphonuclear neutrophils and the mononuclear phagocytes are the two types of cells very much involved in inflammation due to phagocytosis. During this process, the oxygen consumption of the macrophages is increased. The increased oxygen consumption is not utilized for energy purposes; in stead, oxygen is reduced to a series of highly reactive and toxic metabolites which include free radicals (with unpaired electrons) and ultimately water. The pathway of oxygen utilization is called "respiratory burst" *(Ramakrishnan and Rajiswami 1995)* and the metabolites including free radicals are collectively known as reactive oxygen species (ROS). They are (i) superoxide anion with an unpaired electron and negative charge $O_2^{\bullet-}$, (ii) hydrogen peroxide H_2O_2 (iii) hydroxyl free radical $OH^{\bullet}$, and through the latter lipid free radicals $L^{\bullet}$, $LO^{\bullet}$, $LO_2^{\bullet}$ and lipid peroxide LO_2H *(Ramakrishnan 1992)*. The lipid free radicals and peroxide are converted to melondialdehyde which reacts with thiobarbituric acid giving a chromogen. There are a few other end products also which react with thiobarbituric acid. As such, all of them are collectively called thiobarbituric acid reactive substances (TBARS). The quantity of TBARS is decided by the extent of lipid oxidation which, in turn is decided by the quantity of ROS produced. So, the ROS formed due to oxygen thrust (or respiratory burst) is measured as TBARS.

In view of the relationship of inflammatory condition with production TBARS due to respiratory burst of macrophages, TBARS were estimated in the erythrocytes and vitreous in Eales' patients.

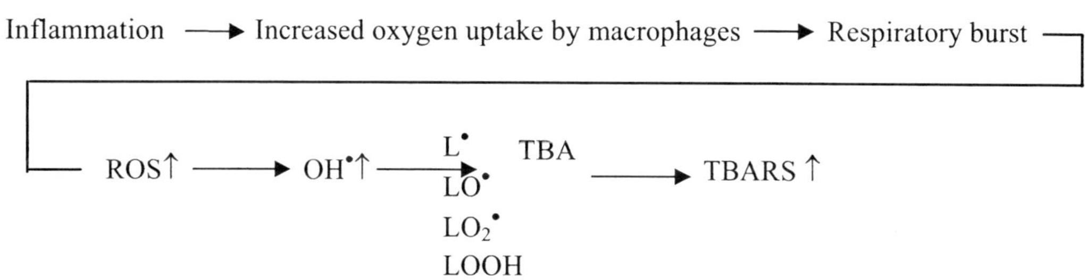

Determination of Thiobarbituric Acid Reactive Substances (TBARS) in Erythrocytes

(*Devasagayam & Tarachand, 1987*)

Malondialdehyde (MDA) produced during peroxidation of lipids, served as an index of lipid peroxidation. MDA reacts with Thiobarbituric acid (TBA) to generate a coloured product, which absorbs at 532 nm.

The erythrocytes were washed thrice with saline after removal of plasma. To the packed cells 1.5 ml of 10 % TCA was added and was allowed to stand for 15 minutes at room temperature. The tubes were centrifuged and to the supernatant 1.5 ml of TBA solution was added and heated in boiling water bath for 15 min. After cooling the tubes, the absorbance was measured at 532 nm.

TBARS were found to be increased in both the erythrocytes and the vitreous confirming the increased production of ROS (*Bhooma et al., 1997*), (*Sulochana et al 1999*) and in platelets (*Srivastava et al, 2000)*.

In a living system which utilizes oxygen for respiration, there will always be the formation of ROS, but it is quenched by antioxidants which are also present in the living beings (just as pathogens are handled by immunoglobulins and interferons). Some antioxidants are endogenously produced while a few are exogenous – taken in the diet.

The endogenously produced antioxidants are glutathione, ceruloplasmin, metallothioneins, hemopexin and the enzymes superoxide dismutase, glutathione peroxidase, glutathione reductase, catalase, glutathione S-transferase and glucose 6 phosphate dehydrogenase. Those taken in the diet to build up a good antioxidant defence are vitamins E, C, A, carotenoids, lycopene, polyphenols, lipoic acid etc.

The antioxidants are also classified as preventive antioxidants and protective antioxidants that is, if the formation of ROS itself is blocked, the antioxidant is called preventive antioxidant (eg ceruloplasmin). If the antioxidant reacts and neutralises the oxidant after the formation of the latter, it is called protective antioxidant (eg. Vit. E, C).

CHEMICAL BASIS FOR THE FORMATION OF ROS

How are the Reactive oxygen species (ROS) formed in living systems even under normal circumstances?

To keep life giving, one has to respire air for his oxygen requirement. The oxygen is utlizaed by each cell at the level of the inner membrane of the mitochondria for biological oxidation and oxidative phosphorylation. The hydrogens and electrons from the metabolites are routed through red-ox systems like $NAD^+/NADH$ to react with molecular oxygen catalyzed by the vital enzyme cytochrome a_3 (cytochrome oxidase). In this process a little oxygen undergoes univalent reduction as it is para magnetic and produces superoxide anion. (*Ramakrishnan, 2001*)

$$\underset{\text{(of air)}}{O_2} \longrightarrow \underset{\text{superoxide anion}}{O_2^{\bullet -}}$$

This superoxide anion, in its turn, triggers a chain of events and causes the production of H_2O_2 and $OH^{\bullet}$ if it is not removed immediately by the enzyme superoxide dismutase. The $OH^{\bullet}$ (free radical) reacts with long chain unsaturated fatty acids like arachidonic acid (*Johnson et al, 1986*) giving Lipid free radical ($L^{\bullet}$), lipoxide free radical ($LO^{\bullet}$), and lipid peroxide free radical ($LO_2^{\bullet}$) and ultimately lipid peroxide LOOH (*Ramakrishnan, 1992*). All those, which have odd electrons, are free radicals and being highly reactive, oxidize membrane proteins and lipids; the membrane integrity is lost.

It was thought that as 88 kDa protein is formed during inflammation with formation of ROS, it could have a role in quenching some oxidants and function as an antioxidant. To prove this prediction, protein purified from both serum and vitreous of patients with Eales disease was tested for anti TBARS activity on erythrocytes as detailed below.

The anti TBARS activity was measured using the method of *Ledwozywa et al* (1986). The extent of lipid peroxidation in fresh erythrocytes was measured as TBARS. The results were expressed as nmoles of malondialdehyde (MDA)dL^{-1} RBC. The quantity of the product, MDA was decreased when the assay was performed in the presence of 100ng of the purified 88 kDa protein to 1.0ml of erythrolysate. This property was used to identify the presence of 88 kDa protein during its purification in fractions collected from preparative electrophoresis and HPLC. The same assay was carried out to assess the effect of various thiol inhibitors such as para chloromercury benzoate (PCMB) and 5, 5^1, dithiobis 2 Nitro benzoic acid (DTNB).

The conventional thiol group inhibitor namely DTNB and PCMB inhibited this activity of the protein, indicating the importance of thiol residues in its function. This was further confirmed by the fact that cysteine residues contributed 8% of total mass of the protein. The *in vitro* demonstration of anti TBARS activity in neutral pH is suggestive of the fact that the contribution by carbohydrate moiety is negligible as enolization of sugar (in alkaline pH) is needed for antioxidant function. The above experiments proved that 88 kDa protein exhibits antioxidation property.

88 kDa Protein as a Preventive Antioxidant

In addition, the thiol containing protein oxidized Ferrous iron to Ferric iron and behaved as ferrooxidase like ceruloplasmin (an endogenous antioxidant)

Ferrous iron reacts with H_2O_2 and generates hydroxyl free radical in Fenton's reaction

$$H_2O_2 + Fe^{2+} \longrightarrow OH^- + OH^\bullet + Fe^{3+}$$

An extension of Fenton's reaction is Haber, Weiss Fentons' dismutation reaction with $O_2^{\bullet-}$ catalysed by Ferrous iron.

$$H_2O_2 + O_2^{\bullet-} \xrightarrow{Fe^{2+}} OH^- + OH^\bullet + O_2$$

These reactions are arrested by ferro oxidases like ceruloplasmin and the newly found 88 kDa protein. The latter is thus functioning as a preventive antioxidant i.e. it prevents the very formation of $OH^\bullet$ and thereby lipid free radicals, through chain reactions as given below.

$$L^\bullet + O_2 \longrightarrow LO_2^\bullet \qquad LH + OH^\bullet \longrightarrow L^\bullet + H_2O$$

$$LH + LO^\bullet \longrightarrow L^\bullet + LOH$$

$$LO_2^\bullet + LH \longrightarrow LOOH + L^\bullet \qquad LH + LO_2^\bullet \longrightarrow L^\bullet + LOOH$$

$$2LOOH \xrightarrow{Fe,\ Cu} LO^\bullet + LO_2^\bullet + H_2O \qquad 2LOOH \xrightarrow{Fe,\ Cu} LO^\bullet + LO_2^\bullet + H_2O$$

LOOH can be scavenged by glutathione peroxidase and glutathione (*Ramakrishnan, 1992*)

88 kDa protein can sequester Ferrous iron and prevent the very formation of $OH^{\bullet}$ (preventive antioxidant).

88 kDa Protein as a Protective Antioxidant

At the same time, it could also have a role as a protective endogenous antioxidant. This is by virtue of its thiol content. In this, its behaviour is similar to that of metallothioneins. The latter contain SH groups in cysteine residues and sequester metal ions including Fe, Cu etc. So the –SH groups in 88 kDa protein too can form complexes with divalent ions through their cysteinyl SH. (sequestering of iron, copper etc). In addition, metallothioneins can quench $O_2^{-\bullet}$ and $OH^{\bullet}$ through their thiol groups. The same property can be expected of 88kDa protein which has cysteinyl SH and which, like metallothioneins, could quench $O_2^{-\bullet}$ and $OH^{\bullet}$. In this, 88 kDa protein could function as a protective (endogenous) antioxidant like GSH i.e. these protective antioxidants protect the membrane from oxidation by destroying ROS after it (ROS) has formed.

88 kDa Protein and Reactive Nitrogen Species (RNS)

Superoxide anion reacts with Nitric oxide (NO) to produce peroxynitrite $(ONOO)^-$ (*Rajesh et al. 2003*). The reaction of NO and $O_2^{-\bullet}$ is facilitated during inflammatory conditions since phagocytes have been shown to generate simultaneously NO and $O_2^{-\bullet}$ and at a similar rate (*Rodenas et al*, 1995) $(ONOO)^-$ is considered a more powerful oxidant than $O_2^{-\bullet}$ because of its higher diffusion coefficient and half life. $ONOO^-$ on entering the cell, rapidly nitrates a variety of macro molecules chiefly at the aromatic rings (say tyrosine). Nitration affects the structure and functions of many proteins including. SOD.

In addition, peroxynitrite radical gets protonated and the product formed decomposes to give $OH^{\bullet}$ free radical. This hydroxyl free radical initiates a chain of reactions on poly unsaturated fatty acids of lipids giving lipid free radicals and ultimately TBARS. Just as, vitamin C and metallothioneins quench oxygen free radicals. 88 kDa protein also with –SH groups can quench oxygen free radicals and protect the membranes. So 88 kDa protein with its – SH groups can be considered to have the dual function of preventive antioxidant and protective antioxidant from both (i) ROS and (ii) ROS derived from RNS.

Comparison of the Structure and Functions of 88 kDa Protein with other Antioxidant/Acute Phase Proteins

Though 88 kDa protein is an antioxidant like ceruloplasmin, transferrin, haptoglobins, hemopexin and metallothioneins it stands alone as a different acute phase protein with antioxidant function. The functions of the various antioxidant proteins and their differences from 88 kDa protein are given below.

Transferrin, a glycoprotein is an iron sequestering protein binds Fe^{3+} and has a mol. wt of 77 kDa. There is no homology in the sequence of N-terminal amino acids of the two proteins.

Haptoglobins (glycoproteins) bind hemoglobin and have a molecular wt of about 90 kDa. They are raised in inflammation (*Murrey et al., 1988*). One of the members of ROS i.e. H_2O_2 is decomposed by haptoglobin-hemoglobin complex. The sequence of N terminal amino acids is different from that of 88 kDa protein..

Hemopexin, also a glycoprotein, is an iron-sequestering protein. It keeps heme in a soluble form. N terminal homology in different .

Ceruloplasmin incorporates Cu. as a structural component. It is a ferroxidase and quite different from -88 kDa protein in sequence and constitution. But both are ferrooxidases and arrest Fenton's reaction.

METALLOTHIONEINS

Metallothioneins are low molecular weight proteins (6.5 to 7.5 kDa) and sequester iron, copper and other divalent ions through their cysteinyl SH groups. Their expression is triggered in heavy metal toxicity and inflammatory conditions. In addition to removing iron and arresting Fenton's reaction, their high cysteine content makes them function as a scavenger of $O_2^{-\bullet}$ and $OH^{\bullet}$ radicals. So the metallothioneins are antioxidants – both preventive and protective. The new protein also like metallothioneins can function as a preventive (i.e. before production of ROS) and protective (i.e. destroying ROS after formation) antioxidant. But, in mol. wt. and N-terminal sequence the two are entirely different.

RETINAL PIGMENT EPITHELIAL PROTECTIVE PROTEIN (RPP)

A novel protein secreted by retinal pigment epithelial cells has been found by *Wu et al* (1996). It inhibits generation of superoxide ($O_2^{-\bullet}$) by activated neutrophils *in vitro*. It is well known that $O_2^{-\bullet}$ is one of the most injurious species through its secondary conversion to H_2O_2, $OH^{\bullet}$ (free radical) and peroxy nitrite ($ONOO^-$) (*Rao et al 1985, 1995*). Most antioxidants are intracellular – unable to move to extra cellular compartment. In the event of inflammation, RPE releases a protein to extra cellular space. The RPP protein is synthesized endogenously by RPE cells. The mechanism of its antioxidant effect is not by quenching the released superoxide (i.e. protective antioxidant); rather the protein intervenes in the activation cascade of the neutrophils and thereby arrests the consequential release of $O_2^{-\bullet}$. (i.e. preventive antioxidant)

Sequence studies have shown that in three of the amino acid sequences, there is some degree of homology with transferrin family protein while 5 other sequences are totally different.

88 kDa protein is different from RPP in sequence homology.

Comparative table of 88 kDa protein with other similar proteins.

Protein	Special property	Different from 88 kDa protein
Transferrin	Binding with iron	Molecular weight (77 kDa), No homology in N terminus
Haptoglobins	Hemoglobin binding, Agglutination, Electrophoretic movement (α_2 region) raised in inflammation, mol.wt 90 kDa.	Seen in all individuals and irrespective of disease.No sequence homology with 88 kDa protein in N terminus.
Ceruloplasmin	Contains copper, ferooxidase activity, endogenous antioxidant.	88 kDa protein not having ceruloplasmin activity with paraphenylene diamine, No sequence homology in N terminus
Metallothioneins	Low molecular wt,both preventive and protective antioxidant, contain – SH	High mol. wt. Though a preventive and protective antioxidant, 88 kDa protein is different in mol wt and / N-terminus.
Retinal pigment epithelial protective protein (RPP)	Has sequence homology in 3 domains with transferrin, but different in 5 domains; arrests the release of $O_2^{-\bullet}$; preventive antioxidant	Mol. wt and N terminus homology are different, also ferro oxidase.
Superoxide Dismutase	Endogenous antioxidant	88 kDa protein has no SOD activity; does not inhibit epinephrine auto oxidation.
Glutathione Peroxidase (GP_x)	Removes H_2O_2	88 kDa does not require GSH for activity, while GP_x needs GSH for its activity.

In summary, the 88 kDa protein is a novel protein, an endogenous preventive and protective antioxidant, different from other antioxidant or iron-sequestering proteins like transferrin, hemopexin, haptoglobins, ceruloplasmin, metallothioneins and Retinal pigment epithelial protective protein (RPP). It is expressed to offer natural defence against oxidant – assault during inflammation and is an acute phase protein.

REFERENCES

Biswas, J., Sharma, T., Gopal, L, Madhavan, HN., Sulochana, KN. & Ramakrishnan, S. (2002). Eales' Disease – an update. *Surv Ophthalmol,* **47**, 1-18.

Bhooma, V., Sulochana, KN., Biswas, J., Ramakrishnan, S. (1997). Eales' disease: accumulation of reactive oxygen intermediates and lipid peroxides and decrease of antioxidants causing inflammation, neovascularization and retinal damage. *Curr Eye Res.* **16***:* 91-95.

Brunette, W.N. (1981). Western blotting. *Anal. Biochem.* **112**, 195-203.

Chase, M.W. (1967). Production of antiserum, *In Manual of Immunology*, edited by William, G.A and Chase, M.W Academic Press, NY, USA. p100-10.

Culliford, B.J (1964). Precipitin reaction in forensic problems. *Nature.* **201**, 1092-94.

Das T, Biswas J, Kumar A, Nagapal PN, Namperumalswamy P, Patnaik B & Tewari, HK. (1994). Eales' disease. *Ind J Ophthalmol.* **42**: 3-18.

Devasagayam, PA. & Tarachand, V. (1987). Decrease in lipid peroxidation in the rat kidney during gestation. *Biochem Biophy Res Commun.* **145**, 134-138.

Eales, H. (1880). Retinal hemorrhages associated with epistaxis and constipation. *Brim. Med. Rev,* **9**, 262-273.

Eales, H. (1882). Primary retinal hemorrhage in young men. *Ophthalmic Rev.* **1**, 41-46.

Johnson, Jr., J.E., Walford, R., Harman, D., & Miquel, J. (1986). Free radicals, aging and degenerative disease: Vol. 8, Modern aging research, New York, Alan R, Liss, Inc. p110.

Ledwozywa M.J., Stepien, A. and Kadziolka A. (1986). The relationship between plasma triglycerides, cholesterol, total lipids and lipid peroxidation products during human atherosclerosis. *Clin. Chim. Acta.* **155**, 275-284.

Lowry, O.H., Rosenborough, N.J., Farr, A.L., & Randall, R.J. (1951). Protein measurement with Folin phenol reagent. *J Biol Chem.* **193**, 265–75.

Lowrell, C.B. (1972). Electrophoretic and electro immunochemical analysis of proteins. *Scand J. Clin Lab. Invest.* **124**, 29–34.

Matsudaria, P. (1987). Sequence from picomole quantities of proteins electroblotted on to polyvinylidine difluoride membranes. *J.Biol.Chem.,* **262**,10035-39.

Morrissey, J.H., (1981). Silver stain for proteins in polyacrylamide gels. A modified procedure with enhanced uniform sensitivity *Anal. Biochem.* **117**, 307-10.

Murray, RK., Granner, DK., Mayes, PA. & Rodwell, VW. (1988). *Harper Biochemistry*, 21st ed Appleton & Lange, East Norwalk, pp. 669.

Puttana, S.T., (1970). Varied fundus picture of central retinal vasculitis. *Trans. Asia Pacific Acad. Ophthalmol.* **3**, 520–22.

Rao, N.A., Thaete, L.G., Delmage, J.M. & Sevanian A., (1985) Superoxide dismutase in ocular structures. *Invest. Ophthalmol Vis. Sci.* **26**, 1778-81.

Rao, N.A., Wu, G.S., & Geetha, P., (1995). Mechanism of tissue injury in uveitis. *Regional immunology.* **6**, 95-100.

Rajesh, M., Sulochana, KN., Amirthalakshmi, S., Krishnakumar, S., Biswas, J. & Ramakrishnan, S. (2003) Presence of a 88 kDa Eales' protein in uveitis, tuberculosis, leprosy and rheumatoid arthritis. *Med Sci Monit.* **9**(1), CR95-99.

Rajesh, M., Sulochana, KN., Punitham, R., Lakshmi, S. & Ramakrishnan, S. (2003). Involvement of oxidative and nitrosative stress in promoting retinal vasculitis in patients with Eales' disease. *Clinical Biochemistry.* **36**(5), 377-385.

Ramakrishnan, S., (1992). *Essentials of Biochemistry & Ocular Biochemistry.* 1 Edn. Annmalai University Publications. Annamalai Nagar, India, p48.

Ramakrishnan, S. & Raji Swami. (1995) *Text Book of Clinical (Medical) Biochemistry & Immunology*: Phagocytic cells, 1 Edn. Chennai (India) T.R. Publications, p436-40.

Ramakrishnan, S., Prasannan, KG. & Rajan R. (2001). *Text Book of Medical Biochemistry:* Biological oxidation and bioenergetics, 3rd Edn. Chennai (India), Orient Longman Limitied 133-153.

Rengarajan, K., Muthukarrupan, V.R., & Namperumalsamy, P. (1989). Biochemical analysis of serum proteins from Eales' patients. *Curr Eye Res.* **8**, 1259–1269.

Rodenas, J., Mitjavila, MT., Carbonell, T. (1995). Simultaneous generation of superoxide by inflammatory cells in rat. *Free Radic Biol Med.* **18**: 869-75.

Spitzans, M., Schwickerath, GT. & Stephen, B. (1975). Clinical picture of Eales' disease. *Clin Exp Ophthalmol,* **73**, 194-98.

Srivatsava, P., Saxena, S., Khanna, KV., Kumar, D., Nath, R. & Seth, KP. (2000). Raised platelet thiobarbituric acid reactive substance in proliferative Eales' disease. *Ind J Ophthalmol,* **48**, 307-09.

Sulochana, KN., Rajesh, M. & Ramakrishnan, S. (2001) Purification and characterization of an 88 kDa novel protein from patients with Eales disease. *Exp Eye Res,* **73**, 547-55.

Sulochana, K.N., Biswas, J. & Ramakrishnan, S. (1999). Eales' disease: increased oxidation and peroxidation products of membrane constituents chiefly lipids and decreased antioxident enzymes and reduced glutathione in vitreous. *Current Eye Res.* **19**, 254–59.

Swamy, MS., Coral, K., Krishnakumar, S., Biswas, J., Ramakrishnan, S., Nagaraj, RH. & Sulochana, KN. (2002). Immunolocalization and quantification of advanced glycation end products in retinal neovascular membranes and serum: a possible role in ocular neovascularization. *Curr Eye Res,* **36**, 139-145.

Talwar, G.P. (1967). Purification of immunoglobulins of different classes. *In a handbook of practical immunology.* Edited by Talwar, G.P., Vikas Publishing PVT LTD, India, p72-83.

Umamaheswari, K., Sulochana, KN. & Ramakrishnan, S. (1999) Occurrence of an 88 kDa protein in Non-infective Intraocular Inflammation. *Insight.* (Vision Research Foundation), XVII(2), 29-31.

Wu, G.S., Swiderek KM & Rao, N.A. (1996). A Novel retinal pigment epithelial protein suppresses neutrophil superoxide generation: Purification and microsequencing analysis. *Exp. Eye. Res.* **63**(6): 727-37.

In: Focus on Eye Research
Editor: O.R. Ioseliani, pp. 173-199
ISBN: 1-59454-434-4

Chapter 8

MODULATION OF PIGMENT EPITHELIUM-DERIVED FACTOR (PEDF) ACTIVITY IN THE EYE

Luigi Notari and S. Patricia Becerra*
National Eye Institute, National Institutes of Health, Bethesda, Maryland

ABSTRACT

Pigment epithelium-derived factor (PEDF), an extracellular serpin protein of 50-kDa, is a major antiangiogenic and neurotrophic factor in the eye. Because PEDF can prevent vessels from invading the cornea, vitreous and retina, and protect photoreceptors and cells from the inner neural retina from apoptotic cell death, its regulation plays an important role in ocular physiology and pathology. Interestingly, its levels are inversely associated with the progression of ocular diseases triggered by neovascularization and neuronal cell death. PEDF is present in high concentrations in the physiological interphotoreceptor matrix and vitreous where it associates with extracellular matrix components such as glycosaminoglycans/proteoglycans and collagens. The retinal pigment epithelium, the main source of PEDF for the eye expresses high levels of *PEDF* transcripts, from which the PEDF polypeptide chains are synthesized and, upon maturation, these are secreted into the interphotoreceptor matrix next to the neural retina. There is biochemical and immunological evidence for a neurotrophic PEDF receptor protein, and for interactions with signal transduction pathways for both neurotrophic and antiangiogenic activities. Regulation of the PEDF activities can be achieved by modulating the mechanisms for its production including transcriptional, and post-translational, secretion, degradation, or by interfering with its mechanisms of action, such as interaction with ECM components, receptors or signaling pathways. We present in this review some experimental evidence on PEDF regulation, and we discuss several possible mechanisms by which PEDF modulation could occur in the eye.

Keywords: PEDF, serpin, neurotrophic, angiogenesis, retina, retainl pigment epithelium, choroidal neovascularization, retinal neovascularization, extracellular matrix, receptor, proteases.

---

* Correspondence concerning this article should be addressed to S. Patricia Becerra National Eye Institute, National Institutes of Health, 7 Memorial Drive, Bethesda, Maryland 20892-0706.

INTRODUCTION

Preservation of the morphology of the retina is vital for our ability to see. Diseases resulting from the destruction of the structure of the retina have a tremendous impact on vision. The neural retina works thanks to intimate interactions among its seven types of neuronal cells. They are nourished by microvessels formed by endothelial cells in the inner retina and in the choroid. In retinitis pigmentosa, the photoreceptor cells loose their structure. In retinopathy triggered by diabetes, neovascularization destroys the beautiful morphology of the inner retina. In macular degeneration, vessels from the choroid invade the neural retina. These disorders threaten the balanced organization of the components of the retina, which end in blindness. Neovascular diseases of the retina include age-related macular degeneration and diabetic retinopathy, and together they comprise the leading causes of adult-onset blindness in developed countries.

The development, morphogenesis, and survival of the neural retina rely on growth, trophic, and survival factors derived mostly from the adjacent retinal pigment epithelium. Pigment epithelium–derived factor (PEDF) was first identified as an RPE-derived protein with potent neuronal differentiating activity in human retinoblastoma cells. PEDF acts in neuronal differentiation and survival in cells derived from the retina and CNS. In addition, its expression is downregulated over the replicative lifespan of mammals. About eight years after its discovery, PEDF was described as a potent antiangiogenic factor for the eye. PEDF acts in preventing aberrant blood vessel growth by inhibiting growth of ocular endothelial cells. This interesting factor is secreted by retinal pigment epithelial cells into the interphotoreceptor matrix, where it acts on photoreceptor cells as a protector and barrier for vessel intrusion from the choroid into the neural retina. Its importance in the development, maintenance, and function of the retina and central nervous system is evident in animal models for inherited and light-induced retinal degeneration, for ischemia-induced retina and laser-induced choroidal neovascularization, as well as for degeneration of spinal cord motor neurons. These observations have increased the interest in the use of PEDF for the development of therapies for diseases involving defective neuronal differentiation or cell survival, such as retinitis pigmentosa, age-related macular degeneration, and amyotrophic lateral sclerosis; as well as in treating diseases in which new blood vessel formation plays a role, such as diabetic retinopathy, age-related macular degeneration, tumor growth, and rheumatoid arthritis.

1. PEDF as a Neurotrophic Factor

There are several lines of evidence for the establishment of PEDF as a multipotent neurotrophic factor that acts upon various types of neurons and from different species. It has been reported that 1) PEDF has a potent neuronal differentiating activity on human retinoblastoma Y-79 cells, an established cell line from human retinoblastoma tumor [1,2] (see Fig. 1); 2) it protects rat retinal neurons from hydrogen peroxide–induced cell death in culture [3]; and 3) it has a morphogenetic effect on photoreceptor neurons of *Xenopus laevis* [4]. The neurotrophic effects of PEDF have also been demonstrated in vivo. PEDF transiently delays the death of photoreceptor cells in mouse models of retinitis pigmentosa (such as the retinal degeneration (*rd/rd*) and retinal degeneration slow (*rds/rds*) mouse models) [5]. It also protects rat photoreceptors cells from light damage [6,7], and the inner retina and retina ganglion cells from ischemia-reperfusion injury [8]. In addition to its effects on retina cells, PEDF has neuronal survival and differentiating activities in neurons from cerebellum, hippocampus and spinal cord, broadening its neurotrophic and neuroprotective effects to the central nervous system. PEDF is a survival factor for rat cerebellar granule cell neurons in primary cultures [9], which protects them against glutamate-induced neurotoxicity [10], and differentially protects immature but not mature cerebellar granule cells against apoptotic cell death [11]. PEDF also protects developing primary rat hippocampal neurons against glutamate toxicity [12], and motor neurons from chronic glutamate-mediated neurodegeneration [13]. It also promotes the survival and neurite-outgrowth of developing avian and murine spinal motor neurons [14]. Thus, PEDF is a multipotent neurotrophic factor that may play a protective role in the retina and CNS in vivo and could be used as a therapeutic agent for the treatment of diseases threaten by neuronal and retinal degenerations.

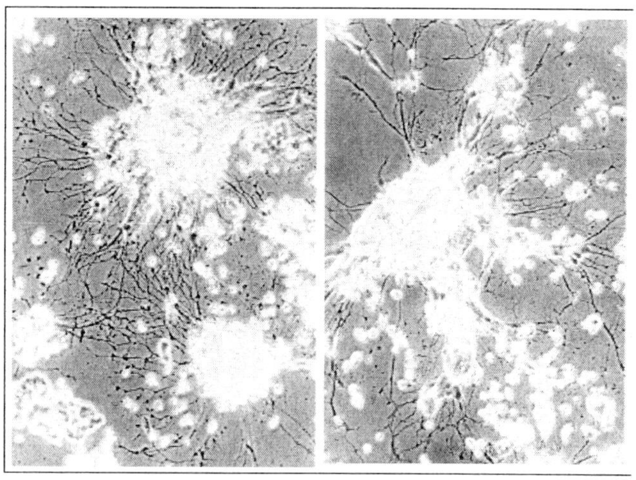

Figure 1. Morphological differentiation of human retinoblastoma Y-79 cells. PEDF protein was purified from media from 293 cells infected with adenoviral vector of human PEDF. Y-79 cells treated with Ad-derived PEDF after 27 days post-attachment are shown. Cells without PEDF were dead at this time point.

2. PEDF as an Antiangiogenic Factor

PEDF has been described as the most potent antiangiogenic factor for the retina [15]. It inhibits endothelial cell migration activated by pro-angiogenic factors (e.g., FGF, VEGF or interleukin-8), suppresses VEGF-induced retinal microvascular endothelial cell proliferation [16] and causes apoptosis of activated endothelial cells [17]. It inhibits aberrant blood vessel growth in models of retinal neovascularization, such as the murine model of ischemia-induced retinopathy [18, 19] and the transgenic mice with increased expression of VEGF in photoreceptors [19]. It prevents choroidal neovascularization upon rupturing the Bruch's membrane by laser-induced injury [19] and also the infiltration of new vessels in cornea induced with exogenous angiogenic stimulators [15]. Consequently, PEDF secreted by RPE cells into the interphotoreceptor matrix, works not only as a protector of photoreceptor cells but as a barrier for vessel intrusion from the choroid into the neural retina. By preventing the infiltration of vessels in the vitreous, aqueous and cornea this interesting extracellular factor allows external light to reach the retina, where the main chemical reactions of the vision process occur. Therefore, PEDF as an antiangiogenic factor may play a protective role in the retina in vivo.

Because pathological neovascularization occurs in tumor growth PEDF has been also tested in cancer models. PEDF can inhibit the invasion of new vessels in tumors, such as melanomas [20, 21], in hepatocellular carcinoma [22, 23], in syngeneic murine models of thoracic malignancies [24], prostate tumors [25]. In addition, it can also act as a tumor stabilizer or suppressor as shown for prostatic and pancreatic growth, Wilm's tumors and neuroblastomas by inducing both endothelial and tumor cell apoptosis, while kidney microvascular density and prostate size and angiogenesis increase in PEDF knockout mice compared with wild type [25, 28]. Thus overexpression of PEDF in animal models has also proven beneficial in preventing pathological angiogenesis, and could be exploited as therapeutic means for the treatment of diseases threaten by aberrant neovascularization.

3. PEDF, an Extracellular Protein in the Vertebrate Eye

Investigations on the identification of PEDF in the native eye have demonstrated that PEDF is expressed and produced in the eye. From the moment of its discovery, PEDF was associated with the retina and identified as a protein secreted by human fetal pigment epithelial cells in culture, hence its name [1]. Preliminary studies showed that the medium conditioned by cultured human fetal epithelial cells induced neuronal differentiation in cultures of Y-79 cells [29]. The molecule responsible for such activity was isolated as a protein of 50-kDa with the ability to induce differentiation in the same cell line.

In the vertebrate eye, the retinal pigment epithelium is the most external compartment of the retina formed by a polarized monolayer of cells. It lies on a connective layer termed Bruch's membrane that constitutes a physical barrier between the retina and the underlying choroid (blood retinal barrier). The interactions and relationships between the retinal pigment epithelium and the inner retina play a role in the development, differentiation, function and survival of the neural retina, and therefore on the visual function itself. Between the retinal pigment epithelium and the more external area of the neural retina, the photoreceptor layer, is the interphotoreceptor matrix (see Fig. 2). The interphotoreceptor matrix is a highly specialized extracellular matrix involved in the interexchange of signaling molecules and nutrients. The biochemical composition of the interphotoreceptor matrix plays an essential part in the release, diffusion, storage, and in the overall regulation of molecules involved in retinal homeostasis and visual processes. The retinal pigment epithelium secretes PEDF in a directional fashion and preferentially toward the apical side, the interphotoreceptor matrix [30]. Using antiserum developed against recombinant human PEDF protein that specifically blocks the PEDF-mediated neurotrophic activity, the presence of PEDF in this matrix is clearly demonstrated. PEDF in the interphotoreceptor matrix is highly concentrated, with estimates reaching 144-250 nM in the soluble interphotoreceptor matrix [30, 31] (Tables 1 and 2). Although it represents about less than 1% of the total soluble interphotoreceptor matrix proteins, the native PEDF can be purified from saline lavages of the bovine interphotoreceptor matrix by ammonium sulfate fractionation followed by S-sepharose ion-exchange column chromatography [31]. Given that the antiserum to PEDF blocks the interphotoreceptor matrix-mediated neurotrophic activity, PEDF is considered the sole component of the interphotoreceptor matrix to play this neurotrophic role.

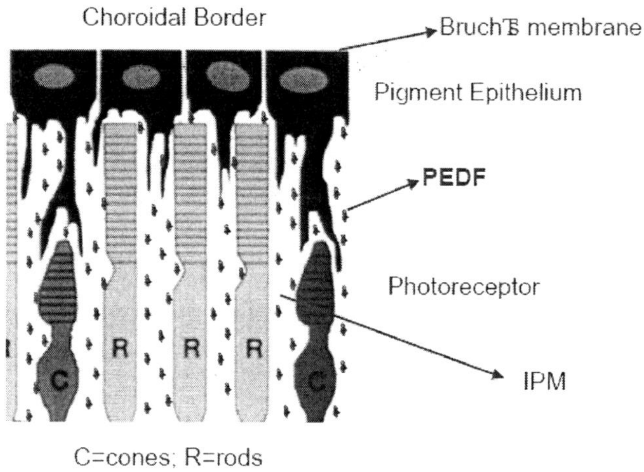

Figure 2. Scheme of the retina to illustrate PEDF secretion by the pigment epithelium to the interphotoreceptor matrix (IPM).

Retinal glial (Muller) cells in culture also secrete PEDF [32], and photoreceptors, inner nuclear layer cells and ganglion cells in adult human retina contain PEDF mRNA [33], indicative of their potential contribution to PEDF deposition in the interphotoreceptor matrix. Similarly, cultures of cells from other ocular tissues, such as from the ciliary epithelium, trabecular meshwork and anterior segments release PEDF to the media and effluents [34; Perruccio et al. *ARVO Annual Meeting*. 2003, Abst. # 1140], suggesting contributions to PEDF accumulations in vitreous and aqueous. Indeed, PEDF is found in the vitreous at concentrations about 20-30 nM, and in the aqueous at lower concentrations (3-6 nM) [30, 35]. Given that the volume of the vitreous is larger than that of the interphotoreceptor matrix and aqueous, purification of PEDF from vitreous is capable of yielding the highest amounts of purified PEDF protein per eye relative to purification protocols starting from other ocular compartments.

Table 1. PEDF Protein in the Bovine Eye

Bovine	µg per eye	µg/ml	nM
IPM[a]	3.3	12.4	250
Vitreous[a]	16	1.6	31
Aqueous[a]	0.3	0.16	3.2

[a]The estimated volume of IPM, vitreous and aqueous were 0.26 ml, 10 ml and 0.15 ml, respectively.

Table 2. PEDF Protein in the Monkey Eye.

Monkey	μg per eye	μg/ml	nM
IPM[a]	0.45	7.2	144
Vitreous[a]	1.2	1	20
Aqueous[a]	0.06	0.3	5.7

[a]The estimated volume of IPM, vitreous and aqueous were 0.063 ml, 1.2 ml and 0.2 ml, respectively.

Outside of the eye, PEDF is also found as a secreted product of a variety of cells and deposited in extracellular matrixes, such as cerebral spinal fluid, human blood serum and bone marrow matrix [36-38]. The molecular interactions that govern the deposition of PEDF in extracellular matrixes like the interphotoreceptor matrix and vitreous have been studied and are discussed below.

4. Structure-Function Relationships

Knowledge of the structure of a polypeptide contributes to the understanding of its function. Thus there is great interest in deciphering the structural determinants for the function of PEDF. Much of the information accumulated to date originates from the PEDF cDNA sequence, identified by Steele et al [39]. Amino acid and cDNA sequence analyses predict that human PEDF is a member of the serine protease inhibitor (serpin) supergene family, with a molecular mass of 46,326 daltons (418 amino acid residues), an asparagine-glycosylation site at position 285-287 (asparagine-leucine-threonine), and an amino-terminal signal peptide associated with secreted proteins. These interesting observations trigger questions about the role of PEDF as a serpin on biological processes such as differentiation, survival, and angiogenesis.

The serpins are a family of serine proteinase inhibitors that share the same overall tertiary structure, consisting of three β-sheets surrounded by eight α-helices [40-42]. The prototype is α_1-antitrypsin or α_1-proteinase inhibitor. This shared structure is also maintained in ovalbumin, one of the several members of the family with no known inhibitory function, i.e. angiotensinogen, cortisol binding globulin, thyroxine binding globulin. The serpin structure confers these proteins a globular conformation with a hinge region or exposed loop susceptible to proteolytic cleavage. The hinge region is located at the C-end of their primary structure. In inhibitory serpins the exposed loop constitutes the reactive center recognized by its target protease as the best substrate acting as bait. Upon binding, the serpin and protease form a complex, preventing further proteolytic activity. One member of the serpin family shares similar biological activity with PEDF. Glia-derived nexin, same as protease nexin-I, (GDN/PN-I) secreted by rat glioma cells promotes neurite outgrowth in mouse neuroblastoma cells, but in contrast to PEDF it inhibits and forms a complex with thrombin. Alignment of primary structures of GDN/PN-I and PEDF indicate a 30% identity.

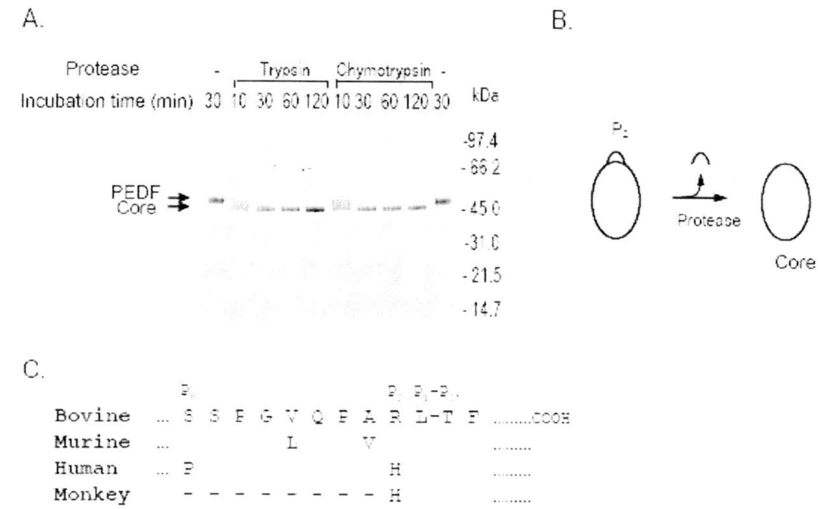

Figure 3. Limited proteolysis of PEDF of 50-kDa with trypsin and chymotrypsin. A. SDS-polyacrylamide gel electrophoresis of the products of 46-kDa polypeptide fragments (core). B. Scheme of cleavage of PEDF with most proteases at the homologous serpin exposed loop. C. Sequence alignment of the serpin exposed loop from bovine, murine, human and monkey PEDF. The bovine and murine proteins have a tryptic recognition site between the P2-P1 positions (Arg-Xxx), while the human and monkey do not. A chymoytyptic recognition site is at P1-P1', the homologous serpin reactive site, in all shown sequences and is specific for leucyl-endopeptidase type inhibition.

Biochemical studies indicate that the native PEDF protein purified from several mammalian sources behaves like a monomeric glycoprotein with an apparent molecular weight of about 50,000 on SDS-PAGE, matching the size predicted from its cDNA [30, 31, 43]. PEDF elutes as a monomeric polypeptide between bovine serum albumin and carbonic anhydrase in size-exclusion column chromatography. It has an isoelectric point of 7.2-7.8, and depending on the pH of its vehicle, it has affinity for anionic or cationic resins and biomolecules such as glycosaminoglycans or collagens. The purified protein is sensitive to glycosidase F, revealing asparagine-linked oligosaccharides that account up to 3,000-Mr of the native protein. The amino-terminal sequence of mature PEDF from several species indicate it starts at position 21 of the PEDF precursor, and that depending on the source, N-acetylation or other post-translational modification might occur at its amino-terminal residue.

The human PEDF polypeptide shares 27% primary sequence homology with α_1-antitrypsin. Comparison of PEDF primary structure to conserved amino acid residues in α_1-antitrypsin necessary for maintaining tertiary structural integrity of serpins displays 90% of amino acid identity, which predicts a serpin tertiary structure for PEDF. The overall folded conformation of serpins has been traditionally studied by controlled proteolysis and amino-terminal sequence determination of the polypeptide products. Proteolysis of serpin proteins with limiting amounts of proteases results in cleavage at sites in the serpin exposed loop leaving a core product smaller than the substrate serpin by 4-6 kDa (see Fig. 3). Control proteolysis with trypsin, chymotrypsin, elastase and subtilisin shows that human, bovine and monkey PEDF are globular proteins containing a hinge region susceptible to cleavage as expected for a serpin [30, 43, 44]. X-ray crystallography confirms that the folded protein conformation of PEDF is that of a serpin [45]. Crystal structures of human PEDF and the serpin prototype are shown in figure 4 to illustrate its similarities. However, in spite of these similarities and unlike most serpins, PEDF does not behave as an inhibitor of serine proteases, it does not form complexes with serine proteases and does not undergo the typical serpin stress-relaxed conformational change upon cleavage of its serpin exposed loop [44]. In this regard PEDF and ovalbumin share the lack of serpin conformational change feature. In contrast to GDN/PN-1, PEDF does not complex with thrombin even in the presence of heparin known to accelerate the inhibition and complex rates of these proteins. Interestingly, cleaved PEDF at its exposed loop exhibits neurotrophic activity, implying that the neurotrophic active site and the hinge region (homologous serpin reactive site) are separated in the primary as well as in the tertiary structure of PEDF.

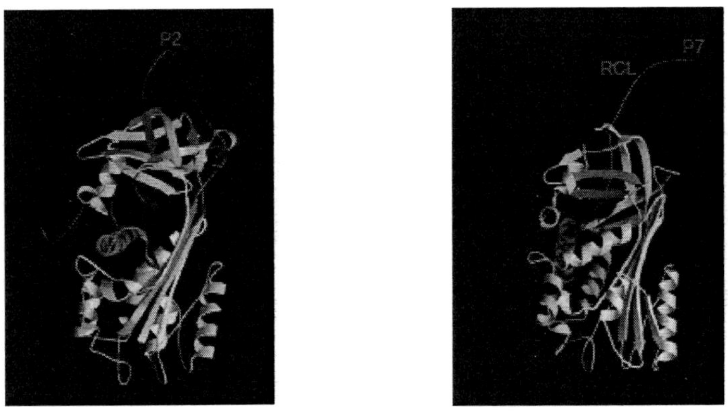

Figure 4. Structures of human PEDF and alpha-1-antitrypsin as obtained from crystallographic data from protein databases PDB, 1MV and 1QMB, respectively. In inhibitory serpins the target protease cleaves the bond between amino acid positions at P1-P1' within the reactive center loop (RCL or serpin exposed loop), the serpin undergoes a conformational change and complexes with the protease preventing it from further acting. Position P2 corresponds to the amino acid position upstream from P1.

Expression vectors containing fragments of PEDF coding sequences provide an excellent source for isolating different regions of the PEDF polypeptide. Segmentation of the PEDF polypeptide becomes instrumental for studies on structure-function. Expression of human fetal *PEDF* sequences was achieved with *Escherichia coli* expression vectors and the human fetal *PEDF* cDNA [44, 46]. Truncated C-end recombinant proteins PEDF (BH, Asp^{44}-Pro^{418}) BP (Asp^{44}-Pro^{267}), BX (Asp^{44}-Leu^{228}) and BA (Asp^{44}-Thr^{121}) retained the ability to differentiate Y-79 cells. The BP and BX proteins also exhibit neurotrophic activities on cerebellar granule cell neurons and motor neurons [11, 14]. Furthermore synthetic peptides designed from the smallest BA region and termed 34-mer (Asp^{44}-Asn^{77}) and 44-mer (Val^{78}-Thr^{121}) retained antiangiogenic and neurotrophic activities, respectively [47, 48; Amaral et al., manuscript in preparation; Filleur et al., Cancer Res. 2005 65:5144-5152]. These observations demonstrate distinct regions on the PEDF primary structure can be distinguished: a proximal with a neurotrophic active site located within amino acid residues 78-121 and an antiangiogenic active site located within amino acid residues 44-77, and a distal with homology to a serpin exposed loop. Thus, the overall native conformation of PEDF might not be required for neurotrophic and antiangiogenic activities and inhibition of serine proteases cannot account for the biological activity of PEDF. During evolution this serpin might have lost its inhibitory activity and gained neurotrophic and antiangiogenic functions. These findings provide an example of the separation of inhibitory and other activities in a serpin.

5. Search for a PEDF Receptor

Given that serine protease inhibition could not explain the biological activities of PEDF, investigations in our laboratory were directed toward the hypothesis that PEDF's neurotrophic activity is mediated by interactions with cell surfaces. Focusing on retinoblastoma and cerebellar granule cells, we prospected for PEDF receptors and found evidence for 1) a saturable, specific, and high-affinity class of binding sites on the surface of both cells, with characteristics of an 80-kDa plasma membrane protein, and 2) the amino-terminal region in PEDF that interacts with these sites [47]. Similarly, we found evidence for saturable, specific and high-affinity class of receptors in spinal motor neurons, expanding its presence to other cell types [48]. However, in contrast to neuronal cells non-neuronal COS-7 cells did not have binding sites for PEDF on their surfaces (Fig. 5 and [47]). A summary of physico-chemical parameters for the interactions between PEDF and sites of cells from different species suggests that PEDF binds to receptor homologues with similar binding affinities (K_d) but varies in numbers of sites per type of cell (B_{max}) (Table 3). The work demonstrated that the first step in the biological activity of PEDF is the binding to receptors on the surface of target cells, a significant advance in the elucidation of PEDF's mechanisms of action.

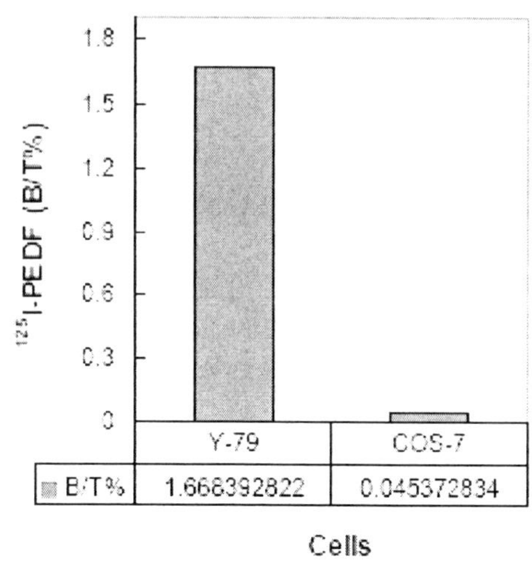

Figure 5. ^{125}I-PEDF binding to receptors in Y-79 and COS-7 cells. Radioligand binding assays were performed with 2 nM ^{125}I-PEDF and retinoblastoma Y-79 cells in suspension and COS-7 cells attached on plastic. Bound radioligand was separated from free and the radioactivity subtracted from non-specific binding performed in assays with a 50-fold molar excess of unlabeled radioligand over radioligand and was plotted. The Y-79 cells contained receptors on its surface, while in COS-7 cells the PEDF-binding sites were not detected.

Table 3. Physicochemical Parameters of PEDF Binding

Cells or tissue	K_d (nM)	B_{max} (sites/unit)
Human retinoblastoma·Y-79 cells	1.7 – 3.6	45,500 – 271,200
Rat cerebellar granule cell neurons	2.3 –4.1	1,000 – 1,200
Bovine retina	2.5 –6.5	1 –48 x 10^{10}
Rat Motor neurons	7.9	48,000

Because PEDF has an effect on retina cells, we then examined the expression of PEDF receptors in native retinas [49]. The collected data provide physico-chemical, pharmacological, and biochemical evidence for PEDF binding to cell-surface receptors distributed discretely in the neural retina of adult steers, *i.e.*, photoreceptors and ganglion cells. These PEDF binding sites have characteristics similar to those in retinoblastoma cells and cerebellar granule cells and correlate with PEDF effects on the survival and morphogenesis of photoreceptor cells *in vivo* and retina cells in culture, suggesting that they may correspond to functional receptors. The data also reveal for the first time that ganglion cells may be targets for PEDF activity. Overall, the data is of particular importance because they provide an anatomical basis for studies to assess PEDF neurotrophic effects on the adult retina. The interactions between PEDF receptors and ligand may trigger the signal transduction events for neurotrophic activity in the retina.

6. Signal Transduction Pathways

Evidence on the downstream events that occur upon binding to cell surface receptors is being obtained. Studies performed with systems other than the retina, such as cerebellar granule cell neurons, further confirm the existence of PEDF neurotrophic receptors in these neurons. One line of evidence for signaling comes from studies on the neuroprotective effect of PEDF against glutamate toxicity. It has been proposed that the effect of PEDF could involve alterations in the intracellular homeostasis of calcium [10] that could interact and modulate the membrane Na^{+}/Ca^{++} exchanger, or increase the expression of intracellular proteins like calbindin or parvalbumin, which are implicated in calcium binding and sequestrating activity. Another line of evidence was derived from the neuronal survival effect of PEDF on the same cells, cerebellar granule cell neurons. Neuronal protection processes require the activation of transcription factors as well as the involvement of antiapoptotic molecules and signals. Because nuclear factor-kB (NF-kB) plays a role in the protection of neuronal cells in several models of apoptotic death induction, Yabe *et al.*, in 2001 [50], investigated the possible involvement of the NF-kB pathway in PEDF neuroprotection activity. In their studies, the level of NF-kB binding to DNA was analyzed using electrophoresis mobility shift assays. A member of the IkB inhibitory proteins normally sequesters NF-kB in the cytoplasmic compartment. When cells are exposed to activators of NF-kB, these IkB proteins are phosphorylated, ubiquitinated, and degraded by proteosomes and then NF-kB is released and it translocates to the nucleus where it binds to responsive elements on the DNA. Upon treatment with PEDF, the authors showed a time dependent decrease in IkBα and IkBβ proteins. Furthermore, when cells were pretreated with BAY-11-7082, an inhibitor of IkB phosphorylation, or with ALLN, which interfere with proteosome activity on IkB, NF-kB activation by PEDF was inhibited. The downstream events following NF-kB activation have then been investigated. The same authors showed that in immature cerebellar granule cells, but not in mature ones, PEDF was able to induce antiapoptotic effectors, like Bcl-2, Bcl-x and Mn-SOD. PEDF was also able to induce other neurotrophic factors like nerve growth factor, brain-derived neurotrophic factor, and glial cell-derived neurotrophic factor [51]. From their results they proposed that PEDF promotes neuronal survival through activation of NFkB, which in turn induces expression of anti-apoptotic and/or neurotrophic factor genes. Although PEDF enhances expression of other neurotrophic factors or chemokines, it does not exert its neuroprotective effect on cerebellar granule cells through their production [51].

In contrast to the neuronal survival effects, the antiangiogenic effects of PEDF have been associated to induction of endothelial cell apoptosis [17, 18]. Several proangiogenic stimuli are able to induce elevated membrane levels of CD95/Fas, a receptor related with apoptotic cell death, whereas antiangiogenic factors like PEDF are able to increase the expression of endothelial Fas ligand (FasL). When expressed simultaneously these two molecules are able to induce apoptosis in endothelial cells, and therefore to inhibit angiogenesis [52]. This provides an example for cooperation between pro- and anti-angiogenic factors in the inhibition of angiogenesis and one explanation for the ability of inhibitors to select remodeling capillaries for destruction.

Induction of angiogenesis by vascular endothelial growth factor (VEGF) or basic fibroblast growth factor requires activation of the nuclear factor of activated T cells (NFAT) [53]. In a recent study by Zaichuk *et al.*, 2004 [17] such activation is blocked by PEDF. Among the upstream regulatory molecules used in NFATc2 regulation by PEDF a dramatic increase in phospho-JNK levels and JNK-dependent substrate phosphorylation by PEDF is observed exclusively in activated endothelial cells. SP600125, a generic JNK inhibitor, reduces NFATc2 phosphorylation and restores nuclear localization in affected endothelial cells. The same compound has no effect on VEGF or bFGF-dependent angiogenesis, but destroys response to PEDF in vitro and in vivo, pointing to JNK kinases and their downstream targets as critical elements of PEDF angioinhibitory signaling. Expression of a novel NFAT target, caspase-8 inhibitor cellular Fas-associated death domain-like interleukin 1beta-converting enzyme inhibitory protein (c-FLIP) that mediates resistance to apoptotic signaling, is coregulated by VEGF and PEDF. The VEGF-dependent increase of NFATc2 binding to the c-FLIP promoter in vivo is attenuated by PEDF. Thus PEDF may counter regulate VEGF or bFGF in angiogenesis via cFLIP controlled by NFAT and its upstream JNK.

Together, it is thought that PEDF would trigger signaling events similar as those described above in the neural and vascular retina to exert its survival and antiangiogenic effects, respectively.

7. PEDF Interacts with Extracellular Matrixes

The complex heterogeneous matrix that surrounds cells and mainly formed by secreted glycosaminoglycans and collagens is called extracellular matrix. It plays important structural and functional roles in development, differentiation, survival and growth of cells. Glycosaminoglycans/proteoglycans and collagens are the most abundant components of interphotoreceptor matrix, vitreous and other extracellular matrixes.

Glycosaminoglycans and proteoglycans are found predominantly in association with cell surfaces as structural components and functional modulators of extracellular matrixes. Glycosaminoglycans are highly sulfated and negatively charged polymers of disaccharide repeats, and proteoglycans are complex glycoconjugates containing a core protein to which several glycosaminoglycan chains (such as heparin, heparan sulfate, chondroitin sulfate, etc.) are covalently attached. Cell-surface associated glycosaminoglycans are thought to act in combination with extracellular proteins as regulators of the neuronal pattern formation, survival and function. They are required for the interaction of several growth/trophic factors with cell surface receptors, and are binding components for cell adhesion proteins. Structurally diverse glycosaminoglycans and proteoglycans are abundant in the developing and mature central nervous system. Heparan and chondroitin sulfate-containing proteoglycans are spatially and temporally distributed across the extracellular spaces of the developing neural retina. In the mature retina these macromolecules maintain a spatial distribution, which is found altered under pathological conditions, *e.g.*, photoreceptor degeneration, age-related maculopathy, diabetes.

Collagens comprise a family of more than 20 proteins with a broad range of structural and physiological functions, which are strictly located in the extracellular space. All collagens are present in tissues as homotrimeric and/or heterotrimeric assemblies and have specific tissue distributions and functions, *e.g.* they are involved in wound healing, cell adhesion, and migration. In the cornea and vitreous they are known to give transparency, strength, and elasticity. Collagen type I is the major protein of the cornea (94% of the total collagen in the bovine cornea) and coassembles in heterotypic fibrils with collagen type V. Collagen type II is the main protein of the vitreous (70-80%) followed by collagens type V, XI and IX [54].

PEDF coexists with glycosaminoglycans in extracellular compartments, such as, the interphotoreceptor matrix, vitreous and aqueous humor. Because of four separate observations: *i)* PEDF is associated with the interphotoreceptor matrix by ionic interactions; *ii)* the major components that confer a negative charge to this extracellular matrix are glycosaminoglycans, such as the sulfated heparan sulfate/heparin, chondroitin sulfates and the non-sulfated hyaluronan; *iii)* glycosaminoglycans are known modulators of several serpins and trophic/growth factors; and *iv)* the sequences of human, bovine and mouse PEDF reveal a conserved region (K189-K197, human sequence numbering) with homology to a characteristic motif found among hyaluronan-binding proteins, the molecular interactions of PEDF with a variety of glycosaminoglycans known in the interphotoreceptor matrix were examined [55; Becerra et al., *Invest. Ophthalmol. Vis. Sci.* 1999; 40, 4, Abst. 42]. We found evidence for PEDF binding affinity for each of these glycosaminoglycans mediated by ionic interactions. Analysis of the GAG-binding region using limited proteolysis and chemical modification showed that while proteolytic cleavage of the serpin-exposed loop and even removal of about 40% from the C-end of the protein does not affect the binding affinity, unfolded protein and PEDF chemically modified on positively charged lysine residues lose their capacity for interaction with heparin. Homology modeling of human PEDF based on the X-ray crystal structures of antithrombin III and ovalbumin revealed a large region at the center of β-sheet A -strands 2 and 3- and helix F that has a basic electrostatic surface potential and is densely populated with lysines exposed to the surface that are available to interact with various glycosaminoglycans/polyanions. Yasui et al [56] by residue-specific chemical modification and site-directed mutagenesis techniques, revealed three clustered basic amino acid residues of mouse PEDF (Arg145, Lys146, and Arg148) that are necessary for heparin binding. Mapping these sites in the crystal structure of human PEDF reveals a novel site for glycosaminoglycan binding in a serpin, which in PEDF is distinct from and non-overlapping with the PEDF neurotrophic active binding region. The glycosaminoglycan-binding property of PEDF represents the likely molecular basis for its association with extracellular matrixes, *e.g.*, interphotoreceptor matrix, vitreous, etc.

PEDF also coexists with collagens in the cornea and vitreous. Because PEDF interacts with bovine corneal and vitreal collagens, we examined the direct binding of PEDF to collagen [57]. By size-exclusion ultrafiltration, radioligand-binding assays, ligand blotting and ligand-affinity column chromatography, it was found that human PEDF binds specifically to collagen types I, II and III, with type I having the highest affinity. Modified PEDF with ^{125}I binds to immobilized collagen I in a specific and saturable fashion (K_d = 0.2 μM). Radioligand competition assays showed that unlabeled PEDF and a recombinant fragment of PEDF (amino acid positions 44-418) compete with ^{125}I-PEDF for the binding to collagen I. However, angiostatin and endostatin (angiogenesis inhibitors) (Fig. 6), and the PEDF-derived synthetic peptide spanning positions 78-121 (44-mer) does not compete [51]. The binding is sensitive to increasing NaCl concentrations, implying an ionic nature for the PEDF-collagen interactions. Because the three-dimensional structure of PEDF reveals two distinct areas with opposite ionic potentials on its surface, the ionic region that interacts with collagen was sought by chemical modifications. Blocking the positively charged lysine residues with fluorescein does not abolish the PEDF affinity for binding collagen I, but increases it, indicating that the positive lysines are not required for binding collagen. However, the negative charged aspartic and glutamic acids of PEDF are required for collagen I binding, given that modification with EDC abolishes the binding affinity for collagen I. More interestingly, neutralizing the charges of the basic region makes the negatively charged surface area more accessible to interact with positively charged collagen. Yasui et al [56] by residue-specific chemical modification and site-directed mutagenesis techniques revealed that the acidic amino acid residues Asp255, Asp257 and Asp299 of mouse PEDF are critical to collagen binding. Mapping of these residues on the crystal structure of human PEDF showed that the collagen-binding site is oriented toward the opposite side of the highly basic surface where the heparin-binding site is localized, and away from the 34-mer and 44-mer region. This site represents the first collagen-binding site described for a serpin. These results indicate that PEDF has two binding sites for different components of the extracellular matrix. The collagen-binding property of PEDF may play a role in surface localization and modulation of its antiangiogenic effects in the eye as well as in other tissues like bone and cartilage.

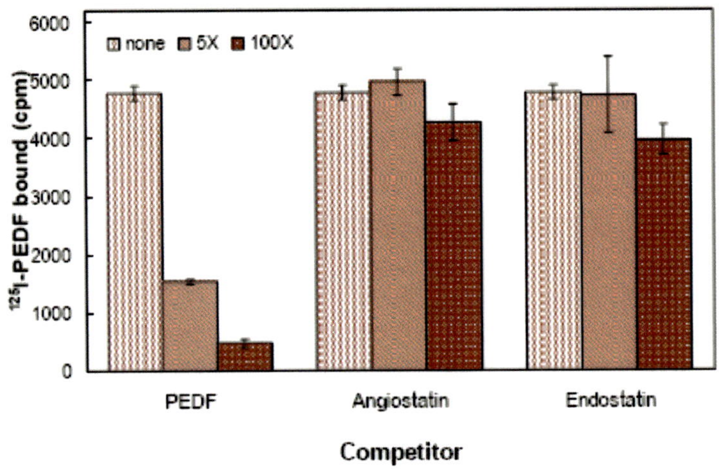

Figure 6. ^{125}I-PEDF ligand competition to immobilized collagen I. Radioligand binding assays were performed with 3 nM ^{125}I-PEDF on collagen I-coated 24-well plates in the presence of competitors unlabeled PEDF, angiostatin and endostatin at 0-, 5- and 100- fold molar excess over radioligand. Angiostatin and endostatin are antiangiogenic factors. Bound ligand was separated from free and the bound radioactivity was plotted. PEDF competed for collagen binding while the other antiangiogenic factors did not.

8. Regulation of PEDF Activity

PEDF expression patterns in the human eye suggest that modulation of this protein over time may play a role in development of normal neural and vascular retina. PEDF mRNA expression is regulated in development and ageing. PEDF mRNA is present in retinal pigment epithelium of the human eye at 17 weeks of gestation, demonstrating its potential for action in vivo during early retinal development [58]. PEDF is secreted from retinal pigment epithelium from fetal human eyes [1] and is detected in photoreceptors and inner retinal cell types in the developing human eyes [33]. Using a mouse model, Behling *et al.*, in 2002 [59] showed that localization and extent of PEDF expression change during the mouse eye development. The authors could not detect PEDF expression in any cells of the retina until late in gestation (E 18.5). After this time in the development, PEDF expression was detected in a variety of ocular cell types, with an evolution of the expression patterns over the next two weeks, in coincidence with the period during which retinal vasculature develops.

PEDF can act like a regulator of cell proliferation. The mechanism by which PEDF induces differentiation is likely to operate through pathways that regulate and drive cells out of the cell cycle into the G_0 state of growth arrest [60]. Similar mechanisms are likely to happen in aging processes. Pignolo et al. [60] showed that PEDF expression was the highest in the actively dividing cells in contrast to lowest expression in senescent cells. Likewise, the inhibition of neovascularization by PEDF has been proposed to be a result of the arrest of endothelial cell proliferation and induction of apoptotic cell death through signals involving the recruitment of MAPK and Fas/FasL pathways [52].

PEDF mRNA expression decreases with passage number of cultured retinal pigment epithelial cells and is accompanied by loss of their proliferative potential and phenotype [58].

It has been proposed that these changes are typical of senescence and that PEDF expression in the human eye is also decreased with age. Although, there are no reports yet on the age-related changes in PEDF expression in the eye, these have been reported in the skin [61]. PEDF, also called EPC-1, is detected primarily in the dermal layer of the skin and its expression declines with increasing donor age. This decline is statistically significant between young (less than 31 years old) and middle-aged (between 30 and 60 years old) donors, becoming less dramatic at older ages. An age-related decline in the retina could lead to lower PEDF-mediated neurotrophic and antiangiogenic activities and an increase of ocular pathologies with age. Although several reports have associated changes in PEDF protein with pathology, the molecular basis for this decline remains unknown.

Indeed, downregulation of PEDF correlates with several ocular neovascular and neurodegenerative diseases, like diabetic retinopathy, age-related macular degeneration, glaucoma and retinitis pigmentosa. It has been shown that the vitreous of patients with choroidal neovascularization due to age-related macular degeneration contained lower levels of PEDF and lacked the antiangiogenic activity of vitreous from age-matched controls [62]. PEDF in the aqueous humor of eyes with retinitis pigmentosa and advanced glaucoma were significantly lower than that in eyes with cataract alone [63]. Comparison between levels of PEDF in vitreous of eyes with diabetic retinopathy and idiopathy macular hole, between proliferative and nonproliferative diabetic retinopathy, and between active and inactive diabetic retinopathy showed lower vitreal concentration of PEDF with higher levels of vascular endothelial growth factor in each case [64]. In experimental animal models for ocular neovascularization, the levels of PEDF have also been found lower than in non-treated animal. An inverse correlation of expression of PEDF and formation of choroidal neovascularization induced by laser injury of Bruch's membrane suggests that decreased expression of PEDF plays a permissive role in the formation of CNV [65]. In mice, penetrating ocular injury suppressed retinal neovascularization and upregulated PEDF expression in the inner retina [66]. These observations suggest that loss of PEDF creates a permissive environment for angiogenesis and neuropathy in patients that may contribute to progression of ocular neovascular and neurodegenerative diseases.

Pathological progression-related changes have also been reported outside of the eye, such as in some prostate cancers. Studies with PEDF gene ablated mice have shown that a developmental deficiency in PEDF can cause profound changes in the size and cellularity of the prostate and pancreas [25]. In both a rat model and in human tumors, the proliferation index and vascular count inversely correlated with PEDF mRNA levels, suggesting loss of PEDF factor expression could be associated with the progression toward a metastatic phenotype in prostate cancer [26]. In neurodegenerative diseases, elevated PEDF protein levels have been detected in the cerebrospinal fluid of patients affected by amylotrophic lateral sclerosis compared with patients with other neurodegenerative diseases [36], suggesting an autoprotective reaction in amylotrophic lateral sclerosis. Similar suggestion has been made from PEDF increases in rodent retinas after laser-induced retinal injuries [67, 68]. These increases might represent an attempt by the tissue to limit neuronal damage, or in other cases to counterbalance the neovascular stimulus.

An increasing number of reports have demonstrated that overexpression of PEDF in animal models for retinal degenerations and ocular neovascularization is beneficial for the protection of the neural and vascular retina. Intravitreal injections of PEDF transiently delayed the death of photoreceptor cells in mouse models of retinitis pigmentosa, retinal degeneration (*rd/rd*), and retinal degeneration slow (*rds/rds*) mice [5]; and protected rat photoreceptors cells from light damage [6,7]. PEDF delivered intravitreally or systemically suppressed ischemia-induced retinal neovascularization in mice models of retinopathy of prematurity [16, 18]. Subretinal transplantation of genetically modified iris pigment epithelial cells expressing PEDF inhibited neovascularization in rat models of choroidal neovascularization induced by laser injury of Bruch's membrane and of oxygen induced ischemic retinopathy, as well as increased the survival and preserved rhodopsin expression of photoreceptor cells in the RCS rat, a model of retinal degeneration [69].

Intravitreal injections of an adenoviral vector encoding PEDF mediated intraocular overexpression of the recombinant PEDF that significantly increased cell survival after ischemia-reperfusion injury of the rat retina [8]. Periocular injection of an adenoviral vector encoding PEDF significantly elevated the intraocular levels of PEDF and inhibited choroidal neovascularization [70]. Adenoviral vectored PEDF gene transfer caused regression on already established ocular neovascularization models (transgenic mice with expression of vascular endothelial growth factor (VEGF) in photoreceptors (rho/VEGF mice) and choroidal neovascularization induced by Bruch's membrane rupturing with laser) by promoting apoptosis of cells within neovascular lesions [71]. Adeno-associated viral-mediated intraocular gene transfer of PEDF also inhibited the development of choroidal and retinal neovascularization in murine models [72, 73].

Given that aberrant regulation of PEDF could be conducive to pathological neovascularization and/or neuronal cell death and its potential use in restoring them, it is of interest to define the mechanisms that govern its regulation and turnover to better exploit this interesting protein as a relevant therapeutic factor for the eye. Alterations of the mechanisms for production or the structural determinants for function and localization modulate the efficacy of PEDF. Regulation of PEDF has been reported at different levels. Several factors affect the PEDF gene expression or the protein concentration of PEDF, for example, hypoxia, a main stimulus for angiogenesis and neuronal cell apoptosis, affects PEDF protein levels.

a. Regulation of Expression of the PEDF Gene

Retinoids, in particular all-*trans*-retinoic acid, are potent regulators of cell proliferation [74] that regulate gene transcription by binding to and activating two classes of nuclear transcription factors, the RA receptors (RARs) and the retinoid X receptors (RXRs). The PEDF promoter has a functional retinoic acid responsive region [75]. It has been shown that PEDF expression can be increased in Y-79 cells, ARPE19, an immortalized cell line derived from RPE cells, and endothelial cells by retinoids, and that PEDF can in turn upregulate the expression of specific RARs and RXRs.

Dexamethasone, a synthetic glucocorticoid used especially as an anti-inflammatory agent, also induces PEDF mRNA expression in both mouse Müller glial cells and C6 rat glioma cells [75], as well as in human trabecular meshwork from human eyes [76]. PEDF protein levels also increase significantly in dexamethasone-treated trabecular meshwork cells over non-treated controls [Perruccio et al. *Invest. Ophthalmol. Vis. Sci.* 2003; 44, 4, Abst. # 1140], indicating a direct effect of dexamethasone on upregulating PEDF expression.

In contrast, leptin, a circulating hormone secreted mainly from adipose tissues involved in the control of body weight, downregulates PEDF gene expression while it upregulates the vascular endothelial growth factor gene in bovine cultured retinal pericytes [77].

Interestingly, like vascular endothelial growth factor, leptin acts as an angiogenic factor and is found elevated in vitreous from patients with angiogenic eye diseases.

b. Post-Translational Regulation of PEDF

To date there is no information reported on PEDF post-transcriptional or translational control to explain changes in expression of PEDF protein through development ageing or in pathological conditions. There is some information on regulation of PEDF activity by post-translational modifications and processes. Glycosylation, as well as folded or unfolded status of the PEDF polypeptide do not affect its biological activities [46]. The recombinant PEDF protein derived from bacteria exhibits the biological activities and properties of the native PEDF. Phosphorylation has been recently reported as a post-translational modification of PEDF protein purified from plasma [78]. Mutagenesis to prevent phosphorylation on Ser24 and Ser114 yielded a PEDF mutant that lacked neurotrophic activity but enhanced antiangiogenic activity, while mutagenesis to prevent phosphorylation on Ser227 reduced PEDF antiangiogenic activity. These observations suggest that differential phosphorylation sites can convert PEDF from a neurotrophic to an antiangiogenic factor.

Upon maturation the protein is secreted from the cells into extracellular matrix. Regulation of secretion may be important. However, little is known about control on intracellular trafficking in the polarized retinal pigment epithelium in preparation for release from the cell. Polarized retinal pigment epithelium secretes components in a directional fashion, by the apicolateral membrane, toward the photoreceptor layer or basolaterally toward the Bruch's membrane and the choroidal vasculature [30, 79, 80]. Because polarization is constantly under the control of regulating factors coming from the choroid and retina, extracellular stimuli may be an important mechanism of controlling PEDF secretion. The fact that extracellular molecules of oxygen can switch the polarity of RPE cells from apical to basal and *vice versa* suggests the possibility for the existence of a stimulus that can specifically target the change of polarity for PEDF secretion to the choroid or toward the interphotoreceptor matrix. Loss of polarity in PEDF production may play a role in the pathogenesis of retinal cells degeneration and choroidal and retinal neovascularization.

Another mechanism for regulating PEDF activity involves interactions between ligand and receptor. It has been proposed that only a very small region of the 44-mer is responsible for interactions with the receptor. Cofactors that induce a conformational change or proteolytic cleavage could expose the neurotrophic 44-mer region making it available for interacting with the receptors and for PEDF activation.

A study on the effects of glycosaminoglycans on the ligand-receptor interactions of PEDF shows that heparan sulfate can be a cofactor that modulates these interactions. Using human retinoblastoma Y-79 cells as a source of functional PEDF receptors [81] it was shown that enzymatic and chemical depletion of sulfated glycosaminoglycans by heparitinase and chlorate treatments decreased the degree of PEDF binding to cell-surface sites in Y-79 cells. Because PEDF has affinity for heparan sulfate and heparin, it was suggested that the PEDF-heparin/heparan sulfate complex may somehow facilitate encounters between PEDF and its receptor, *e.g.*, by inducing a conformational change in PEDF, which might accelerate the ligand-receptor interactions. In addition, the receptor may also form a complex with heparin/HS to facilitate interactions with the ligand. These observations offer interesting possibilities of regulation of the activity of PEDF. The ratio and amount of production of heparin and heparan sulfate by cells bearing PEDF receptors may be an important mechanism to control the activity of PEDF as is the modulation of the rate of expression of PEDF receptors. The data present in literature on the action of PEDF on different cells may have not considered the presence of these cofactors in the media. Modulation of the PEDF ligand-receptor interactions by glycosaminoglycans opens also the possibility that different glycosaminoglycans may modulate differently the affinity of PEDF for its receptors, by increasing or even decreasing it in some cases. Thus, the differentiation and survival of cells in vivo may be regulated not only by the expression of PEDF and its receptor but also by the temporal and spatial expression of glycosaminoglycans.

The glycosaminoglycan-PEDF as well as the collagen-PEDF interactions may play important roles *in vivo* in regulating the local availability of PEDF and/or in modulating its biological activities, *e.g.* antiangiogenic activities in the cornea and vitreous. PEDF in the vitreous, cornea and Bruch's membrane may also be regulated by the temporal and spatial expression of collagens. The collagen binding property of PEDF suggests that PEDF regulates cell interactions and has a function as a cell adhesion molecule and/or substrate adhesion molecule. At the molecular level, PEDF has binding sites for collagens and glycosaminoglycans, which are characteristic features of cell adhesion molecules. The actual affinity of PEDF for extracellular matrix may be even higher than that for individual extracellular matrix molecules, as its affinity for collagen increases when the glycosaminoglycan-binding site of PEDF is neutralized and *vice versa* and could even change with the pH of the extracellular matrix. Therefore, qualitative and quantitative changes of extracellular matrix molecules, *e.g.* collagen, glycosaminoglycans, as well as pH changes of extracellular matrix, which occur through development, with aging and in certain pathologic conditions, such as corneal dystrophies, diabetic retinopathy, and wound healing, [54, 82-87], may alter molecular assembly and the location of the antiangiogenic activities of PEDF.

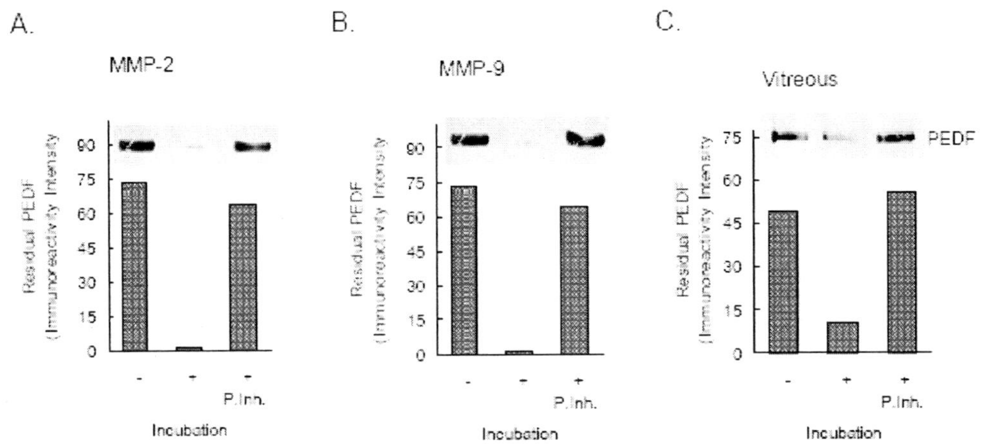

Figure 7. PEDF Protein Degradation by matrix metalloproteinase type-2 and type-9 and in monkey vitreous. A and B, westerns against Ab-PEDF show PEDF product levels after degradation with MMP-2 and MMP-9 at a 1:1000 protease:substrate ratio (w:w). C. Westerns against Ab-PEDF showing PEDF product levels in vitreal extracts after incubations at 37°C. Quantification of PEDF immunoreactivity shows that incubation with protease inhibitors that included the calcium chelator EDTA prevented degradation of PEDF. Vitreous contains EDTA-sensitive proteases that degrade PEDF. P. Inh., protease inhibitors mix.

Changes in the expression or degradation of collagen may affect PEDF deposition in extracellular matrixes. For example, degradation of collagens by matrix metalloproteinases may allow PEDF to be liberated as a diffusible factor or degraded as well by the same proteases. As shown in figure 7 extracellular matrix metalloproteinases can efficiently degrade PEDF protein.

c. Extracellular Degradation of PEDF: Interaction with Proteases

Given that PEDF and proteases coexist in extracellular matrixes we studied the biological implications of their biochemical interactions. Previous studies had shown that the homologous serpin reactive loop located at the C-terminal end of the PEDF molecule has sensitive cleavage recognition sites for proteases such as trypsin, chymotrypsin, and subtilisin. The rest of the folded PEDF polypeptide is resistant to the attack by most of proteases. PEDF of 50-kDa can be cleaved in a controlled reaction with serine proteases like chymotrypsin, leaving limited products that can be resolved on SDS-PAGE as protein fragments migrating at about 46-kDa and 4kDa (Becerra et al., 1995; Stratikos et al., 1996). In addition and unlike other members of the serpin superfamily, PEDF biological activity is not suppressed by the cleavage of the homologous serpin exposed loop, which contains the structural determinant for inhibition by members of the serpin superfamily, being its structure stabilized by additional structural elements probably selected in an evolutionary process. In inhibitory serpins, like α_1-antichymotrypsin and glia-derived nexin/protease nexin, the biological activities are directly related to inhibition of serine proteases, and cleavage of the serpin-exposed loop abolishes their serpin inhibitory property [88-90]. Because PEDF behaves like a substrate rather than an inhibitor, like ovalbumin, angiotensinogen and maspin, cleavage at its exposed loop could result in proteolytic processing. The effects of cleavage at this region could induce a change in its folded protein conformation to uncover structural determinants for biological function, such as the receptor-binding site, and therefore enhance its biological effects. However, so far there are no reports of an enhancement in biological activities upon cleavage at the serpin-exposed loop of PEDF.

PEDF loss in the retina is a recurrent event in retinal pathological conditions like age-related macular degeneration and diabetic retinopathy, and in hypoxic-related retinal diseases that result in retinal and choroidal neovascularization, and neuronal cell death. Interestingly, the expression and secretion of matrix metalloproteinases type-2 and type-9 also correlates positively with the progression of neovascular ocular diseases [91, 92]. These two proteases belong to the matrix metalloproteinases family of Zn^{++} and Ca^{++} dependent extracellular peptidases [93]. Their classical and most studied role is that of an extracellular matrix degrading activity principally for collagens. But recently an increasing number of "non-conventional" substrates' for matrix metalloproteinases have been identified, including several growth factors, cytokines, and vasoactive molecules. The vitreous contains matrix metalloproteinases and the physiological retinal pigment epithelium secretes PEDF and matrix metalloproteinase-2 from its apicolateral membranes towards the interphotoreceptor matrix. In our laboratory we have found that the levels of PEDF protein in soluble extracts from the vitreous and interphotoreceptor matrix decrease upon incubation of these extracts, leaving no limited products to be detected by SDS-polyacrylamide gel electrophoresis. Only calcium chelators, such as EDTA were able to prevent such proteolytic degradation, while inhibitors of other than the metalloproteinase class, like the cysteine protease inhibitor leupeptin, the serine proteinase inhibitors AEBSF and aprotinin, or the specific calpain inhibitor E-64, did not have any effect on PEDF proteolysis prevention. These results imply a complete degradation of PEDF by enzymes sensitive to calcium chelators present in the vitreous and interphotoreceptor matrix, and lead us to investigate the direct effect of matrix metalloproteinases type 2 and type 9 on PEDF protein. When PEDF was incubated in *in-vitro* reactions with MMP-2 or MMP-9 in the presence of $CaCl_2$, it was completely degraded in a time and protease concentration dependent fashion, and without limited products to be detected by either Coommassie blue staining or Ab-PEDF immunostaining after SDS-polyacrylamide gel elctrophoresis [Notari et al., *Invest. Ophthalmol. Vis. Sci.* 2005; 46:2736-2747]. Furthermore, PEDF treated with matrix metalloproteinases lost its biological properties of inducing retinal survival and inhibiting angiogenesis.

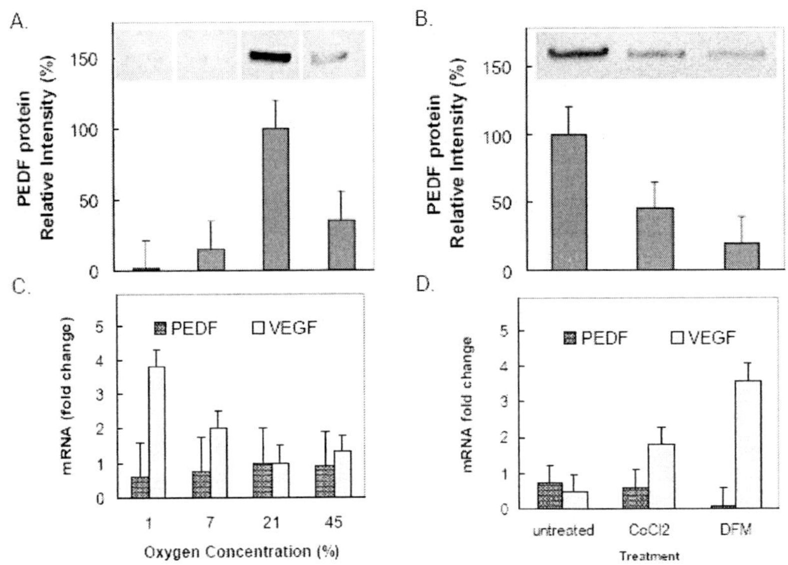

Figure 8. The effect of oxygen on PEDF in human retinoblastoma Weri cells. Panels A and C show the effect of oxygen on PEDF protein levels in the media and mRNA levels, respectively. Panels B and D show the effect of hypoxic mimetics $CoCl_2$, an "iron analog" at 100 μM, or deferoxamine mesylate (DFM), an iron chelator on PEDF at 260 μM on protein levels in the media and mRNA levels in the cells, respectively. Changes in protein levels in the media do not correlate with the PEDF mRNA levels, suggesting regulation of PEDF is at a post-transcriptional level.

Matrix metalloproteinases are regulated by a variety of stimulators for the remodeling of extracellular matrixes in many biological processes such as cell differentiation, survival, growth, death and migration. Hypoxia, a main stimulus for angiogenesis and neuronal cell apoptosis, and vascular endothelial growth factor, the main pro-angiogenic factor in the eye, are inducers of expression and activators of matrix metalloproteinases [94, 95]. It has been reported that hypoxia and vascular endothelial growth factor can also decrease PEDF levels in the media of cultured cells such as human retinoblastoma Weri cells [15], retinal glial (Muller) cells [32] and retinal pigment epithelial cells [Notari et al., *Invest. Ophthalmol. Vis. Sci.* 2005; 46:2736-2747]. However, the PEDF mRNA levels remain unchanged (see Fig. 8), suggesting regulation of PEDF at a post-transcriptional level. In vascular endothelial growth factor- or hypoxic-treated cell cultures, and in hypoxic-induced rat retinas, there is an increase in matrix metalloproteinase type 2 type 9 activities that correlate with a decrease in PEDF protein. Because hypoxia can upregulate the expression of vascular endothelial growth factor via the hypoxia-inducible factor 1α, we have proposed that hypoxia can attenuate PEDF activities by vascular endothelial growth factor-mediated induction of metalloproteinase-directed degradation of PEDF protein (see Fig. 9). A decrease in oxygen concentration results in an enhanced ration between vascular endothelial growth factor and PEDF. This proposal provides a new mechanism for PEDF regulation at a post-translational and post-secretion level, through proteolytic degradation, which is novel for a member of the serpin superfamily. It explains the vascular endothelial growth factor/PEDF ratio changes in hypoxia-related diseases and could be part of the angiogenic switch and neuronal cell death.

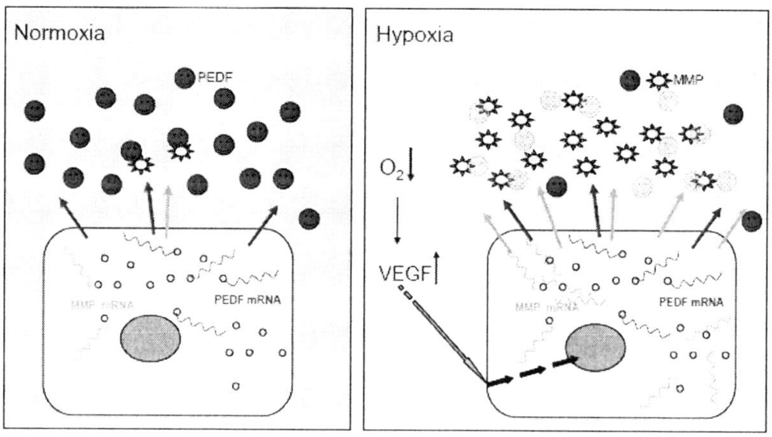

Figure 9. Scheme to illustrate a mechanism for downregulation of PEDF by hypoxia. When oxygen tension decreases, vascular endothelial growth factor (VEGF) is induced; this in turn induces metalloproteinase (MMP) gene expression. The MMPs are synthesized, secreted and activated in the extracellular matrix where they act to degrade and inactivate the extracellular PEDF protein decreasing its neurotrophic and antiangiogenic potentials. The MMP-mediated degradation of PEDF is induced by hypoxia via the angiogenic factor VEGF. In addition, hypoxia favors an increase of VEGF/PEDF ratios via MMP-mediated degradation of PEDF.

Conclusion

The neurotrophic and antiangiogenic properties and the association with senescence make PEDF a key factor for the development, survival and function of the eye. Positive and negative modulation of the activities of PEDF can be achieved at different levels and have an impact in ocular function. PEDF can be modulated by altering the mechanisms of production and of action, such as ageing, hypoxia, metalloproteinases as negative modulators; and retinoids, the anti-inflamatory dexamethasone, heparin sulfate and inhibitors of metalloproteinases as positive modulators. These mechanisms of regulation may be exploited for its use as a therapeutic agent against diseases triggered by angiogenesis and neuronal death.

REFERENCES

[1] Tombran-Tink J, Chader GG, Johnson LV. PEDF: a pigment epithelium-derived factor with potent neuronal differentiative activity. *Exp Eye Res* 1991;53:411-4.

[2] Seigel GM, Tombran-Tink J, Becerra SP et al. Differentiation of Y79 retinoblastoma cells with pigment epithelial-derived factor and interphotoreceptor matrix wash: effects on tumorigenicity. *Growth Factors* 1994;10:289-97.

[3] Cao W, Tombran-Tink J, Chen W et al. Pigment epithelium-derived factor protects cultured retinal neurons against hydrogen peroxide-induced cell death. *J Neurosci Res* 1999;57:789-800.

[4] Jablonski MM, Tombran-Tink J, Mrazek DA et al. Pigment epithelium-derived factor supports normal development of photoreceptor neurons and opsin expression after retinal pigment epithelium removal. *J Neurosci* 2000;20:7149-57.

[5] Cayouette M, Smith SB, Becerra SP et al. Pigment epithelium-derived factor delays the death of photoreceptors in mouse models of inherited retinal degenerations. *Neurobiol Dis* 1999;6:523-32.

[6] Cao W, Tombran-Tink J, Elias R et al. In vivo protection of photoreceptors from light damage by pigment epithelium-derived factor. *Invest Ophthalmol Vis Sci* 2001;42: 1646-52.

[7] Imai D, Yoneya S, Gehlbach PL et al. Intraocular gene transfer of pigment epithelium-derived factor rescues photoreceptors from light-induced cell death. *J Cell Physiol* 2004.

[8] Takita H, Yoneya S, Gehlbach PL et al. Retinal neuroprotection against ischemic injury mediated by intraocular gene transfer of pigment epithelium-derived factor. *Invest Ophthalmol Vis Sci* 2003;44:4497-504.

[9] Taniwaki T, Becerra SP, Chader GJ et al. Pigment epithelium-derived factor is a survival factor for cerebellar granule cells in culture. *J Neurochem* 1995;64:2509-17.

[10] Taniwaki T, Hirashima N, Becerra SP et al. Pigment epithelium-derived factor protects cultured cerebellar granule cells against glutamate-induced neurotoxicity. *J Neurochem* 1997;68:26-32.

[11] Araki T, Taniwaki T, Becerra SP et al. Pigment epithelium-derived factor (PEDF) differentially protects immature but not mature cerebellar granule cells against apoptotic cell death. *J Neurosci Res* 1998;53:7-15.

[12] DeCoster MA, Schabelman E, Tombran-Tink J et al. Neuroprotection by pigment epithelial-derived factor against glutamate toxicity in developing primary hippocampal neurons. *J Neurosci Res* 1999;56:604-10.

[13] Bilak MM, Corse AM, Bilak SR et al. Pigment epithelium-derived factor (PEDF) protects motor neurons from chronic glutamate-mediated neurodegeneration. *J Neuropathol Exp Neurol* 1999;58:719-28.

[14] Houenou LJ, D'Costa AP, Li L et al. Pigment epithelium-derived factor promotes the survival and differentiation of developing spinal motor neurons. *J Comp Neurol* 1999;412:506-14.

[15] Dawson DW, Volpert OV, Gillis P et al. Pigment epithelium-derived factor: a potent inhibitor of angiogenesis. *Science* 1999;285:245-8.

[16] Duh EJ, Yang HS, Suzuma I et al. Pigment epithelium-derived factor suppresses ischemia-induced retinal neovascularization and VEGF-induced migration and growth. *Invest Ophthalmol Vis Sci* 2002;43:821-9.

[17] Zaichuk TA, Shroff EH, Emmanuel R et al. Nuclear factor of activated T cells balances angiogenesis activation and inhibition. *J Exp Med* 2004;199:1513-22.

[18] Stellmach V, Crawford SE, Zhou W et al. Prevention of ischemia-induced retinopathy by the natural ocular antiangiogenic agent pigment epithelium-derived factor. *Proc Natl Acad Sci U S A* 2001;98:2593-7.

[19] Mori K, Duh E, Gehlbach P et al. Pigment epithelium-derived factor inhibits retinal and choroidal neovascularization. *J Cell Physiol* 2001;188:253-63.

[20] Garcia M, Fernandez-Garcia NI, Rivas V et al. Inhibition of xenografted human melanoma growth and prevention of metastasis development by dual antiangiogenic/antitumor activities of pigment epithelium-derived factor. *Cancer Res* 2004;64:5632-42.

[21] Abe R, Shimizu T, Yamagishi S et al. Overexpression of pigment epithelium-derived factor decreases angiogenesis and inhibits the growth of human malignant melanoma cells in vivo. *Am J Pathol* 2004;164:1225-32.

[22] Matsumoto K, Ishikawa H, Nishimura D et al. Antiangiogenic property of pigment epithelium-derived factor in hepatocellular carcinoma. *Hepatology* 2004;40:252-9.

[23] Wang L, Schmitz V, Perez-Mediavilla A et al. Suppression of angiogenesis and tumor growth by adenoviral-mediated gene transfer of pigment epithelium-derived factor. *Mol Ther* 2003;8:72-9.

[24] Mahtabifard A, Merritt RE, Yamada RE et al. In vivo gene transfer of pigment epithelium-derived factor inhibits tumor growth in syngeneic murine models of thoracic malignancies. *J Thorac Cardiovasc Surg* 2003;126:28-38.

[25] Doll JA, Stellmach VM, Bouck NP et al. Pigment epithelium-derived factor regulates the vasculature and mass of the prostate and pancreas. *Nat Med* 2003;9:774-80.

[26] Halin S, Wikstrom P, Rudolfsson SH et al. Decreased pigment epithelium-derived factor is associated with metastatic phenotype in human and rat prostate tumors. *Cancer Res* 2004;64:5664-71.

[27] Crawford SE, Stellmach V, Ranalli M et al. Pigment epithelium-derived factor (PEDF) in neuroblastoma: a multifunctional mediator of Schwann cell antitumor activity. *J Cell Sci* 2001;114:4421-8.

[28] Abramson LP, Stellmach V, Doll JA et al. Wilms' tumor growth is suppressed by antiangiogenic pigment epithelium-derived factor in a xenograft model. *J Pediatr Surg* 2003;38:336-42; discussion -42.

[29] Tombran-Tink J, Johnson LV. Neuronal differentiation of retinoblastoma cells induced by medium conditioned by human RPE cells. *Invest Ophthalmol Vis Sci* 1989;30:1700-7.

[30] Becerra SP, Fariss RN, Wu YQ et al. Pigment epithelium-derived factor in the monkey retinal pigment epithelium and interphotoreceptor matrix: apical secretion and distribution. *Exp Eye Res* 2004;78:223-34.

[31] Wu YQ, Notario V, Chader GJ et al. Identification of pigment epithelium-derived factor in the interphotoreceptor matrix of bovine eyes. *Protein Expr Purif* 1995;6:447-56.

[32] Eichler W, Yafai Y, Keller T et al. PEDF derived from glial Muller cells: a possible regulator of retinal angiogenesis. *Exp Cell Res* 2004;299:68-78.

[33] Karakousis PC, John SK, Behling KC et al. Localization of pigment epithelium derived factor (PEDF) in developing and adult human ocular tissues. *Mol Vis* 2001;7:154-63.

[34] Ortego J, Escribano J, Becerra SP et al. Gene expression of the neurotrophic pigment epithelium-derived factor in the human ciliary epithelium. Synthesis and secretion into the aqueous humor. *Invest Ophthalmol Vis Sci* 1996;37:2759-67.

[35] Wu YQ, Becerra SP. Proteolytic activity directed toward pigment epithelium-derived factor in vitreous of bovine eyes. Implications of proteolytic processing. Invest *Ophthalmol Vis Sci* 1996;37:1984-93.

[36] Kuncl RW, Bilak MM, Bilak SR et al. Pigment epithelium-derived factor is elevated in CSF of patients with amyotrophic lateral sclerosis. *J Neurochem* 2002;81:178-84.

[37] Petersen SV, Valnickova Z, Enghild JJ. Pigment-epithelium-derived factor (PEDF) occurs at a physiologically relevant concentration in human blood: purification and characterization. *Biochem J* 2003;374:199-206.

[38] Kozaki K, Miyaishi O, Koiwai O et al. Isolation, purification, and characterization of a collagen-associated serpin, caspin, produced by murine colon adenocarcinoma cells. *J Biol Chem* 1998;273:15125-30.

[39] Steele FR, Chader GJ, Johnson LV et al. Pigment epithelium-derived factor: neurotrophic activity and identification as a member of the serine protease inhibitor gene family. *Proc Natl Acad Sci U S A* 1993;90:1526-30.

[40] Stein PE, Leslie AG, Finch JT et al. Crystal structure of uncleaved ovalbumin at 1.95 A resolution. *J Mol Biol* 1991;221:941-59.

[41] Wright HT, Qian HX, Huber R. Crystal structure of plakalbumin, a proteolytically nicked form of ovalbumin. Its relationship to the structure of cleaved alpha-1-proteinase inhibitor. *J Mol Biol* 1990;213:513-28.

[42] Loebermann H, Tokuoka R, Deisenhofer J et al. Human alpha 1-proteinase inhibitor. Crystal structure analysis of two crystal modifications, molecular model and preliminary analysis of the implications for function. *J Mol Biol* 1984;177:531-57.

[43] Stratikos E, Alberdi E, Gettins PG et al. Recombinant human pigment epithelium-derived factor (PEDF): characterization of PEDF overexpressed and secreted by eukaryotic cells. *Protein Sci* 1996;5:2575-82.

[44] Becerra SP, Sagasti A, Spinella P et al. Pigment epithelium-derived factor behaves like a noninhibitory serpin. Neurotrophic activity does not require the serpin reactive loop. *J Biol Chem* 1995;270:25992-9.

[45] Simonovic M, Gettins PG, Volz K. Crystal structure of human PEDF, a potent anti-angiogenic and neurite growth-promoting factor. *Proc Natl Acad Sci U S A* 2001;98:11131-5.

[46] Becerra SP, Palmer I, Kumar A et al. Overexpression of fetal human pigment epithelium-derived factor in Escherichia coli. A functionally active neurotrophic factor. *J Biol Chem* 1993;268:23148-56.

[47] Alberdi E, Aymerich MS, Becerra SP. Binding of pigment epithelium-derived factor (PEDF) to retinoblastoma cells and cerebellar granule neurons. Evidence for a PEDF receptor. *J Biol Chem* 1999;274:31605-12.

[48] Bilak MM, Becerra SP, Vincent AM et al. Identification of the neuroprotective molecular region of pigment epithelium-derived factor and its binding sites on motor neurons. *J Neurosci* 2002;22:9378-86.

[49] Aymerich MS, Alberdi EM, Martinez A et al. Evidence for pigment epithelium-derived factor receptors in the neural retina. *Invest Ophthalmol Vis Sci* 2001;42:3287-93.

[50] Yabe T, Wilson D, Schwartz JP. NFkappaB activation is required for the neuroprotective effects of pigment epithelium-derived factor (PEDF) on cerebellar granule neurons. *J Biol Chem* 2001;276:43313-9.

[51] Yabe T, Herbert JT, Takanohashi A et al. Treatment of cerebellar granule cell neurons with the neurotrophic factor pigment epithelium-derived factor in vitro enhances expression of other neurotrophic factors as well as cytokines and chemokines. *J Neurosci Res* 2004;77:642-52.

[52] Volpert OV, Zaichuk T, Zhou W et al. Inducer-stimulated Fas targets activated endothelium for destruction by anti-angiogenic thrombospondin-1 and pigment epithelium-derived factor. *Nat Med* 2002;8:349-57.

[53] Oukka M, Ho IC, de la Brousse FC et al. The transcription factor NFAT4 is involved in the generation and survival of T cells. *Immunity* 1998;9:295-304.

[54] Bishop PN. Structural macromolecules and supramolecular organisation of the vitreous gel. *Prog Retin Eye Res* 2000;19:323-44.

[55] Alberdi E, Hyde CC, Becerra SP. Pigment epithelium-derived factor (PEDF) binds to glycosaminoglycans: analysis of the binding site. *Biochemistry* 1998;37:10643-52.

[56] Yasui N, Mori T, Morito D et al. Dual-site recognition of different extracellular matrix components by anti-angiogenic/neurotrophic serpin, PEDF. *Biochemistry* 2003;42: 3160-7.

[57] Meyer C, Notari L, Becerra SP. Mapping the type I collagen-binding site on pigment epithelium-derived factor. Implications for its antiangiogenic activity. *J Biol Chem* 2002;277:45400-7.

[58] Tombran-Tink J, Shivaram SM, Chader GJ et al. Expression, secretion, and age-related downregulation of pigment epithelium-derived factor, a serpin with neurotrophic activity. *J Neurosci* 1995;15:4992-5003.

[59] Behling KC, Surace EM, Bennett J. Pigment epithelium-derived factor expression in the developing mouse eye. *Mol Vis* 2002;8:449-54.

[60] Pignolo RJ, Cristofalo VJ, Rotenberg MO. Senescent WI-38 cells fail to express EPC-1, a gene induced in young cells upon entry into the G0 state. *J Biol Chem* 1993;268: 8949-57.

[61] Francis MK, Appel S, Meyer C et al. Loss of EPC-1/PEDF expression during skin aging in vivo. *J Invest Dermatol* 2004;122:1096-105.

[62] Holekamp NM, Bouck N, Volpert O. Pigment epithelium-derived factor is deficient in the vitreous of patients with choroidal neovascularization due to age-related macular degeneration. *Am J Ophthalmol* 2002;134:220-7.

[63] Ogata N, Matsuoka M, Imaizumi M et al. Decreased levels of pigment epithelium-derived factor in eyes with neuroretinal dystrophic diseases. *Am J Ophthalmol* 2004;137:1129-30.

[64] Ogata N, Nishikawa M, Nishimura T et al. Unbalanced vitreous levels of pigment epithelium-derived factor and vascular endothelial growth factor in diabetic retinopathy. *Am J Ophthalmol* 2002;134:348-53.

[65] Renno RZ, Youssri AI, Michaud N et al. Expression of pigment epithelium-derived factor in experimental choroidal neovascularization. *Invest Ophthalmol Vis Sci* 2002;43:1574-80.

[66] Stitt AW, Graham D, Gardiner TA. Ocular wounding prevents pre-retinal neovascularization and upregulates PEDF expression in the inner retina. *Mol Vis* 2004;10:432-8.

[67] Ogata N, Wada M, Otsuji T et al. Expression of pigment epithelium-derived factor in normal adult rat eye and experimental choroidal neovascularization. *Invest Ophthalmol Vis Sci* 2002;43:1168-75.

[68] Ogata N, Tombran-Tink J, Jo N et al. Upregulation of pigment epithelium-derived factor after laser photocoagulation. *Am J Ophthalmol* 2001;132:427-9.

[69] Semkova I, Kreppel F, Welsandt G et al. Autologous transplantation of genetically modified iris pigment epithelial cells: a promising concept for the treatment of age-related macular degeneration and other disorders of the eye. *Proc Natl Acad Sci U S A* 2002;99:13090-5.

[70] Gehlbach P, Demetriades AM, Yamamoto S et al. Periocular injection of an adenoviral vector encoding pigment epithelium-derived factor inhibits choroidal neovascularization. *Gene Ther* 2003;10:637-46.

[71] Mori K, Gehlbach P, Ando A et al. Regression of ocular neovascularization in response to increased expression of pigment epithelium-derived factor. *Invest Ophthalmol Vis Sci* 2002;43:2428-34.

[72] Mori K, Gehlbach P, Yamamoto S et al. AAV-mediated gene transfer of pigment epithelium-derived factor inhibits choroidal neovascularization. *Invest Ophthalmol Vis Sci* 2002;43:1994-2000.

[73] Auricchio A, Behling KC, Maguire AM et al. Inhibition of retinal neovascularization by intraocular viral-mediated delivery of anti-angiogenic agents. *Mol Ther* 2002;6:490-4.

[74] Maden M. Retinoid signalling in the development of the central nervous system. *Nat Rev Neurosci* 2002;3:843-53.

[75] Tombran-Tink J, Lara N, Apricio SE et al. Retinoic acid and dexamethasone regulate the expression of PEDF in retinal and endothelial cells. *Exp Eye Res* 2004;78:945-55.

[76] Lo WR, Rowlette LL, Caballero M et al. Tissue differential microarray analysis of dexamethasone induction reveals potential mechanisms of steroid glaucoma. *Invest Ophthalmol Vis Sci* 2003;44:473-85.

[77] Yamagishi S, Inagaki Y, Amano S et al. Up-regulation of vascular endothelial growth factor and down-regulation of pigment epithelium-derived factor messenger ribonucleic acid levels in leptin-exposed cultured retinal pericytes. *Int J Tissue React* 2002;24: 137-42.

[78] Maik-Rachline G, Shaltiel S, Seger R. Extracellular phosphorylation converts pigment epithelium-derived factor from a neurotrophic to an antiangiogenic factor. *Blood* 2004.

[79] de SSP, Calabro A, Nishiyama K et al. Glycosaminoglycan synthesis and secretion by the retinal pigment epithelium: polarized delivery of hyaluronan from the apical surface. *J Cell Sci* 2001;114:199-205.

[80] Dunn KC, Marmorstein AD, Bonilha VL et al. Use of the ARPE-19 cell line as a model of RPE polarity: basolateral secretion of FGF5. *Invest Ophthalmol Vis Sci* 1998;39: 2744-9.

[81] Alberdi EM, Weldon JE, Becerra SP. Glycosaminoglycans in human retinoblastoma cells: heparan sulfate, a modulator of the pigment epithelium-derived factor-receptor interactions. *BMC Biochem* 2003;4:1.

[82] Robert L, Legeais JM, Robert AM et al. Corneal collagens. *Pathol Biol (Paris)* 2001;49:353-63.
[83] Kern P, Sebert B, Robert L. Increased type-III/type-I collagen ratios in diabetic human conjunctival biopsies. *Clin Physiol Biochem* 1986;4:113-9.
[84] Lu DW, Chang CJ, Wu JN. The changes of vitreous pH values in an acute glaucoma rabbit model. *J Ocul Pharmacol Ther* 2001;17:343-50.
[85] Holmes JM, Zhang S, Leske DA et al. Metabolic acidosis-induced retinopathy in the neonatal rat. *Invest Ophthalmol Vis Sci* 1999;40:804-9.
[86] Nishikawa T, Giardino I, Edelstein Det al. Changes in diabetic retinal matrix protein mRNA levels in a common transgenic mouse strain. *Curr Eye Res* 2000;21:581-7.
[87] Reiser KM, Amigable MA, Last JA. Nonenzymatic glycation of type I collagen. The effects of aging on preferential glycation sites. *J Biol Chem* 1992;267:24207-16.
[88] Mast AE, Enghild JJ, Nagase H et al. Kinetics and physiologic relevance of the inactivation of alpha 1-proteinase inhibitor, alpha 1-antichymotrypsin, and antithrombin III by matrix metalloproteinases-1 (tissue collagenase), -2 (72-kDa gelatinase/type IV collagenase), and -3 (stromelysin). *J Biol Chem* 1991;266:15810-6.
[89] Potempa J, Fedak D, Dubin A et al. Proteolytic inactivation of alpha-1-anti-chymotrypsin. Sites of cleavage and generation of chemotactic activity. *J Biol Chem* 1991;266:21482-7.
[90] Cunningham DD, Van Nostrand WE, Farrell DH et al. Interactions of serine proteases with cultured fibroblasts. *J Cell Biochem* 1986;32:281-91.
[91] Noda K, Ishida S, Inoue M et al. Production and activation of matrix metalloproteinase-2 in proliferative diabetic retinopathy. *Invest Ophthalmol Vis Sci* 2003;44:2163-70.
[92] Plantner JJ, Jiang C, Smine A. Increase in interphotoreceptor matrix gelatinase A (MMP-2) associated with age-related macular degeneration. *Exp Eye Res* 1998;67: 637-45.
[93] Brinckerhoff CE, Matrisian LM. Matrix metalloproteinases: a tail of a frog that became a prince. *Nat Rev Mol Cell Biol* 2002;3:207-14.
[94] Lamoreaux WJ, Fitzgerald ME, Reiner A et al. Vascular endothelial growth factor increases release of gelatinase A and decreases release of tissue inhibitor of metalloproteinases by microvascular endothelial cells in vitro. *Microvasc Res* 1998;55:29-42.
[95] Burbridge MF, Coge F, Galizzi JP et al. The role of the matrix metalloproteinases during in vitro vessel formation. *Angiogenesis* 2002;5:215-26.

In: Focus on Eye Research
Editor: O.R. Ioseliani, pp. 201-214
ISBN: 1-59454-434-4

Chapter 9

Adhesion of *Pseudomonas Aeruginosa* to High Molecular Weight Glycoprotein Species in Human Tears

Lina Panayiota Aristoteli[1,*] ***and Mark D. P. Willcox***[1,2]
[1]The Cooperative Research Centre for Eye Research and Technology,
University of New South Wales,
[2]The Vision Cooperative Research Centre[2],
Sydney NSW 2052 Australia.

Abstract

Introduction: Mucin in the tear film forms the first line of ocular protection where it facilitates bacterial adhesion and removal from the eye, and forms the scaffold for tear defence proteins to be anchored in the tear film. *P. aeruginosa* is an opportunistic pathogen that has emerged as an important causative agent of bacterial keratitis. The interaction of mucin in tears and *P. aeruginosa* isolated from contact lens wear was undertaken in the present study to identify mucin species that bind to this bacterium and the nature of this interaction. Method: Open eye basal tears were collected from healthy volunteers, pooled, and tear constituents were thereafter separated by agarose gel electrophoresis. Separated tear proteins/glycoproteins were blotted to nitrocellulose for either characterisation by lectin staining or adhesion to biotin-labelled *P. aeruginosa* strains Paer1 and 6294. Results: Tear mucin under reducing conditions, produced at least five mucin species greater than 200 kDa. Of these, Paer1 and 6294 preferentially bound to the highest molecular weight mucin species near the origin of the gel, and shown by concurrent *S. nigra* lectin staining to contain sialic acid linked by an $\alpha(2\rightarrow6)$ linkage. The presence of $\alpha(2\rightarrow6)$ linked sialic acid was a unique feature of this mucin compared with the other species. The adhesion of *P. aeruginosa* to the distinct mucin species was not due to free biotin label, indicating its quite specific nature. Conclusion: A qualitative assay of biotin-labelled bacteria adhesion to mucins separated from tears by agarose electrophoresis was developed, where at least five high molecular weight glycoprotein species greater than 200 kDa were identified. The present study observed the adhesion of ocular *P.*

* Correspondence concerning this article should be addressed to Dr. Lina Panayiota Aristoteli, HRI; 145-147 Missenden Rd Camperdown NSW 2050 Australia. Tel: (061) 2 9550 3560; Fax: (061) 2 9550 3302; E-mail address: l.aristoteli@hri.org.au.

aeruginosa strains to a distinct tear glycoprotein species containing $\alpha(2\rightarrow6)$ linked sialic acid residues.

INTRODUCTION

The precorneal tear film has generally been thought to consist of three layers, the lipid, aqueous, and mucous layers, although recent evidence suggests that there is no distinct aqueous layer in the tear film[1]. A function of the tear film is to provide a smooth optical surface for the cornea to maintain visual acuity. The primary refractive power of the cornea is acquired from the air and tear film interface, thus the tear film must be a quality optical surface for favourable refractive properties. Indeed, the removal of the tear film in humans has been demonstrated to cause a loss in the quality of vision. [2].

The thickness of the human tear film has been documented to be in the range of 3 μ m [3], 10.4 μm [4] or 40 μm [5] with mucin as the predominant component[1, 5, 6]. A mucin gradient seems to exist from a high concentration near the epithelial cells to a more dilute mucin region towards the lipid layer[1]. Secretory MUC5AC mucin, originating from conjunctival goblet cells[7], is the prevalent mucin type in the tear film, having a concentration of approximately 60 μg/ml in tears[8]. MUC2, although probably of considerably less concentration than MUC5AC, and a soluble form of the membrane mucin sialomucin complex (MUC4), have also been detected in tears[9], while the presence of MUC1 in tears is more controversial[10-12]. Recently, two isoforms of the protein DMBT1, a mucin-like membrane associated glycoprotein containing sialyl-Le^a carbohydrates have also been identified in tear fluid[13]. Other mucin types have been described as being produced by conjunctival, corneal or lacrimal gland epithelial surfaces, but as yet have not been detected in tears; these include MUC5B, MUC7, MUC11, MUC15, MUC16 [7, 14-18]. A distinguishing feature of the ocular mucins is that they show much less variation in the thickness along the length of the molecule, due to differences in degree of glycosylation, compared with other mucins and this may be associated with the need to maintain the transparency of the eye[19].

Mucin also forms the first line of ocular protection from invading pathogens and other potential toxins/allergens. It facilitates bacterial adhesion and removal from the eye under normal circumstances[20], where bacteria adherent to tear film mucin are removed to mucous threads in the lower fornix and then the skin at the inner canthus[21]. There has also been an implication that mucin forms the scaffold for tear defence proteins to be anchored in the tear film [22, 23]. *P. aeruginosa* is the most commonly isolated bacterium from cases of microbial keratitis associated with contact lens wear [24] and is also associated with the production of an inflammatory response of the cornea during contact lens wear, contact lens induced red eye[25]. The removal of mucin from the ocular surface results in increased adhesion of *P. aeruginosa* to the underlying corneal cells, confirming its protective role[26]. *P. aeruginosa* has been shown to be able to bind to mucin, and it appears that flagella proteins are important in this interaction[27-29]. Furthermore, we and others have shown that several strains of *P. aeruginosa* can adhere to ocular mucin[26, 30, 31]. Since mucin is the main constituent of the tear film and functions to protect the ocular surface, the interaction of mucin in tears and *P. aeruginosa* isolated from contact lens wear was undertaken in the present study to identify tear mucin species that bind to this bacterium.

METHODS

Collection of Open Eye Tears

Basal tears consist of tear fluid collected without mechanical or chemical stimulation of tear flow and most accurately reflect the composition of the tear film on the normal eye as compared to reflex tears that are predominantly lacrimal gland in origin[32]. Open eye basal tears were collected from healthy volunteers using a disposable calibrated 20 μl glass capillary tube (Crown Scientific, Moorebank NSW) by a published method[33]. Thereafter, tears were pooled and centrifuged at 12 000 g for 10 minutes to remove cellular debris. The tear supernatant was stored at -86°C until further use.

Electrophoresis and Blotting of Tear Components

High molecular weight glycoproteins observed in non-reduced tear samples are mainly attributed to sIgA and its associated components [33] as the native sIgA complex has a molecular weight of 385 kDa[32]. Under reducing conditions, the sIgA complex dissociates into 85, 64 and 28 kDa fragments, corresponding to the secretory component, heavy chain and light chain of sIgA respectively[34]. Thus, in order to ensure the presence of mucin species, tear samples were assayed under reducing conditions to eliminate the possibility of bacterial adhesion to sIgA components.

Frozen tear samples were thawed at room temperature and the appropriate volume of reducing 4 X sample buffer (0.2 g SDS, 4 ml glycerol, 4 ml 4% (w/v) bromophenol blue, 2.5 ml 1 M Tris-HCl pH 6.8, Milli-Q water to 10 ml, and 4 mM DTT) was added. The samples were subsequently boiled at 100°C for 5 minutes and, after cooling, were re-centrifuged at 12 000 g for 10 minutes to clarify the extract, and the supernatant was loaded onto the gel for electrophoresis.

Agarose electrophoresis was conducted by the method of Thornton[35]. Briefly, a 1 % (w/v) agarose gel was prepared in electrophoresis running buffer (40 mM Tris-acetate, 1mM EDTA, pH 8.0, 0.1% (w/v) SDS) in a horizontal sub-cell (20 cm length; NovaLine, Novex, Sydney, Australia). 15 μl of tears in sample buffer were loaded into wells and electrophoresis commenced at 30 volts overnight at room temperature. Molecular weight standards were routinely applied to the gel for calibration purposes (Kaleidoscope Pre-stained Standards, Bio-Rad).

Proteins/glycoproteins separated by agarose electrophoresis were transferred onto nitrocellulose membrane (0.2 μm pure nitrocellulose, Bio-Rad) overnight by capillary blotting using 4 × standard sodium citrate buffer (0.6 M sodium chloride/0.06 M sodium citrate, pH 7.0) as the transfer buffer. The membrane was dried for half an hour at room temperature, washed briefly with PBS and blocked for either lectin studies or bacterial adhesion assays.

Lectin Analysis of High Molecular Weight Tear Components

Lectin staining of blots was based on a modification of a cited procedure. [36]Membranes were blocked for 1 hour with PBS + 0.5 % (w/v) Tween-20 (PBST). Blotted tear proteins were probed with a panel of biotin-labelled lectins that were *Triticum vulgaris* (Wheat Germ Agglutin (WGA); specific for N-acetyl-β-D-glucosamine and a secondary affinity for sialic acid; Sigma), *Sambucus nigra* bark agglutin (SNA; specific for α-NeuNAc-[2→6]-Gal and α-NeuNAc-[2→6]-GalNAc, with a secondary affinity for α-NeuNAc-[2→3]-Gal; Vector Laboratories, Burlingame, CA, USA), *Bandeira simplifolica* (BS-I; specific for α-D-galactose with a secondary affinity for terminal N-acetyl-α-D-galactosamine; Sigma), *Ulex europaeus I* (Gorse, Furze; specific for L-fucose; Sigma). Membranes were incubated with the lectins at a concentration of 1 μg/ml lectin in PBST for 2 hours on a rocking platform at room temperature. After washing six times, 10 minutes each with PBST, the membranes were incubated with ExtrAvidin-peroxidase (Sigma) at a dilution of 1: 2 000 dilution (v/v) in PBST for 1 hour. Membranes were washed a further three times, for 10 minutes each wash, with PBST then another three washes for 10 minutes each wash with PBS. Blots were developed using a solution consisting of 80 ml PBS, two tablets of 3,3'-Diaminobenzidine tetrahydrochloride (DAB; 10 mg/ tablet, Sigma) dissolved in 10 ml methanol, two tablets of 4-chloro-1-naphthol (4CN; Sigma) dissolved in 10 ml methanol and 40 μl hydrogen peroxide solution (30 % solution BDH Laboratory Supplies, Poole, England), adding 25 ml developer to each membrane.

Bacterial Adhesion Assay

P. aeruginosa strain Paer1, originally isolated from a contact lens related acute red eye (CLARE) event, and 6294, from a microbial keratitis (corneal ulcer) patient were obtained from the culture collection at the Cooperative Research Centre for Eye Research and Technology and were stored in tryptone soya broth (TSB; Oxoid, Basingstoke, Hampshire, England) supplemented with 30 % (v/v) glycerol (Ajax, NSW, Australia) at -86°C. For each experiment, bacterial strains were taken from -86°C and subcultured on chocolate blood agar plates (Oxoid Australia, West Heidelberg, Victoria) at 35°C for 18 hours. For more consistent results, the strains were routinely subcultured another time on chocolate blood agar plates at 35°C for 18 hours, to subsequently produce uniform plate growth. Bacteria were harvested from the plates with PBS, by gently scrapping with an ethanol-flamed hockey stick and washed three times in PBS by centrifugation at 2 000g for 10 minutes.

Bacterial strains were brought to the log-phase of growth by incubation in TSB at a starting OD_{660} of 0.1 by 150 rpm orbital shaking for 4 hours in a 37°C water bath. After washing three times in PBS by centrifugation at 2 000 g for 10 minutes, bacterial pellets were stored at 4°C overnight.

The concentration of log-phase grown *P. aeruginosa* was adjusted to OD_{660} 1.0 with PBS, and biotin (EZ-Link™ Sulfo-NHS-LC-Biotin; Pierce, Rockford, IL, USA) was added from a 10 mg/ml biotin stock in PBS to a final concentration of 0.5 mg/ml. Bacteria were incubated with biotin for 20 minutes on a rocking platform at room temperature, washed three times by centrifugation at 2 000 g for 10 minutes to remove unbound label and the pellets were resuspended in the original volume of PBS. The negative control was a free biotin solution consisting of 0.5 mg/ml biotin in PBS with no bacteria.

The blotted membrane was blocked for 2 hours with 0.5% (w/v) casein (Sigma) in PBS, washed three times briefly in PBS and incubated with biotin labelled bacteria or free biotin for 2 hours on a rocking platform at ambient temperature. Unbound bacteria were washed three times for 10 minutes each in PBS and membranes were incubated in ExtrAvidin-peroxidase (1:2 000 dilution in PBS + 0.1 % Tween-20). The membrane was washed three times for 10 minutes each and was developed using a solution consisting of 80 ml PBS, two tablets of 3,3'-Diaminobenzidine tetrahydrochloride (DAB; 10 mg/ tablet, Sigma) dissolved in 10 ml methanol, two tablets of 4-chloro-1-naphthol (4CN; Sigma) dissolved in 10 ml methanol and 40 µl hydrogen peroxide solution (30 % solution BDH Laboratory Supplies, Poole, England), adding 25 ml developer to each membrane.

For the determination of hydrophobic interactions involved in *P. aeruginosa* adhesion to mucin in tears, a final concentration of 0.5M tetramethylurea was used[37]. The appropriate volume of chemical was added to the biotinylated bacterial suspension immediately prior to bacterial addition to the membrane. The tetramethylurea and biotinylated bacteria mixture was applied to the membrane, incubated for two hours and the procedure followed as mentioned above.

RESULTS

Comparison of Tear Assay Parameters

Initially, tear samples were routinely centrifuged at 12 000 g for 10 minutes to remove insoluble debris, solubilized in reducing sample buffer and then boiled for 5 minutes. The denatured samples were thereafter applied to the gel for electrophoresis. In most cases, a 'smeary' profile of tears was observed under these conditions, encompassing the entire range of molecular weight values (results not shown). The 'smear' effect was alleviated once the insoluble residue present after boiling the tear sample was removed by centrifugation prior to its application for electrophoresis. Thus tears were routinely re-centrifuged after boiling for the consistent migration of tear components during electrophoresis. An insoluble pellet was not observed after centrifugation of tears solubilized in non-reducing sample buffer and not boiled.

Figure 1. The identification of high molecular weight tear mucin species separated by 1% (w/v) agarose gels under reducing conditions and stained with WGA lectin. Arrowheads denote the presence of at least four different mucin species over 218 KDa in tears.

Large dimension agarose (Figure 1) exhibited increased migration of tear mucins into the gel and more effective separation of glycoprotein species than low percentage SDS-PAGE gels (Figure 3). Agarose gels were superior in tear mucin separation as observed by comparative WGA staining where at least four high molecular weight glycoprotein species were detected over 200 kDa in the agarose gel (Figure 1).

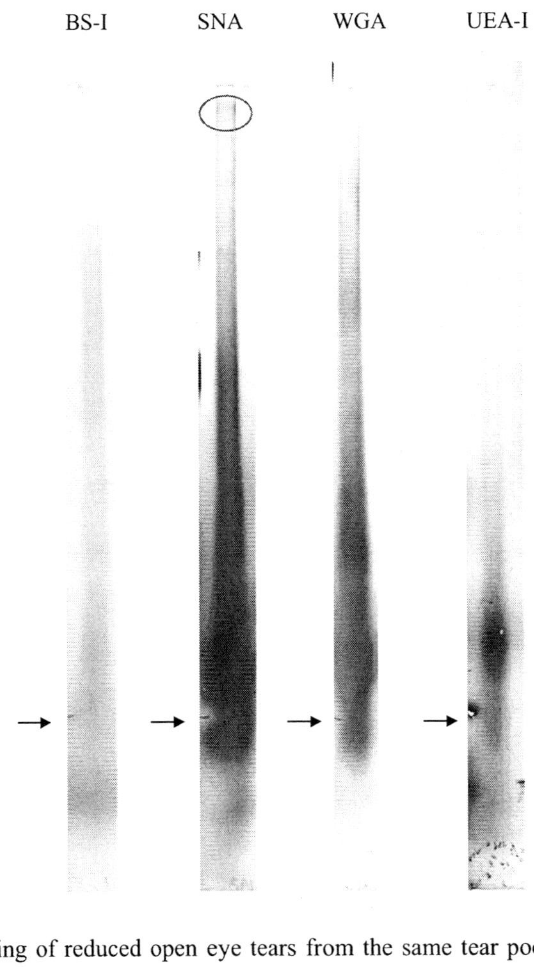

Figure 2. Lectin staining of reduced open eye tears from the same tear pool using a 1% agarose gel. *Bandeira simplifolica I (BS-I); Sambucus nigra agglutin; (SNA) Wheat germ agglutin; (WGA) Ulex europaeus I (UEA-I).* Arrows denote the position of the 218 KDa molecular marker. Circle indicates distinct glycoprotein species in SNA blot only.

Lectin Characterisation of Tears

The glycoprotein profile of open eye tears was investigated using lectin probing of tear samples from the same tear pool (Figure 2). Wheat germ agglutin (WGA) or lectin from *Triticum vulgaris* with an affinity for n-acetyl-β-D-glucosamine and sialic acid identified at least four mucin species greater than 200 kDa . The residues detected by *Bandeira simplifolica* (BS-I) include α-D-galactose and terminal N-acetyl-α-D-galactosamine residues, and exposure to tear components exhibited a profile similar to that observed with WGA lectin. *Ulex europaeus* lectin (Gorse, Furze), detecting L-fucose, had a low affinity for the predominant two tear glycoproteins just greater than 200 kDa. The lectin *Sambucus nigra*, primarily detecting α-NeuNAc-[2→6]-Gal and α-NeuNAc-[2→6]-GalNAc, extensively stained a high molecular weight mucin species near the origin of the gel that was not detected by the other lectins tested. Although other mucin species greater than 200 kDa were detected with *Sambucus nigra* lectin, these were also stained by wheat germ agglutin lectin. The common staining pattern of lower molecular weight mucin species results from the secondary affinity of both lectins for sialic acid linked by a 2→3 linkage.

Biotinylation Adhesion Assay

The biotinylation adhesion assay of tears separated by 5% SDS-PAGE electrophoresis and transferred onto nitrocellulose confirmed that *P. aeruginosa* was able to bind to a high molecular weight mucin smear in reduced tears (Figure 3). However, it was only with the resolution of higher molecular weight tear species with agarose gels, that showed *P. aeruginosa* strains Paerl and 6294 predominantly adhered to the high molecular weight mucin species in reduced tears substantially greater than 200 kDa and found near the origin of the gel (Figures 4A and 5). The adhesion of *P. aeruginosa* to the highest molecular weight mucin species was repeatable at least three times. This tear species was not appreciably stained by corresponding WGA lectin staining of the same pooled tear sample by WGA in corresponding blots of tear samples (Figure 4B), but in fact correlated *with S. nigra* staining of this mucin species (Figure 2).

In some cases both Paer1 and 6294 also bound lower molecular weight mucin species on the agarose gel blot, just above 218 kDa, probably corresponding to the tear species represented in the 5% SDS-PAGE blot bound by the bacteria (Figure 3). However, staining of the highest molecular weight mucin occurred first indicating a higher specificity of bacterial adhesion to this tear mucin species. In addition, there was no adhesion of free biotin label to any tear component under the present circumstances, and tetramethylurea did not affect binding, confirming the specificity of the results obtained (results not shown).

a b

← 218 KDa

Figure 3. The adhesion of biotin-labelled Paer1 to titrated volumes of open eye tears separated by 5% SDS-PAGE gel electrophoresis. Lane a: 3 μl; lane b: 5 μl.

Thus, it is concluded that *P. aeruginosa* preferentially adhered to a high molecular weight polymeric mucin in tears containing sialic acid linked to galactose or n-acetyl-galactosamine by a 2→6 linkage, as stained by *S. nigra* lectin. In some cases, adhesion to lower molecular weight components by both strains was noted, but this adhesion took longer to develop.

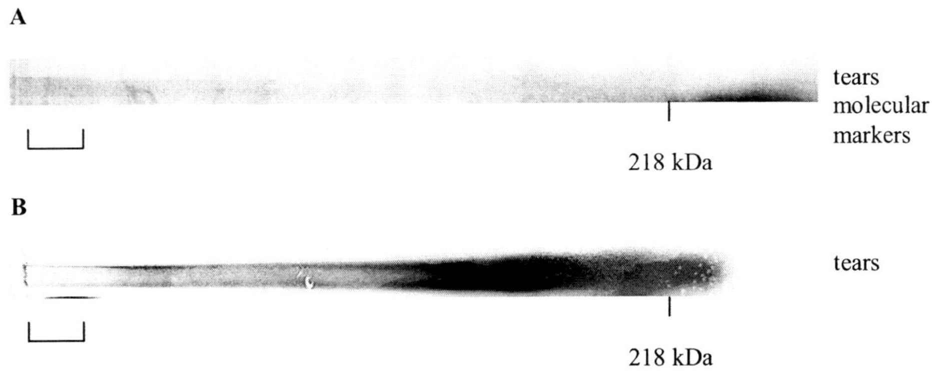

Figure 4. Adhesion of biotin-labelled Paer1 to high molecular weight tear glycoproteins separated by 1 % agarose electrophoresis under reducing conditions and transferred to nitrocellulose (A) and complementary tear profile stained with wheat germ agglutin lectin (B). Brackets indicate tear species bound by bacteria and its complementary region in the WGA blot.

Figure 5. Adhesion of biotin-labelled *P. aeruginosa* strain 6294 to tear components separated by a 1% (w/v) agarose gel. Circle denotes tear species preferentially bound by Paer6294 and bracket indicates lower molecular weight tear glycoprotein species bound by bacteria to a lesser extent.

DISCUSSION

The present study sought to investigate the adhesion of *P. aeruginosa* strains to tear glycoproteins. The results indicate that *P. aeruginosa* strains preferentially adhered to a high molecular weight polymeric glycoprotein, most likely a mucin species, that was reactive with *S. nigra* lectin, containing sialic acid linked by a 2→6 linkage to galactose or N-acetyl-galactosamine. The interaction was not due to non-specific hydrophobic interactions. Also, there seemed to be at least four other glycoprotein species in reduced tear samples of molecular weight greater than 200 kDa, that were able to adhere to *P. aeruginosa* to a lesser extent.

In the current study, at least five distinct glycoprotein species were identified in reduced tears and the use of large dimension agarose gels was imperative for the separation of all glycoprotein species. The identification of at least four mucin species greater than 200 kDa in reduced tears has been documented[10, 11, 38], and other studies, like the present, have also observed higher amounts of lower molecular weight mucin species just over 200 kDa (450-500 kDa) in tears than high molecular weight mucin species[10, 11, 13]. Lower molecular weight species seem to be polymorphic, exhibiting considerable variation in molecular weight between subjects where in some individuals it may migrate as two separate bands[10, 11].

Lectin staining has characterised the glycoprotein profile of tear glycoprotein species in this study (Figure 2). Relatively low molecular weight glycoproteins over 200 kDa contained N-acetyl-glucosamine and $\alpha(2\rightarrow3)$-linked sialic acid, consistent with another study that found sialic acid linked to galactose by a $2\rightarrow3$ linkage, but not sialic acid linked by a $2\rightarrow6$ linkage, and abundant N-acetyl-glucosamine residues by WGA staining in mucin species just over 200kDa[39]. Moreover, sialic acid is present in three out of the four tear glycoproteins species over 200 kDa[10, 11]. In addition, relatively low molecular weight species contained galactose and/or terminal N-acetyl-galactosamine, and at least two of the glycoprotein species had fucose residues. The identification of tear glycoprotein species above 200 kDa as mucin *per se* stems from the detection of Galβ1-3GalNAc-Ser/Thr residues suggesting the presence of core O-glycosidic structures[39, 40].

The highest molecular weight mucin species near the origin of the gel was distinct due to the absence of n-acetylglucosamine carbohydrate residues (WGA staining), and the presence of sialic acid linked to galactose and N-acetyl-galactosamine with a $2\rightarrow6$ linkage. *P. aeruginosa* had a primary affinity for the highest molecular weight polymeric mucin that was reactive with *S. nigra* lectin, despite the seemingly higher concentrations of lower molecular weight mucin species in the reduced tear samples. This was the only mucin species containing sialic acid with a $2\rightarrow6$ linkage, implying that *P. aeruginosa* has a higher affinity for this particular sialic acid configuration.

Sialic acid with this configuration has been detected in goblet cells and the epithelium of the lacrimal duct, where tears exit the eye[41], suggesting that this secretory mucin is responsible for microbial defence facilitating the removal of pathogens from the eye. Furthermore, goblet cells in the normal human conjunctiva contain mucin with sialic acid comprising a $2\rightarrow6$ linkage[42], indicating that the high molecular weight mucin species involved in the adhesion of *P. aeruginosa* is probably a goblet cell derived secretory-type mucin.

The adhesion of *P. aeruginosa* to $\alpha(2\rightarrow6)$ linked sialic acid has been identified in the immature mouse model where prior scarification of the cornea was not needed for *P. aeruginosa* infection[43]. The inhibition of *P. aeruginosa* adhesion to the cornea *in vivo* by exogenous sialic acid, significantly protected immature mice from septicaemia and death due to *P. aeruginosa* infection of the cornea[44]. Hence, the adhesion of *P. aeruginosa* to $\alpha(2\rightarrow6)$ linked sialic acid was a critical initial step in the ocular pathogenesis in immature mice[44]. It seems paradoxical that a pathogen may bind to secretory sialic acid in mucin to prevent their adhesion to the underlying epithelium, and also bind sialic acid on membrane-bound mucin on the corneal epithelium to initiate pathogenesis. In fact, a recent study has found that *S. pyogenes* adhered to $\alpha(2\rightarrow6)$ sialic acid on both secretory mucin, and membrane-bound mucin on cultured pharyngeal cells[45]. It seems likely that *P. aeruginosa* binds to $\alpha(2\rightarrow6)$ sialic acid in tears to be removed from the eye, though with contact lens wear, the same receptor may allow it to adhere to the tear film, degrade the mucin network and bind to the corneal epithelial cells.

It is also worthy of note that there was a higher amount of sialic acid in salivary mucin glycopeptides from cystic fibrosis patients, that correlated with increased *P. aeruginosa* adhesion to cystic fibrosis mucin glycopeptides than from non-cystic fibrosis patients[46]. The characterisation of *P. aeruginosa* mucin receptors, with respect to sialic acid, has been limited to $\alpha(2\rightarrow3)$ linked sialic acid such as in sialyl-Le^x structures. In these studies, *P. aeruginosa* strains have a high affinity for sialyl-Le^x epitopes and 6-sulfo-sialyl-Le^x, more than that observed with Le^a, Le^x, Le^y, and 3'sulfo-Le^x structures[47, 48]. *P. aeruginosa* was also able to adhere to a neoglycolipid bearing $\alpha(2\rightarrow6)$ linked sialic acid in a thin layer chromatography assay but not in a microtitre adhesion assay[49].

P. aeruginosa was also able to bind the other low molecular weight species greater than 200kDa that contain $\alpha(2\rightarrow3)$ linked sialic acid, though clearly with a lower affinity than the species near the origin of the gel.

The adhesion of strain 6294 to sialoglycoproteins in tears observed in this study is in conflict with other studies[50, 51]. Neuraminidase treatment of collected tear washings increased the adhesion of 6294 to tear components compared with adhesion to untreated tear washings[50]. This implies that sialic acid was not needed for *P. aeruginosa* adhesion to tear components. Further, *P. aeruginosa* was not able to bind to purified high molecular weight sialoglycoproteins isolated from closed eye tears in a microtitre adhesion assay, although adhesion was apparent to commercial BSM[51]. A possible reason for the discrepancy between the results of McNamara and colleagues and the present study may be that the isolation and purification of sialoglycoproteins from tears had altered the structure or bacterial-binding epitope in the former study. The adhesion of bacteria to tear mucin species separated by electrophoresis seems less intrusive than tears separated by vigorous purification procedures. Alternatively, closed eye tears may contain a different mucin composition than open eye tears that were used in this study. Also, the isolated high molecular weight glycoproteins for their adhesion assay may have been mucin species that bacteria were not able to avidly adhere from results in the current assay, such as the species just below the highest molecular weight mucin species.

Conclusion

At least five high molecular weight glycoproteins were observed greater than 200 kDa in reduced tears and mucin-adherent *P. aeruginosa* strains preferentially bound to the highest molecular weight polymeric mucin species containing sialic acid linked by a $2\rightarrow6$ linkage, although a secondary affinity was noted to smaller mucin species. It is hypothesised that this polymeric mucin species is involved in the mucosal defence of the eye, as an active component in tears adhering to pathogens and facilitating their removal from the eye and preventing adhesion to epithelial cells.

Acknowledgments

This study was supported in part by grants from the Australian Commonwealth Government under the Cooperative Research Centres Programme, and the American Optometric Foundation.

REFERENCES

[1] Chen, H.-B., Yamabayashi, S., Ou, B., Tanaka, Y., Ohno, S. & Tsukahara, S. (1997). Structure and composition of rat precorneal tear film. A study by an in vitro cryofixation. Invest. *Ophthalmol. Vis. Sci.,* **38**, 381-387.

[2] Dursun, D., Monroy, D., Knighton, R., Tervo, T., Vesaluoma, M., Carraway, K., Feuer, W. & Pflugfelder, S. C. (2000). The effects of experimental tear film removal on corneal surface regularity and barrier function. *Ophthalmology,* **107**, 1754-1760.

[3] King-Smith, P. E., Fink, B. A., Fogt, N., Nichols, K. K., Hill, R. M. & Wilson, G. S. (2000). The thickness of the human precorneal tear film: evidence from reflection spectra. Invest. *Ophthalmol. Vis. Sci.,* **41**, 3348-3359.

[4] Creech, J., Do, L., Fatt, I. & Radke, C. (1998). In vivo tear-film thickness determination and implications for tear-film stability. *Curr. Eye Res.,* **17**, 1058-1066.

[5] Prydal, J. I., Artal, P., Woon, H. & Campbell, F. W. (1992). Study of human precorneal tear film thickness and structure using laser interferometry. Invest. *Ophthalmol. Vis. Sci.,* **33**, 2006-2011.

[6] Nichols, B. A., Chiappino, M. L. & Dawson, C. R. (1985). Demonstration of the mucous layer of the tear film by electron microscopy. *Invest. Ophthalmol. Vis. Sci.,* **26**, 464-473.

[7] Jumblatt, M. M., McKenzie, R. W. & Jumblatt, J. E. (1999). MUC5AC mucin is a component of the precorneal tear film. *Invest. Ophthalmol. Vis. Sci.,* **40**, 43-49.

[8] Zhao, H., Jumblatt, J. E., Wood, T. O. & Jumblatt, M. M. (2001). Quantification of MUC5AC protein in human tears. *Cornea,* **20**, 873-877.

[9] Pfugfelder, S. C., Liu, Z., Monroy, D., Li, D.-Q., Carvajal, M. E., Price-Schiavi, S. A., Idris, N., Solomon, A., Perez, A. & Carraway, K. L. (2000). Detection of sialomucin complex (MUC4) in human ocular surface epithelium and tear fluid. *Invest. Ophthalmol. Vis. Sci.,* **41**, 1316-1326.

[10] Sack, R. A., Bogart, B., Sathe, S., Beaton, A. & Lew, G. (1998). *Characterisation and origin of major high-molecular-weight tear sialoglycoproteins.* In D.A. Sullivan, D.A. Dartt, and M.A. Meneray (Eds.), Lacrimal Gland, Tear Film, and Dry Eye Syndromes 2, (pp. 235-238). New York, Plenum Press.

[11] Sack, R. A., Bogart, B. I., Beaton, A., Sathe, S. & Lew, G. (1997). Diurnal variations in tear glycoproteins:evidence for an epithelial origin for the major non-reducible ^{3}450 kDa sialoglycoprotein(s). *Curr. Eye Res.,* **16**, 577-588.

[12] Davies, J., Carlstedt, I., Nilsson, A.-K., Håkannson, A., Sabharwal, H., Van Alphen, L., Van Ham, M. & Svanborg, C. (1995). Binding of Haemophilus influenzae to purified mucins from the human respiratory tract. *Infect. Immun.,* **63**, 2485-2492.

[13] Schulz, B. L., Oxley, D., Packer, N. H. & Karlsson, N. G. (2002). Identification of two highly sialylated human tear-fluid DMBT1 isoforms: the major high-molecular-mass glycoproteins in human tears. *Biochem. J.,* **366**, 511-520.

[14] Davidson, H. J. & Kuonen, V. J. (2004). The tear film and ocular mucins. *Vet. Ophthalmol.,* **7**, 71-77.

[15] Watanabe, H., Fabricant, M., Tisdale, A. S., Spurr-Michaud, S. J., Lindberg, K. & Gipson, I. K. (1995). Human corneal and conjunctival epithelia produce a mucin-like glycoprotein for the apical surface. *Invest. Ophthalmol. Vis. Sci.,* **36**, 337-344.

[16] Gipson, I. K., Yankauckas, M., Spurr-Michaud, S. J., Tisdale, A. S. & Rinehart, W. (1992). Characteristics of a glycoprotein in the ocular surface glycocalyx. *Invest. Ophthalmol. Vis. Sci.,* **33**, 218-227.

[17] Van den Steen, P., Rudd, P. M., Dwek, R. A. & Opdenakker, G. (1998). Concepts and principles of O-linked glycosylation. *Crit. Rev. Biochem. Mol. Biol.,* **33**, 151-208.

[18] Paulsen, F. P., Corfield, A. P., Hinz, M., Hoffmann, W., Schaudig, U., Thale, A. B. & Berry, M. (2003). Characterisation of mucins in human lacrimal sac and nasolacrimal duct. *Invest. Ophthalmol. Vis. Sci,* **44**, 1807-1813.

[19] McMaster, T. J., Berry, M., Corfield, A. P. & Miles, M. J. (1999). Atomic force microscopy of the submolecular architecture of hydrated ocular mucins. *Biophys. J.,* **77**, 533-541.

[20] Smolin, G. (1987). The role of tears in the prevention of infections. *Int. Ophthalmol. Clin., 27*, 25-26.

[21] Tiffany, J. M. (1997*). Tears and conjunctiva.* In J.J. Harding (Ed.), Biochemistry of the Eye, (pp. 1-15). London, Chapman and Hall.

[22] Corfield, A. P., Carrington, S. D., Hicks, S. J., Berry, M. & Ellingham, R. (1997). Ocular mucins: purification, metabolism and functions. *Prog. Ret. Eye Res.,* **16**, 627-656.

[23] Argüeso, P. & Gipson, I. K. (2001). Epithelial mucins of the ocular surface: structure, biosynthesis and function. *Exp. Eye Res.,* **73**, 281-289.

[24] Willcox, M., Sankaridurg, P., Lan, J., Pearce, D., Thakur, A., Zhu, H., Keay, L. & Stapleton, F. (2000). *Inflammation and infection and effects of the closed eye.* In D. Sweeney (Ed.), Silicone hydrogels: The rebirth of continuous wear contact lenses, (pp 45-75). Oxford, Butterworth-Heinemann.

[25] Holden, B. A., La Hood, D., Grant, T., Newton-Howes, J., Baleriola-Lucas, C., Willcox, M. D. P. & Sweeney, D. F. (1996). Gram-negative bacteria can induce contact lens related acute red eye (CLARE) responses. *CLAO J.,* **22**, 47-52.

[26] Fleiszig, S., Zaidi, T., Ramphal, R. & Pier, G. (1994). Modulation of Pseudomonas aeruginosa adherence to the corneal surface by mucus. *Infect. Immun.,* **62**, 1799-1804.

[27] Ramphal, R., Guay, C. & Pier, G. (1987). Pseudomonas aeruginosa adhesins for tracheobronchial mucin. *Infect. Immun.,* **55**, 600-603.

[28] Scharfman, A., Arora, S. K., Delmotte, P., Van Brussel, E., Mazurier, J., Ramphal, R. & Roussel, P. (2001). Recognition of Lewis x derivatives present on mucins by flagellar components of Pseudomonas aeruginosa. *Infect. Immun,* **69**, 5243-5248.

[29] Arora, S. K., Ritchings, B. W., Almira, E. C., Lory, S. & Ramphal, R. (1998). The Pseudomonas aeruginosa flagellar cap protein, FliD, is responsible for mucin adhesion. *Infect. Immun.,* **66**, 1000-1007.

[30] Aristoteli, L. P., Bojarski, B. & Willcox, M. D. P. (2003). Isolation of conjunctival mucin and differential interaction with Pseudomonas aeruginosa strains of varied pathogenic potential. *Exp. Eye Res.,* **77**, 699-710.

[31] Aristoteli, L. P. & Willcox, M. D. P. (2001). Adhesion of Pseudomonas aeruginosa ocular isolates to mucin. *Clin. Exp. Ophthalmol.,* **29**, 143-146.

[32] Kuizenga, A., Identification and characterisation of proteins in human tear fluid, in Department of Ophthalmology. 1992, University of Amsterdam: Amsterdam.

[33] Sack, R. A., Tan, K. O. & Tan, A. (1992). Diurnal tear cycle: evidence for a nocturnal inflammatory constitutive tear fluid. *Invest. Ophthalmol. Vis Sci.,* **33**, 626-640.

[34] Kuizenga, A., van Haeringen, N. J. & Kijlstra, A. (1991). SDS-Minigel electrophoresis of human tears. Invest. *Ophthalmol. Vis. Sci,* **32**, 381-386.

[35] Thornton, D., Howard, M., Devine, P. & Sheehan, J. (1995). Methods for separation and deglycosylation of mucin subunits. *Anal. Biochem.,* **227**, 162-167.

[36] Gravel, P. & Golaz, O. (1996). *Identification of glycoproteins on nitrocellulose membranes using lectin blotting.* In J.M. Walker (Ed.), The Protein Protocols Handbook, (pp. 603-617). Totowa, NJ, Humana Press Inc.

[37] Shuter, J., Hatcher, V. B. & Lowy, F. D. (1996). Staphylococcus aureus binding to human nasal mucin. *Infect. Immun.,* **64**, 310-318.

[38] Wells, P. A., Ashur, M. L. & Foster, C. S. (1986). SDS-gradient polyacrylamide gel electrophoresis of individual ocular mucus samples from patients with normal and diseased conjunctiva. *Curr. Eye Res.,* **5**, 823-831.

[39] Argüeso, P., Herreras, J. M., Calonge, M., Citores, L., Pastor, J. C. & Girbés, T. (1998). Analysis of human ocular mucus: effects of neuraminidase and chitinase enzymes. *Cornea,* **17**, 200-207.

[40] Kuizenga, A., van Haeringen, N. J. & Kijlstra, A. (1991). Identification of lectin binding proteins in human tears. Invest. *Ophthalmol. Vis. Sci.,* **32**, 3277-3284.

[41] Paulsen, F., Thale, A., Kohla, G., Schauer, R., Rochels, R., Parwaresch, R. & Tillmann, B. (1998). Functional anatomy of human lacrimal duct epithelium. *Anat. Embryol.,* **198**, 1-12.

[42] Berry, M., Ellingham, R. B. & Corfield, A. P. (1996). Polydispersity of normal human conjunctival mucins. *Invest. Ophthalmol. Vis. Sci.,* **37**, 2559-2571.

[43] Hazlett, L., Rudner, X., Masinick, S., Ireland, M. & Gupta, S. (1995). In the immature mouse, Pseudomonas aeruginosa pili bind a 57-kd (a2-6) sialylated corneal epithelial cell surface protein: a first step in infection. *Invest. Ophthalmol. Vis. Sci.,* **36**, 634-643.

[44] Hazlett, L. D., Moon, M. & Berk, R. S. (1986). In vivo identification of sialic acid as the ocular receptor for Pseudomonas aeruginosa. *Infect. Immun.,* **51**, 687-689.

[45] Ryan, P. A., Pancholi, V. & Fischetti, V. A. (2001). Group A streptococci bind to mucin and human pharyngeal cells through sialic acid-containing receptors. *Infect. Immun.,* **69**, 7402-7412.

[46] Carnoy, C., Ramphal, R., Scharfman, A., Lo-Guidice, J.-M., Houdret, N., Klein, A., Galabert, C., Lamblin, G. & Roussel, P. (1993). Altered carbohydrate composition of salivary mucins from patients with cystic fibrosis and the adhesion of Pseudomonas aeruginosa. *Am. J. Respir. Cell Mol. Biol.,* **9**, 323-334.

[47] Scharfman, A., Degroote, S., Beau, J., Lamblin, G., Roussel, P. & Mazurier, J. (1999). Pseudomonas aeruginosa binds to neoglycoconjugates bearing mucin carbohydrate determinants and predominantly to sialyl-Lewis x conjugates. *Glycobiology,* **9**, 757-764.

[48] Scharfman, A., Delmotte, P., Beau, J., Lamblin, G., Roussel, P. & Mazurier, J. (2000). Sialyl-Lex and sulfo-sialyl-Lex determinants are receptors for P. aeruginosa. *Glycoconj. J.,* **17**, 735-740.

[49] Ramphal, R., Carnoy, C., Fievre, S., Michalski, J., Houdret, N., Lamblin, G., Strecker, G. & Roussel, P. (1991). Pseudomonas aeruginosa recognises carbohydrate chains containing type 1 (Galb1-3GlcNAc) or type 2 (Galb1-4GlcNAc) disaccharide units. *Infect. Immun.,* **59**, 700-704.

[50] McNamara, N. A. & Fleiszig, S. M. J. (1998). *Human tear film components bind Pseudomonas aeruginosa.* In D.A. Sullivan, D.A. Dartt, and M.A. Meneray (Eds.),

Lacrimal Gland, Tear Film, and Dry Eye Syndromes 2, (pp. 653-658). New York, Advances in Experimental Medicine and Biology: Plenum Press.

[51] McNamara, N. A., Sack, R. A. & Fleiszig, S. M. J. (2000). *Mucin-bacterial binding assays*. In A.P. Corfield (Ed.), Glycoprotein Methods and Protocols: The Mucins, (pp. 429-437). Totowa, NJ, Humana Press.

In: Focus on Eye Research
Editor: O.R. Ioseliani, pp. 215-228

ISBN: 1-59454-434-4

Chapter 10

REFRACTIVE INDEX OF LENS FIBER MEMBRANES IN DIFFERENT PARTS OF THE CRYSTALLINE LENS - IMPACT ON LENS TRANSPARENCY

Ralph Michael* and Rafael I. Barraquer
Institut Universitari Barraquer, Universitat Autònoma de Barcelona, SPAIN

ABSTRACT

Purpose: Local variations in refractive index are the physical cause of light scattering in a material or tissue. The goal of this study was to further add to the understanding of the process of light propagation in the crystalline lens by directly measuring local variations in refractive index by phase contrast microscopy.
Methods: Refractive index was estimated by immersion refractometry. Cryo-sections of quick-frozen human donor lenses were embedded in a graded series of bovine serum albumin solutions, and in immersion oil, ranging in refractive index from 1.34 to 1.52.
Results: Fiber membranes in the lens cortex prove to have a refractive index considerably above that of fiber cytoplasm at the same location. Fiber membranes in the lens nucleus have a refractive index approximately the same as that of fiber cytoplasm at the same location.
Discussion: In the lens cortex, transparency is obtained by a high spatial order of the lens fiber lattice to compensate for the light scattering caused by differences in refractive index between fiber membranes and cytoplasm. In the lens nucleus, high spatial order is less important, because the minor differences in the refractive index between fiber membranes and fiber cytoplasm lead only to minimal scattering.

Keywords: Crystalline lens, Cataract, Transparency, Cell membrane, Refractive index

* Correspondence concerning this article should be addressed to Ralph Michael, Institut Universitari Barraquer, Laforja 88, E-08021 Barcelona, Spain; E-mail address: ralphm@co-barraquer.es

INTRODUCTION

Loss of transparency in the crystalline lens is denoted as cataract. Cataract is one of the most common diseases reducing visual acuity in elderly people. It is an age-related multifactorial disease. Potential factors inducing cataract are for instance metabolic diseases, certain drugs, different types of radiation, genetic factors, ocular inflammation and physical injury. Alterations and damages to the lens are accumulating over lifetime, because there is no cell shedding in the lens cortex and nucleus. For optimal vision, all lens fiber cells developing before and after birth must remain transparent until old age.

In the crystalline lens there are mainly two types of potential scattering elements: the crystallins in the fiber cytoplasm and the fiber membranes. Most commonly, local peripheral lens opacities and cataract are seen as a protein aggregation disease [1, 2]. Increase in light scattering is attributed to the increase in the high molecular weight fraction of proteins.

The impact on transparency of fiber membranes and their age and disease-related changes is discussed to a lesser extent in the literature. Trokel [3] and Hemenger [4] discussed the importance of the regular spatial arrangement of the lens fiber membranes for lens transparency. Hemenger calculated the angular dependence of scattered light with an exponentially decaying correlation function considering the differences in refractive index of fiber membranes and fiber cytoplasm. He hypothesized that the lens fiber lattice is the main source for small-angle (< 8°) intraocular light scattering [4]. Bettelheim attributed about 50% of the light scattering in the normal lens to the fiber membranes [5]. Lipid peroxidation leading to degeneration and disintegration of the fiber membranes is sometimes discussed as an early event in cataractogenesis [6, 7].

Local variations in refractive index are the basic physical cause for light scattering in optical media. The average refractive index of living cells depends mostly on the protein concentration. A typical mammalian cell has an average protein content of 18 mass% [8], corresponding to a refractive index of about 1.37. The protein concentration in the center of the human lens is about 32 vol%, with a refractive index of about 1.41 [9]. The main components of cell membranes are phospholipids, cholesterol and membrane-spanning proteins and usually have a higher refractive index than the proteins in the cytoplasm. The refractive index of membranes is about 1.48 [10]. This difference in refractive index between cytoplasm and membranes will have an impact on the light scattering properties of the lens.

Fibers in the central part of the lens are usually less regularly ordered and have an irregular tortuous surface as compared with the lens cortex [11-13]. Theoretically this would cause larger variations in the refractive index and hence induce more light scattering in the lens center. However, there are no reports to the effect that the nucleus of a normal lens would scatter light more than the cortex. Indeed, in the normal lens the nucleus appears to be as transparent as the cortex [2, 14]. In this discussion the refractive index of the membranes is crucial. However, there is little or no information available on the refractive index of lens membranes. Therefore, it was decided to measure the refractive index of the membranes in different parts of the human lens.

Differences in refractive index influence the phase of the propagating light waves. This effect is used in phase and interference contrast microscopy as an optical contrasting technique for unstained biological specimen. We employed phase contrast microscopy to measure variations in refractive index. For this we used the technique known as immersion refractometry, first proposed by Zernike [15] and further developed by Barer & Joseph [16]. A similar immersion technique has been applied earlier on a macroscopic scale by Bettelheim and Wang [17] to estimate the refractive index at the surface of bovine lenses.

METHODS

Human eyes were obtained from the Cornea Bank Amsterdam after dissection of the corneas for transplantation. The research adhered to the tenets of the Declaration of Helsinki for using human postmortem material. Eight lenses (mean age 66 years, from 54 to 75 years) with no visible opacities were dissected from the eye and quick-frozen in liquid ethane at -176°C. Cryoprotection with sucrose is commonly employed to reduce morphological artefacts in the tissue due to freezing. Infiltration with sucrose was avoided in this study because it could possibly influence the refractive indices in the tissue. For the same reason, lenses were not fixed prior to the quick-freezing.

The refractive index of cell components can be estimated by immersion refractometry [16]. Cells or tissue sections are embedded in an immersion medium of known refractive index and inspected in phase contrast microscopy. When the refractive index of the embedding medium matches that of an element in the tissue, this element has no contrast. Elements with a higher refractive index than the embedding medium appear darker, and those with lower refractive index, brighter than the embedding medium. In this way, quantitative data on the refractive index can be obtained from simple morphological inspection in phase contrast microscopy. The phase contrast effects are relatively insensitive to gradual phase changes, being maximal at regions with steep phase changes [18]. The immersion medium should not change the hydration status of the cells or be birefringent.

Dissected pieces of the quick-frozen lenses were cryo-sectioned in the sagittal plane (10 μm) and embedded in a graded series of protein-water solutions (bovine serum albumin - BSA from Sigma, USA, Article No. A 9647) and in two different oils. The refractive index of a protein solution can be calculated with the Gladstone-Dale formula [16] : $n = n_m + \alpha * C$; where n_m is the refractive index of the solvent (for water $n_m = 1.333$), α is the specific refractive increment in cm^3/g and C the concentration of proteins in g/cm^3. The specific refractive increment for the majority of proteins is 0.1845 cm^3/g [16]. The above formula can be used to calculate the refractive index of BSA solutions, but also for the refractive index of the crystallins in the lens cells. For an approximate conversion of protein concentration from vol% to g/cm^3, the density of dry lens proteins can be considered as 1.40 g/cm^3 [19].

Throughout the text, the refractive index is given relative to air, for light with a wavelength of 589 nm and at 20°C. The cytoplasm of a standard cell has a refractive index of about 1.35 [20], the fiber cells in the lens nucleus have an average refractive index of about 1.41 [9] and normal cell membranes of about 1.48 [10]. Therefore the immersion media has to span refractive index values between 1.33 and about 1.50. The highest concentration of BSA in water that will remain in a liquid state is about 46% corresponding to a refractive index of 1.42. For media with higher refractive index, other substances have to be employed. Glycerol-water solutions (refractive index adjustable from 1.34 to 1.47) had to be excluded because glycerol would cause dehydration, which would alter the refractive index of the tissue. Therefore it was decided to use inert oils as immersion media with refractive indices over 1.42. The refractive index of the employed immersion solutions was measured with an Abbe refractometer: 1.343 (BSA 6%), 1.384 (BSA 28%), 1.418 (BSA 46%), 1.470 (Olive oil, extra virgin, Borges, Spain) and 1.517 (microscopy immersion oil from Merck, USA).

The embedded lens sections were inspected with a Zeiss-Universal-Stand microscope (Zeiss, Germany) with a Plan-Neofluar® objective of 40x, a numerical aperture of 0.75 and a phase ring (phase shift $\lambda/4$ and 20 % transmission). Illumination according to Köhler was strictly adhered to. Digital images with a resolution of 764x574 were taken with a Sony 3 CCD camera (Sony, Japan) keeping constant settings. The histograms of the images were linearly equalized in the same way for all acquired images.

In a first series of experiments (4 lenses), sagittal lens sections were inspected along a line close to the optical axis at the level of the epithelium and in two different regions at 50 and 500 μm below the lens capsule. In a second series of experiments (another 4 lenses), regions at 250, 1000 and 2000 μm below the lens capsule were inspected. Considering an average anterior-posterior lens thickness for the adult human lens of 4900 μm [13], the 50 to 500 μm regions can be considered to be located in the lens cortex and the regions at 1000 and 2000 μm below the capsule as part of the lens nucleus.

RESULTS

A panel of representative images, taken at different locations below the capsule in the optical axis using immersion media with increasing refractive index, is shown in figure 1. Nuclei and organelles in the epithelial cells and fiber cell membranes are clearly visualized in these phase contrast images, but no sub-structures are seen inside the lens fiber cytoplasm. This latter is in accordance with the ultrastructural observation that the anterior and posterior end parts of even young fibers have no or very few organelles and exhibit a homogeneous distribution of proteins. Moreover the images of the epithelium show the spatial resolution of the method. At a refractive index of 1.34 the heterochromatin can easily be distinguished from the euchromatin by its dark contrast and reflects the known highly condensed character of the heterochromatin.

In an immersion medium with a refractive index of 1.34, the lens fiber membranes up to 1000 μm are seen dark against a bright background, showing that the membranes have a higher refractive index than 1.34 (figure 1). For the most superficial fiber membranes (50 μm), this appearance shifts from dark to bright between a refractive index of 1.42 and 1.47 (figure 1). For the fiber membranes at 1000 μm below the capsular surface the shift is between 1.34 and 1.38. These observations clearly indicate that upon maturation the refractive index of fiber membranes significantly changes.

The refractive index of tissue elements of interest is estimated as follows: If an embedding medium is found which matches the refractive index of the tissue element, i.e. the tissue element has no contrast, the index of this medium is considered to be the refractive index of this tissue element. If there is a shift from dark to bright of a tissue element from one embedding medium to the next, the intermediate refractive index between both embedding media is considered to be a good estimate of the refractive index of this tissue element. For example, if the membranes appear dark in 1.34 and bright in 1.38, the refractive index for these membranes is taken as 1.36 (Figure 1, 1000 μm).

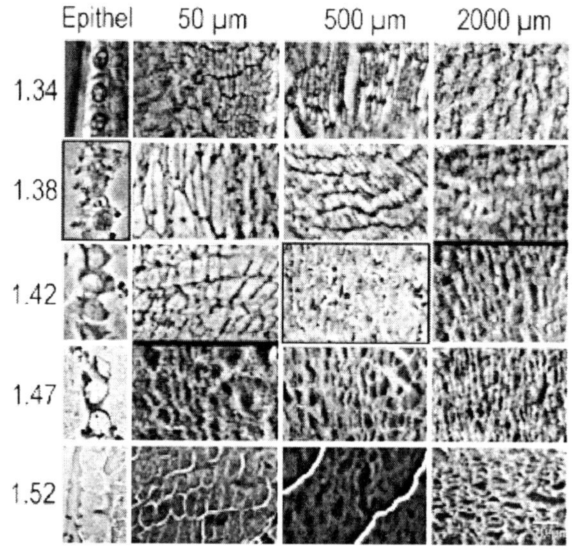

Figure 1. Panel of sample phase-contrast images of cryo-sections of human lenses taken at different locations below the capsule (top) using immersion media with different refractive indices (left). If the membranes appear dark, this indicates that the refractive index of the membranes is higher than that of the immersion medium; bright membranes indicate that the refractive index of the membranes is lower. The turning point of membrane contrast is indicated with a black line and the matching point by a black frame. The scale bar on the lower right is valid for all images. (Reprinted from [26], Copyright 2003, with permission from Elsevier.)

The results of the refractive index estimations of the epithelial cell nuclei and the fiber membranes from 8 lenses are summarized in figure 2. Refractive index values for the nuclei range between 1.38 and 1.40 (average of 1.39). The refractive index of the fiber membranes in the lens cortex at 50, 250 and 500 µm is higher than in the lens nucleus at 1000 and 2000 µm, ranging in the cortex between 1.42 and 1.44 (average of 1.43) and ranging in the nucleus between 1.36 and 1.40 (average 1.38). Interestingly, to see that there seems to be a rather abrupt change in the refractive index of fiber membranes between cortex and nucleus.

CONCLUSION

As far as we are aware, the refractive index of lens fiber membranes has not been measured before. However, various techniques have been used to measure the overall refractive index of the lens: microradiography [9], Raman spectroscopy [21] and application of an optic fiber probe [22]. Roth & Kluxen [23] traced a laser beam (which was directed into the eye) by using a Scheimpflug camera. The refractive index in the lens was calculated simply with Snellens formula. All these techniques give estimates of the refractive index with different spatial resolution, but so far the resolution has not permitted estimation at the level of single lens cells. Because the lens consists to over 98% of water and proteins [19, 24], the data obtained with the techniques mentioned above can be considered to show the refractive index of the lens fiber cytoplasm. The contribution from the lens fiber membranes can be ignored in these studies, because the membranes were not resolved and they contribute less than 2% to the wet weight of the lens.

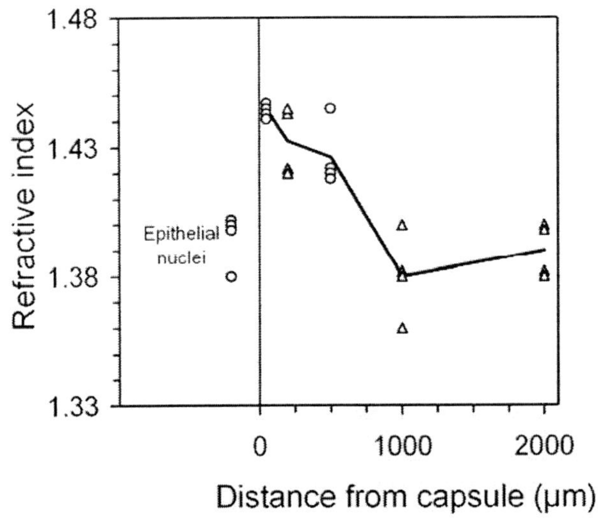

Figure 2. Refractive index of human lens epithelial cell nuclei and fiber membranes as estimated from the current experiment (for details see Materials and Methods). Circles represent the results of the first series of experiments (measurements in two different regions 50 and 500 μm below the lens capsule) and triangles that of the second series of experiments (regions 250, 1000 and 2000 μm below the lens capsule). One symbol represents the estimation from one lens and the solid line is drawn through the average from 4 lenses. (Reprinted from [26], Copyright 2003, with permission from Elsevier.)

The comparison of the refractive indices of lens cytoplasm (data taken from literature) and lens fiber membranes (current experiment) reveals a considerable difference between the two in the lens cortex and an overlap of values in the lens nucleus (Figure 3A). That the refractive index of the lens cytoplasm increases from cortex to lens center due to the increase in protein concentration has been known for a long time [25]. That the refractive index of the lens fiber membranes decreases from cortex to lens center and approaches that of the cytoplasm is a new finding [26].

The refractive index of membranes of living cells is about 1.48 [10] and that of model lipid bilayers ranges between 1.47 and 1.52 [27]. Our data from the human lens, especially the lens nucleus, are below these values. This may be explained by the relatively high cholesterol-to-phospholipid ratio of the membranes in the lens, being between 0.8 and 3.5 [24]. Average values of this ratio in other mammalian cells are between 0.3 and 0.4 [28]. The cholesterol-to-phospholipid ratio is not only higher in the lens, but also increases gradually from lens cortex to lens center [24, 29, 30] and may be the reason for the decrease in refractive index.

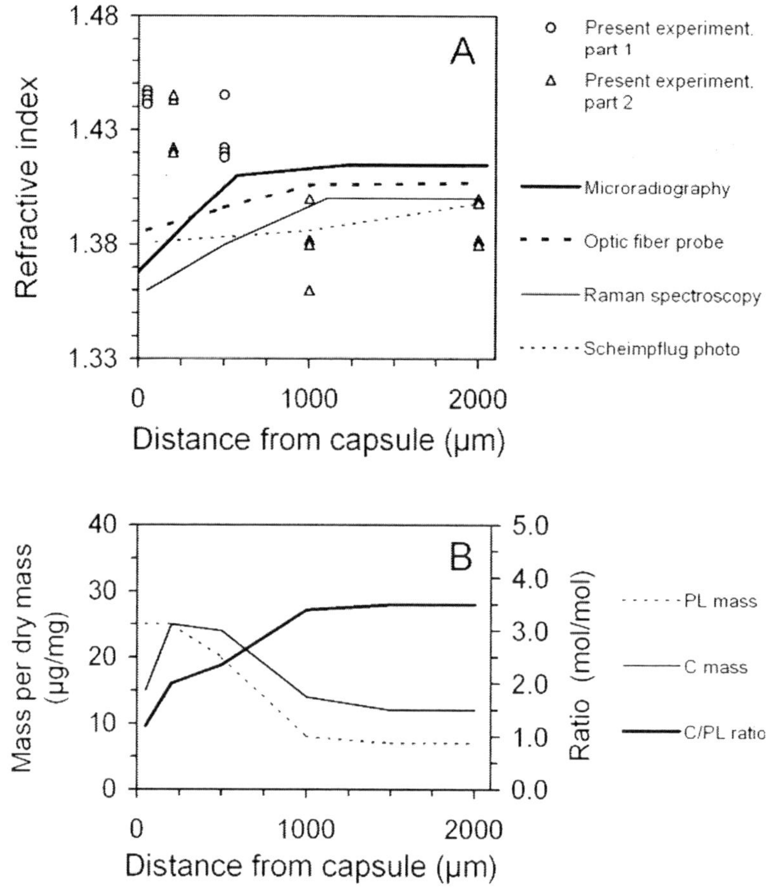

Figure 3. Above a comparison of the estimated refractive index of human lens fiber membranes as found in the present experiment and refractive index data of the fiber cytoplasm as given in the literature (A): Microradiography [9], Optic fiber probe [22], Raman spectroscopy [21], Scheimpflug photography [23]. Below a summary of local changes of the phospholipid (PL) and cholesterol (C) of human lens membranes and the cholesterol-to-phospholipid (C/PL) ratio (B). Data from Li et al [24].

The cholesterol content is rapidly increasing in the superficial lens cortex (Figure 3 B). Both phospholipids and cholesterol are decreasing in the intermediate and deep lens cortex and remain constant throughout the lens nucleus. The lower phospholipid content and the decrease in double bonds in the fiber membranes of the lens nucleus as compared to that in the lens cortex is reflected in routine electron micrographs of OsO_4 treated lens tissue; membranes in the cortex appear as electron dense lines whereas in the nucleus they appear as electron lucent lines flanked by more electron dense cytoplasm (Figure 4 A, C and E). OsO4 is reduced by the polar head groups of lipids and by their double bonds, but is not reduced by cholesterol and therefore fiber membranes in the lens cortex are stained, but not in the lens center (Figure 4 C and E).

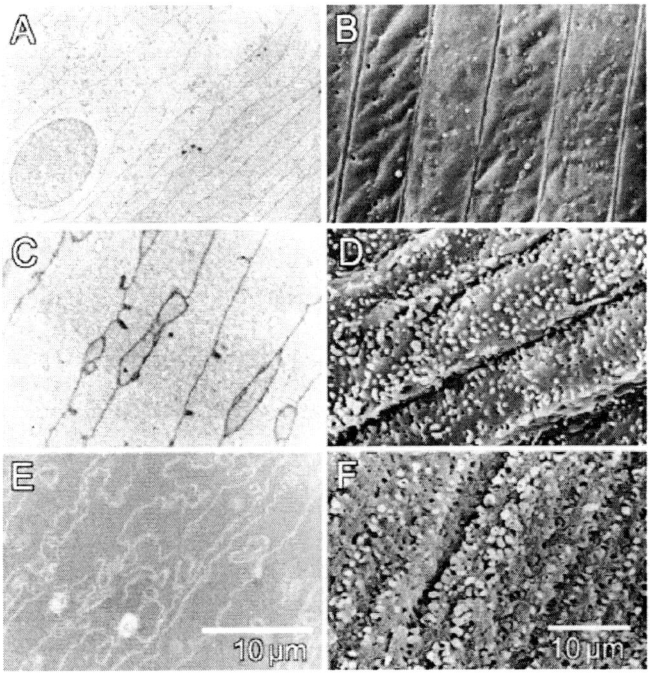

Figure 4. Images from transmission electron microscopy (left) and scanning electron microscopy (right) of human lens fibers. In the superficial cortex (A, B), the intermediate cortex (C, D) and in the lens nucleus (E, F).

The cholesterol-to-phospholipid ratio is constantly increasing from the most superficial cortex to the deep cortex and remains constant in the lens nucleus (Figure 3 B). This dependence is almost reciprocal to the observed refractive index changes of the fiber membranes. According to Li et al. [24] less than one third of the membrane surface in the lens nucleus is formed by a phospholipid bilayer. They speculate that the membranes consist of a mosaic of phospholipid and cholesterol patches.

From a cell biological point of view, lens fibers in the superficial cortex are growing and maturing and therefore have need of properly functioning membranes as in other cells. This means that they must have membranes with a normal cholesterol-to-phospholipid ratio that allows insertion of membrane spanning proteins as for instance transporters and water and ion channels. This implies that the membranes of these growing and maturing fibers have a high refractive index, comparable to that of membranes of other cell types. In contrast, lens fibers in the deep cortex and nucleus have very limited biological activity and therefore do not require the same type of membranes as in the cortex. This might explain why the observed changes in the membranes do not have an adverse effect on the integrity of the nuclear fibers. The lower refractive index improves the optical quality of the lens nucleus as outlined in the hypothesis given below.

Phase contrast images in the mid-cortical region frequently show bodies of about 1 µm diameter, which seem to be associated with the fiber membranes (Figure 5 A). Gilliland [31] reports "rare, but distinct, circular 1-3 µm diameter objects" and Al-Ghoul [32] "multilamellar membrane aggregates and globular bodies" in human age-related nuclear cataracts. Membrane-bound bodies of similar size also were found in an electron microscopic study of human lenses with early cataractous changes [33] (figure 5 B). Since these bodies exhibit steep local variation in refractive index, they certainly will contribute to increased light scattering in the lens as has been associated with these so-called dot-like opacities [33].

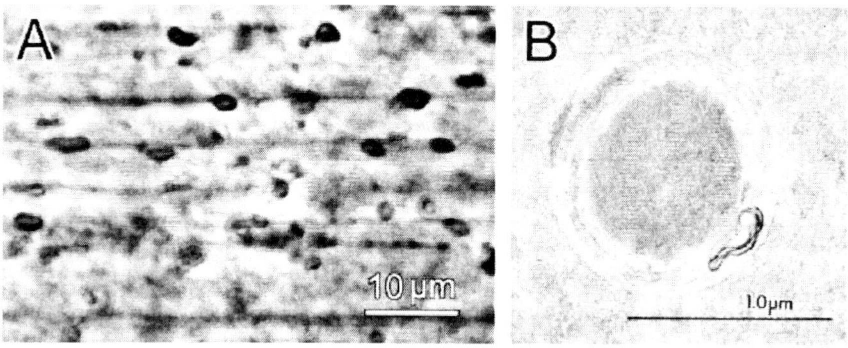

Figure 5. Phase contrast image of a human lens 500 µm below the lens capsule and taken with an immersion medium of refractive index 1.38, showing dark membrane-associated bodies (A). Multilamellar body as frequently found in human lenses with early cortical opacities (B). (Figure 5 A reprinted from [26], Copyright 2003, with permission from Elsevier and figure 5 B reprinted from [33] with permission by Marcel Dekker Inc.)

Lens fiber membrane morphology changes dramatically from the lens cortex towards the lens center. As observed especially in scanning electron micrographs (Figure 4 B, D and F) the superficial lens fibers have a smooth surface with few ball-and-sockets (Figure 4 B). In the deeper cortex, the surface is more irregular with many ball-and-sockets and interdigitating edge protrusions, about 1/10 to 1 µm in size (Figure 4 D). This irregularity is even more pronounced in the lens center (Figure 4 F). Intuitively one would expect that these irregularities may lead to more intense light scattering. However, since our results show that there is almost no difference in refractive index between cytoplasm and membranes in the lens center this intuitive expectation of increased light scattering in the nucleus has no physical basis and actually explains the low scattering properties and good transparency of the center of the non-cataractous human lens.

In the superficial cortex the difference in refractive index is quite considerably and on account of this a pronounced light scattering would be expected. However, the fibers in the superficial cortex are neatly ordered and have a smooth surface (Figure 4 A, B). Interference theory explains that this regular spatial order minimizes light scattering arising from these local variations in refractive index between cytoplasm and membranes in the lens cortex. Interference can be either constructive i.e. superimposed waves reinforce each other or destructive i.e. that waves cancel each other. Regularly spaced scattering centers lead to constructive interference at specific points in space and to destructive interference at all other points in space (Figure 6). Hence, the light passes the material in one direction only. Irregularly spaced scattering centers lead to constructive interference in many different directions, meaning that the light is scattered away from the incident light path (Figure 6).

Diffraction and interference effects originating from cortical lens fibers can be demonstrated experimentally. The lenticular halo is a diffraction effect attributed to the lens fibers in vivo and explained by treating the fibers optically as a periodic variation in refractive index (Figure 7 A, B and C) [4,34,35]. It can be observed around a small source of light in an otherwise dark room as a series of colored rings around the light source. Many people with normal eyes can see traces of these rings, especially when the pupil is dilated. Colored rings of this nature are well known in physics and ophthalmology, as for instance the ciliary corona due to uniform particles within the eye (Figure 7 C) [34].

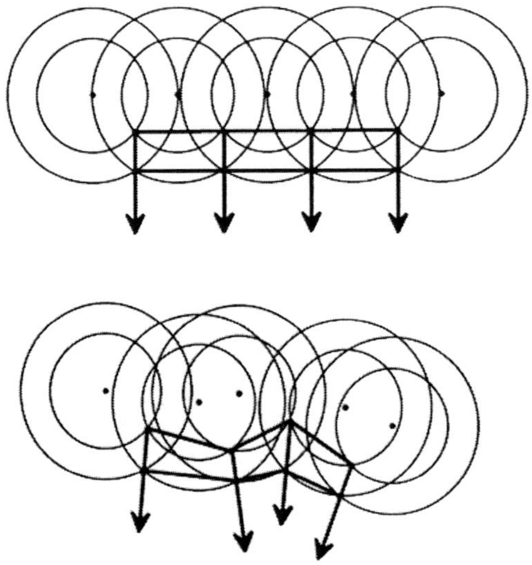

Figure 6. Schematic diagram of resultant light scattering from regularly spaced scattering centers (above) and irregularly spaced (below).

Peripheral lens fibers have a very regular order as illustrated in figure 7 A and D, which shows a cross-section in the equatorial or coronary plane of a rat lens. This fiber lattice in the lens cortex forms a structure of periodic variation in refractive index which fulfills the most basic definition of a diffraction grating: "a repetitive array of elements which produce periodic alterations in the phase, amplitude or both of an emerging wave" [36]. Simpson explains the lenticular halo with the help of a drawing of a circular grating: Figure 7 B. It shows a biconvex lens with its equatorial plane in the plane of the paper, the focal point F in a parallel plane beyond the paper and the light source above the paper. An optical grating is shown etched to the outer zone of the lens, the lines of the grating being radial. If monochromatic yellow light falls on a small segment of the circular grating (point G in figure 7 B), it will produce three images of the source on the focal plane. One will be at the main focus, F; where it combines with the white light from the clear central part of the lens, and two diffracted images at Y an Y'. Monochromatic red light will form red spots at R and R' and violet light at V and V' [34].

It is interesting that Simpson mentions that the diffractive effect is limited to the periphery of the lens. The central part of the lens, although built up of similar fibers, shows no diffraction and therefore may be considered to be optically homogeneous [34]. This is in accordance with our finding that there are only minor differences in the refractive index between fiber membranes and cytoplasm in the lens nucleus.

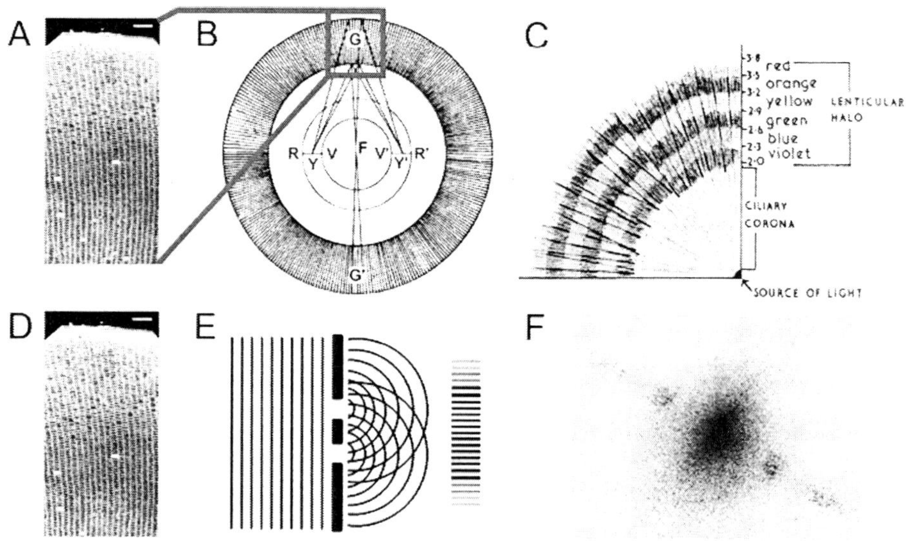

Figure 7. Diffraction and interference effects originating from cortical lens fibers. Midcoronary paraffin lens section stained with wheat germ agglutinin (A and D) to illustrate the regular order of the lens fibers in the periphery of the crystalline lens. Tissue from a rat lens showing about 250 μm lens cortex below the lens capsule (scale bar is 25 μm). Diagram of a circular grating (B) [34] formed by the cortical lens fibers and a diagram of light waves at a barrier (E). Lenticular halo with details of colored rings; numbers are denoting angle in degree (C) [34]. Interference pattern showing low angle laser light scattering from a section of human transparent lens cortex (F) [37]. Images C and F are negative, the dark streaks representing bright rays and dark spots bright light. (Figure 7 B and C reprinted from[34] with permission from BMJ Publishing Group Ltd, Figure 7 F reprinted from [37], Copyright 1973, with permission from Elsevier.)

Philipson [37] demonstrated that a piece of human lens tissue indeed can produce a interference pattern when illuminated with monochromatic light (Figure 7 F). Helium neon laser light was passed through thin slices of lens substance. The interference pattern registered from human cortex corresponded to a spacing of 7 μm. Philipson suggests that the interference maxima was most likely caused by the lens fiber membranes or the intercellular spaces. This experimental interference pattern in figure 7 E is also a good illustration for the theory of constructive / destructive interference in the crystalline lens. Superimposed waves can reinforce each other (constructive interference) or cancel each other (destructive interference) producing the well known interference pattern.

SUMMARY

In the lens cortex, transparency is obtained by the high spatial order of the fiber lattice to compensate for the light scattering caused by fluctuations of the refractive index between membranes and cytoplasm. In the lens nucleus, high spatial order is not a prerequisite for transparency, because scattering is minimal due to the minor differences in the refractive index between fiber membranes and cytoplasm (Figure 8).

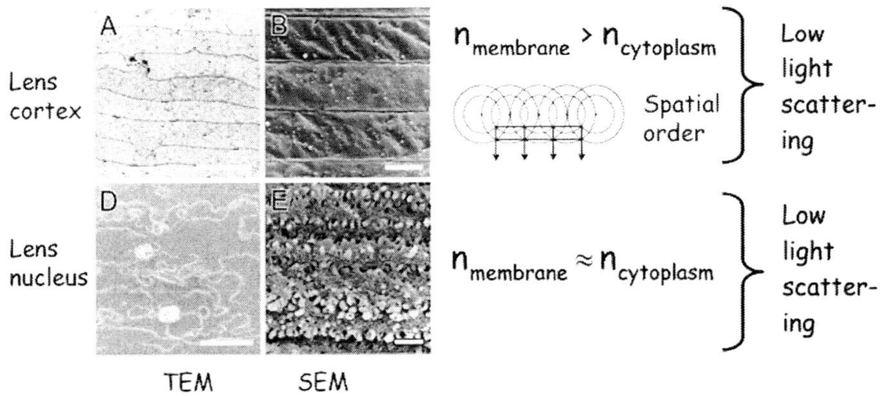

Figure 8. Explanatory figure on the relation of spatial lens fiber order and light scattering considering differences in refractive index (n) between lens fiber membranes and lens fiber cytoplasm in the lens cortex and lens nucleus. Transmission electron micrographs (TEM) (A, D) and scanning electron micrographs (SEM) (B, E) of human lens fibers of the superficial cortex (A, B) and in the lens nucleus (D, E). On the right hand side a schematic representation to explain the cause for minimal light scattering in the lens cortex and nucleus, respectively. Scale bar is 5 µm.

ACKNOWLDGEMENT

The authors wish to thank Gijs Vrensen from Leiden University Medical Center for making available the transmission and scanning electron micrographs (Figure 4 and 8) and for the numerous discussions about lens morphology and membrane chemistry. We would like to thank Elisabeth Pels and her co-workers from the Cornea Bank Amsterdam for making available the human lenses. The human eyes were donated for transplantation purposes. We thank Jan van Marle from the University of Amsterdam for his help with phase contrast microscopy in his lab and Tom van den Berg from The Netherlands Ophthalmic Research Institute for his support and constructive criticism. This study was financed in part by a fellowship to Ralph Michael: Marie Curie Fellowship of the European Community program Quality of Life (QLK6-CT-1999-51159), Brussels, Belgium.

REFERENCES

[1] Benedek GB. Cataract as a protein condensation disease. *Invest Ophthalmol Vis Sci.* 1997;38:1911-21.

[2] van den Berg TJ, Spekreijse H. Light scattering model for donor lenses as a function of depth. *Vision Res.* 1999;39:1437-45.

[3] Trokel S. The physical basis for transparency of the crystalline lens. *Invest Ophthalmol.* 1962;1:493-501.

[4] Hemenger RP. Small-angle intraocular light scatter: a hypothesis concerning its source. *J Opt Soc Am [A] [A].* 1988;5:577-82.

[5] Bettelheim FA. Physical basis of lens transparency. In: Maisel H. *The ocular lens, structure, function and pathology.* New York: Marcel Dekker Inc.; 1985:265-95.

[6] Babizhayev MA, Costa EB. Lipid peroxide and reactive oxygen species generating systems of the crystalline lens. *Biochim Biophys Acta.* 1994;1225:326-37.

[7] Hightower KR, McCready JP, Borchman D. Membrane damage in UV-irradiated lenses. *Photochem Photobiol.* 1994;59:485-90.

[8] Alberts B, Bray D, Lewis J, Raff M, Roberts K, Watson JD. Chapter 3: Macromolecules: Structure, Shape, and Information. *Molecular biology of the cell.* New York: Garland Publishing; 1994:89-138.

[9] Fagerholm PP, Philipson BT, Lindström B. Normal human lens - the distribution of protein. *Exp Eye Res.* 1981;33:615-20.

[10] Beuthan J, Minet O, Helfmann J, Herrig M, Muller G. The spatial variation of the refractive index in biological cells. *Phys Med Biol.* 1996;41:369-82.

[11] Taylor VL, Al-Ghoul KJ, Lane CW, Davis VA, Kuszak JR, Costello MJ. Morphology of the normal human lens. *Invest Ophthalmol Vis Sci.* 1996;37:1396-410.

[12] al-Ghoul KJ, Costello MJ. Light microscopic variation of fiber cell size, shape and ordering in the equatorial plane of bovine and human lenses. *Mol Vis.* 1997;3: <http://www.molvis.org/molvis/v3/a2/>

[13] Al-Ghoul KJ, Nordgren RK, Kuszak AJ, Freel CD, Costello MJ, Kuszak JR. Structural evidence of human nuclear fiber compaction as a function of ageing and cataractogenesis. *Exp Eye Res.* 2001;72:199-214.

[14] Van den Berg TJTP. Light scattering by donor lenses as a function of depth and wavelength. *Invest Ophthalmol Vis Sci.* 1997;38:1321-32.

[15] Zernike F. Phase contrast, a new method for the microscopic observation of transparent objects. *Physica.* 1942;9:686

[16] Barer R, Joseph S. Refractometry of living cells. *Q J Microsc Sci.* 1954;95:399-423.

[17] Bettelheim FA, Wang TJ. Topographic distribution of refractive indices in bovine lenses. *Exp Eye Res.* 1974;18:351-6.

[18] Barer R. Phase contrast and interference microscopy in cytology. In: Pollister AW. *Physical techniques in biological research.* New York: Academic Press; 1966:1-55.

[19] Philipson B. Distribution of protein within the normal rat lens. *Invest Ophthalmol.* 1969;8:258-70.

[20] Johnsen S, Widder EA. The physical basis of transparency in biological tissue: ultrastructure and the minimization of light scattering. *J Theor Biol.* 1999;199:181-98.

[21] Siebinga I, Vrensen GF, De Mul FF, Greve J. Age-related changes in local water and protein content of human eye lenses measured by Raman microspectroscopy. *Exp Eye Res.* 1991;53:233-9.

[22] Smith G, Pierscionek BK. The optical structure of the lens and its contribution to the refractive status of the eye. *Ophthalmic Physiol Opt.* 1998;18:21-9.

[23] Roth EH, Kluxen G. In-vivo-Messung der Brechungsindex-Verteilung der menschlichen Linse mit Hilfe eines Scheimpflug-Fotos des vorderen Augenabschnitts und einem Helium-Neon-Laserstrahl. *Fortschr Ophthalmol.* 1990;87:312-6.

[24] Li LK, So L, Spector A. Membrane cholesterol and phospholipid in consecutive concentric sections of human lenses. *J Lipid Res.* 1985;26:600-9.

[25] Gullstrand A. Die optische Abbildung in heterogenen Medien und die Dioptrik der Kristallinse des Menschen Uppsala & Stockholm, Almqvist & Wiksell, *1908.*

[26] Michael R, van Marle J, Vrensen GF, van den Berg TJ. Changes in the refractive index of lens fibre membranes during maturation--impact on lens transparency. *Exp Eye Res.* 2003;77:93-9.

[27] Salamon Z, Tollin G. Optical anisotropy in lipid bilayer membranes: coupled plasmon-waveguide resonance measurements of molecular orientation, polarizability, and shape. *Biophys J.* 2001;80:1557-67.

[28] Alberts B, Bray D, Lewis J, Raff M, Roberts K, Watson JD. Chapter 10: Membrane structure. *Molecular biology of the cell.* New York: Garland Publishing; 1994:477-95.

[29] Duindam HJ, Vrensen GF, Otto C, Puppels GJ, Greve J. New approach to assess the cholesterol distribution in the eye lens: confocal Raman microspectroscopy and filipin cytochemistry. *J Lipid Res.* 1995;36:1139-46.

[30] Duindam JJ, Vrensen GF, Otto C, Greve J. Aging affects the conformation of cholesterol in the human eye lens. *Ophthalmic Res.* 1996;28 Suppl 1:86-91.

[31] Gilliland KO, Freel CD, Lane CW, Fowler WC, Costello MJ. Multilamellar bodies as potential scattering centers in human age-related nuclear cataracts. *Mol Vis.* 2001;7: 120-30.

[32] Al-Ghoul KJ, Lane CW, Taylor VL, Fowler WC, Costello MJ. Distribution and type of morphological damage in human nuclear age-related cataracts. *Exp Eye Res.* 1996;62:237-51.

[33] Vrensen G, Kappelhof J, Willekens B. Morphology of the aging human lens. II. Ultrastructure of clear lenses. *Lens Eye Toxic Res.* 1990;7:1-30.

[34] Simpson GC. Ocular halos and coronas. *Br J Ophthalmol.* 1953;37:450-86.

[35] van den Berg T, Hagenouw M. Ciliary corona and lenticular halo. *J Cataract Refract Surg.* 2001;27:10-1.

[36] Hecht E. Chapter 10. Diffraction. Optics Reading MA, Addison-Wesley, *1998.* 433, 511

[37] Philipson B. Changes in the lens related to the reduction of transparency. *Exp Eye Res.* 1973;16:29-39.

INDEX

C

D

E

F

G

H

I

K

L

M

N

O

P

R

S

T

U

V

W

Y

Z